HISTORY OF THE
ROYAL MEDICAL SOCIETY
1737–1937

THE EDINBURGH UNIVERSITY PRESS

Sole Agent

OLIVER AND BOYD

TWEEDDALE COURT, EDINBURGH

98 GREAT RUSSELL STREET

LONDON, W.C. 1

ANDREW DUNCAN, SENIOR

This portrait is attributed to Sir John Watson Gordon and hangs in the Society's Hall

HISTORY OF THE ROYAL MEDICAL SOCIETY
1737–1937

BY

JAMES GRAY, M.A., F.R.S.E.

EDITED BY

DOUGLAS GUTHRIE
M.D., F.R.C.S.E.

Lecturer in History of Medicine
University of Edinburgh

WITH A FOREWORD BY

SIR ROBERT HUTCHISON, BART.
M.D., LL.D., F.R.C.P.

EDINBURGH
AT THE UNIVERSITY PRESS
1952

PRINTED IN GREAT BRITAIN
BY R. AND R. CLARK LTD, EDINBURGH

FOREWORD

IT is surprising that a history of the Royal Medical Society has not been written before, for, with its more than two hundred years of existence, it is perhaps the oldest medical society in Great Britain. Add to this its close association with the Edinburgh Medical School, with which the Society is practically coeval, and the large number of its members who have afterwards become famous names in Medicine, and it would seem to be a subject ready to the hand of the medical historian.

It is equally matter for surprise that the history, now that it has been written, should be the work of a layman, as the author, Mr. James Gray, was not himself a doctor though he was closely connected with the profession through his brother-in-law, the late Dr. George Anderson, who was Secretary of the British Medical Association.

Mr. Gray seems to have derived a special interest in the Royal Medical Society from his grandfather, Mr. J. R. Young, to whom he was much attached and who had himself served the Society for many years as its devoted honorary treasurer and general business adviser.

Unfortunately, Mr. Gray died in 1942 at the comparatively early age of fifty-six, but he had devoted much time in the later years of his life to collecting the material for this book, and every reader of it will appreciate how heavy a task this must have been, for the author not only describes the origin and growth of the Society in detail, but has much to tell us about the early history of the Edinburgh Medical School, besides giving sketches of many members of the Society who afterwards rose to eminence. It is tragic that he did not live to see his History in book form, publication having been delayed by the war and subsequent difficulties, but the writing of it was to him a real and disinterested labour of love, and it would have pleased him to know that it was among the first productions of the recently established Edinburgh University Press.

The book, I feel sure, will be read with pleasure not only by those interested in Medical history but by all old Edinburgh men and especially by past or present members of the " Royal Medical ". To the latter it will recall many pleasant Friday evenings spent in the discussion both of " private " and " public " business in the Society's Hall, and the mutual sharpening of wits which took place there, to say nothing of the many friendships to which such meetings gave rise. Indeed, for many years the Royal Medical Society provided one of the few opportunities which students at a non-residential University, such as Edinburgh, had of exchanging ideas and making social contacts with their fellows.

For myself, looking back over nearly sixty years, I feel that the Society was one of the most formative influences of my undergraduate days, and I have no doubt that many other of its old members would say the same. It is therefore with confidence and pleasure that I cordially commend Mr. Gray's book as a worthy life-story of an institution, alike venerable and useful.

ROBERT HUTCHISON

EDITORIAL NOTE

ALTHOUGH the manuscript by Mr. James Gray has been abridged to some extent, care has been taken to preserve continuity, and to produce an account of the Society without greatly altering the original wording and style. The Editor had the advantage of discussing the project with Mr. Gray shortly before his death, and he has sought to carry out the author's ideas as closely as possible.

The task has been greatly facilitated by the co-operation of Dr. H. P. Tait, who assisted in the work of proof-reading.

For a work of this nature, a good index is essential. The duty of preparing it was undertaken by Dr. J. C Corson, with his customary skill and accuracy.

D. G.

CONTENTS

CONTENTS

CONTENTS

ILLUSTRATIONS

CHAPTER I

THE History of the Royal Medical Society cannot be clearly
understood without some reference to the development of
Edinburgh as a centre of medical teaching, a reference which
will be expanded as this first chapter proceeds.   The torch
of learning, which had been lit in Greece by Hippocrates and
his followers, was handed on to Salerno, thence to Mont-
pellier and to Padua, from there to Leyden, and, early in the
eighteenth century, to Edinburgh.   It was a Leyden student,
Sir Robert Sibbald (1641–1722) who, in 1685, was appointed
the first Professor of Medicine in the Town's College, as
Edinburgh University was then called, and it was another
famous Edinburgh man, Dr. Archibald Pitcairne, who
actually became Professor of Medicine at Leyden in 1692
and who numbered among his students there Hermann
Boerhaave, who succeeded him, and Richard Mead, who
became a leading London physician.

Thus was Leyden linked with Edinburgh, although it was
not until the time of Monro that the Faculty of Medicine
was founded in Edinburgh University.

In 1720 Alexander Monro, *primus*, delivered his inaugural
lecture on assuming the Chair of Anatomy at the age of
twenty-two, having been specially educated, with this end in
view, by his father, John Monro, who, while serving as army
surgeon on the Continent, had noted the success of the Leyden
School, and had resolved to found a similar medical school in
Edinburgh.   It was natural that alongside the Medical School

1

there should have arisen various medical societies with the object of promoting study and research in medical science and of publishing the results of the work. Indeed it was as a means of ensuring such publications that the first medical societies were founded.

In the autumn of 1734 six students of medicine, " fired by the example of their masters, who had nothing more at heart than the improvement of those who committed themselves to their tuition ",[1] began to hold informal meetings for the discussion of dissertations, written by themselves, on medical subjects. This little association laid the foundation of the Medical Society, which was formally constituted in 1737, and incorporated by Royal Charter in 1778.

The first manuscript code of laws of the Royal Medical Society is entitled " Regulations of a Society instituted at Edinburgh for Improvement in Medical Knowledge " and it is dated 1737. Though the titles are similar, this Society, founded by students, had no connection with the " Society for the Improvement of Medical Knowledge," formed in Edinburgh in 1731. The latter was instituted for the purpose of publishing essays written by members or communicated to them, and it was composed of the medical professors at Edinburgh, and of medical practitioners. The secretary was Alexander Monro, *primus*, to whom we have already referred as the first systematic Professor of Anatomy in the University of Edinburgh, and the founder of the Medical School of Edinburgh. The Transactions of the Society were published at different periods, in five volumes, under the title of *Medical Essays and Observations*, a publication which was one of the principal causes of enlarging the fame of the Medical School of the University of Edinburgh.[2] In 1739, this Society developed into the Philosophical Society, and, in 1783, became the Royal Society of Edinburgh. The first article in the first volume of *Medical Essays and Observations*, published in 1732, is a

---

[1] J. Fothergill, *Works* (ed. J. C. Lettsom), vol. ii, p. 367.
[2] *Transactions of the Royal Society of Edinburgh*, vol. i, Part I, p. 5; Bower, *History of the University of Edinburgh*, vol. ii, pp. 337-338.

description of Edinburgh ; and as the Essays were published under the care of Monro, the description, probably written by him, is a proper introduction to a history of the Royal Medical Society of Edinburgh, which owes its origin to an informal association of six of his students in 1734, only eight years after he had founded the Faculty of Medicine in the University of Edinburgh.

" The City of Edinburgh . . . stands chiefly on the Ridge of a Hill, which, at its lowest Part, the Palace of Holyrood-house, is 94 Feet higher than the Level of the Sea, and gradually ascends from thence . . . to its highest Part, the Castle-hill. All this Ridge of a Hill is one large fine Street, which is divided near the middle by cross Building, and a Gate, (the *Netherbow*). The upper Division is properly the City, and commonly is called the *High-Town*, and the lower Half is named the *Cannongate*.

" The Lanes (*Closes*) going off from the High-street, are narrow and steep, especially those of the North-side, on which Side the Houses are not continued down to the Foot of the Hill, but on the Brow there are Gardens between the Buildings and the fresh Water Lake (the *Nore-Loch*). On the Side of this Loch, nearest the Town, the Butchers have their Slaughter-houses, and the Tanners and Skinners their Pits. Several Lanes (the *Wynds*) on the South-side of the Street are larger, and not so steep as the others above mentioned, are built on both sides, and terminate in a narrow Street (the *Cowgate*) that runs parallel everywhere with the High-street. It is a common Tradition that this low Part of the Town was formerly a Loch, in regard of which the one now remaining on the opposite Side of the City was called *Nore-Loch* ; and there are now Plenty of Springs everywhere in the *Cowgate* ; and after violent Rains, the Water makes its Way, in great Quantities, through the Floors of the Ground-storeys there. From the *Cowgate* other Lanes are continued Southwards to the City-wall, which is built on another Ridge, almost parallel to the High-street : Where these Lanes are not, there are Gardens, Burying-places *etc.* within the Wall ; and beyond it, from the Gates, are some large Suburbs.

" Between the low Street or *Cowgate* and this South-wall, most of the Brewers have their Work-houses, for the Convenience of Water.

" The *Cannongate* or lower Part of the Town, the larger Share of which is properly without the Liberties of the City, has narrow Lanes going off from each Side of the Street ; but the Houses not being built far down, there is considerable Space for Gardens, that are all planted and laboured.

" The Houses in *Edinburgh* are of Stone, and are allowed by Law to be five Storeys high to the Street, but are generally higher backwards. They are built very close on each other ; and one Stair often serves two Houses, each of which contains a Family in every Storey ; the Height of the Houses, Narrowness of the Lanes, and Number of People entering by one Stair, may therefore in some measure apologize for neither Stairs nor Lanes being so clean as in some other Places where such Crowds are not confined to such a narrow Spot of Ground.

" No River or Rivulet runs through the Town, or nearer it than three-fourths of a Mile ; but the City is plentifully provided with fine Spring-water, conveyed about three Miles through Leaden Pipes. The Markets are here plentifully furnished with Fleshes, Fishes, Fruits, Herbs and Roots. The common Draught is small Ale sold at Two pence a Pint . . . the People of Fashion having Plenty of Claret, and all other Sorts of Wines. All except the poorer Labourers use Wheat-bread ; these indeed feed much on Oat-meal : And all Sorts burn Pit-coal in their Fires.

" The Number of Inhabitants in Edinburgh and Cannongate is reckoned to amount to some Hundreds more than Thirty two thousand . . . this we judge to be rather too small a Calcul for such a crowded healthy Place as this is."

Such was the City of Edinburgh, when the Faculty of Medicine was established in the University there, in 1726. That event, and the developments which followed it, can only be understood correctly in the light of the fact that Edinburgh owes the foundation of its University to the Corporation of the City. The Town Council were the sole patrons until the Universities (Scotland) Act, 1858, deprived them of part of their patronage. During a great part of its history the University was called the " Town's College ". At the outset in 1583 it was literally a College because some of the students resided within its walls. And it remained a College until the beginning of the eighteenth century, because, during the whole of that period, the domestic practice of " regenting " was the mode of teaching. A Regent taught his class all the subjects of their curriculum. " The point at which it would seem most proper to drop the designation of ' College ' and to begin to speak of ' the University of Edinburgh ' will be from that date when its patrons abolished the tutorial system and substituted Professors of special subjects for the Regents of Philosophy." [1] This happened in 1708, when the Faculty of Arts was established.

The beginning of the study of botany in the College of Edinburgh is far before that of any other medical subject. The Chair of Botany was founded in 1676, when the Town Council gave Mr. James Sutherland, Keeper of the Physic Garden, a yearly salary of £20 and annexed his profession of botany " to the rest of the liberal sciences taught in the College ". The Physic Garden, a small enclosure, lay to the east of the North Bridge on part of the low-lying ground later occupied by the London and North Eastern Railway Company. In 1695 the Keeper was more formally appointed to be Professor of Botany in the College, with his former salary of £20. In the same year his position was further improved by an arrangement with the Surgeons who had then received their patent from William and Mary. This patent empowered the Surgeons " to examine all who practised anatomy, surgery, and pharmacy within the three Lothians, and the Counties of Peebles, Selkirk, Roxburgh, Berwick, and Fife ".[2] The Professor of Botany immediately requested the Surgeons to assess their apprentices and pupils at a fee of one guinea

[1] Sir A. Grant, *The Story of the University of Edinburgh*, vol. i, p. 184.
[2] J. Gairdner, *Historical Sketch of the Royal College of Surgeons of Edinburgh*, pp. 12-13.

each for instruction in botany. He was to acknowledge the Surgeons as his patrons, to attend upon them in the garden and demonstrate the plants, whenever they should have inclination, and wait upon them " at a solemn public herbarizing in the feilds four severall times in every year ".[1]

In 1685, Sir Robert Sibbald, Dr. James Halket, and Dr. Archibald Pitcairne, three accomplished physicians in Edinburgh, were appointed Professors of Medicine in the College. But these appointments were merely titular, and such lectures on medicine as were given in the University before 1726 formed part of the general arts course. Sir Alexander Grant has described the appointments as " the tentative outset—a sort of false dawn—of the University Medical School ".[2] The degree of M.D. was given as an honorary one, as that of LL.D. is given to-day, and it did not imply any knowledge of medicine beyond that expected of all educated men. Only twenty-one medical degrees were conferred by the University before the establishment of the Faculty of Medicine in 1726 ; and of these, two were admissions *ad eundem*, granted to medical graduates of other universities, and the others were conferred " at the instance and by the recommendation of the Royal College of Physicians ".[3]

The idea of providing a technical training for medical practitioners arose when surgeons realised their need of a knowledge of anatomy. As early as 1505, nine years before the birth of Vesalius, the Barber-Surgeons of Edinburgh were granted permission by the municipal authorities to " have anis in the yeir ane condampnit man efter he be deid to mak anatomea of quhairthrow we may haif experience Ilk ane to instruct uthers And we sall do suffrage for the soule ".[4] This remarkable provision for dissection is contained in the first charter, called a seal of cause, of the Surgeons of Edinburgh, granted by the Town Council in 1505, and ratified by James IV in 1506. For two centuries afterwards, however,

[1] Gairdner's *Sketch*, p. 19.
[2] *The Story of the University of Edinburgh*, vol. i, p. 294.
[3] *Ibid.* p. 312.   [4] Gairdner's *Sketch*, p. 5.

no progress was made in anatomy or medical science in Scotland owing to the unsettled state of the country. A great advance was made in 1697, when the Surgeons of Edinburgh built an anatomical theatre of their own, and performed dissections there. In 1705 they appointed Robert Eliot, one of their number, at his own request, to be their Professor of Anatomy, during pleasure. A few months later, the Town Council, as patrons of the University, associated him with that institution by allowing him a salary of £15 a year, on condition that he took charge of " the rarities in the Colledge ", and made " ane exact inventar " of them.[1] In 1708 the Town Council, on the recommendation of the President of the Surgeons, appointed Adam Drummond, surgeon apothecary, to be conjoint professor with Eliot. And in 1716 they appointed John M'Gill, Deacon of the Surgeons, as the President was then designated, to be conjoint professor with Drummond, in room of Eliot deceased. In 1720 Drummond and M'Gill resigned their conjoint Chair in favour of Alexander Monro.

About 1720 Monro's father, John Monro, who had been Deacon of the Surgeons in 1712–13, communicated to the Physicians and Surgeons a plan which he had long had in his mind of having the various branches of medicine and surgery taught in a regular manner at Edinburgh and which was eagerly approved by them ; and with their support, regular professorships of anatomy and medicine were instituted in the University.[2] He dedicated his only son to this project, " the founding of a Seminary of Medical Education in his native country ". Alexander Monro, *primus*, justified his father's confidence in him. After instruction in anatomy, chemistry and botany at Edinburgh, he studied in London under Cheselden, at Paris under Bouget and Thibaud, and at Leyden where " he became the favourite and admiring pupil of the great Boerhaave ". Soon after his return to Edinburgh, the Surgeons unanimously recommended him, as " one of their number ", to the Lord Provost and Town of

[1] *Ibid.* p. 17.
[2] Dr. Donald Monro, *Life of Alexander Monro, primus*, p. xii.

Edinburgh to be Professor of Anatomy within the city ; and he was elected, during pleasure. In 1722 he successfully applied to the Town Council to be nominated Professor, not during pleasure but *ad vitam aut culpam*, in the University.[1] " Thus he was the means of laying down a precedent, which was in direct violation of the repeated acts of the Council, but which has been strictly adhered to ever since." [2] He retained his appointment from the Surgeons, as their Professor of Anatomy, and taught in their theatre.[3] In April 1725 a report was spread that body-snatchers had violated graves in the Greyfriars Churchyard and that they were students of Monro. A furious mob surrounded Surgeons' Hall. The Hall was only saved from destruction by prompt and firm action by the authorities. Monro applied to the Town Council for a theatre within the University, and for permission to move his specimens, and commence teaching there. " And thus the Chair of Anatomy was removed from the premises and the partial control of the College of Surgeons ; it ceased indefinitely to belong to ' this City and College ' ; it was localised within the University. . . ." [4]

Monro's next step was to obtain associates to lecture on other branches of medicine in the College. Rightly did Dr. Andrew Duncan, senior, eulogise Monro as the father and founder of the Medical School of Edinburgh. " The endeavours of the young professor were strenuously exerted for exciting in others the same enthusiasm with which he was himself animated. These endeavours were soon crowned with success ; and he obtained associates in every respect correspondent to his wishes." [5] On 9th February 1726, Drs. St. Clair, Rutherford, Innes and Plummer, who were teaching the various branches of medicine in Surgeons' Hall, petitioned the Town Council to introduce the profession of medicine into the College, and to appoint the petitioners " to teach and profess the same ". The Town Council " were of

[1] Gairdner's *Sketch*, p. 18.
[2] Bower, *History of the University of Edinburgh*, vol. ii, p. 182.
[3] Gairdner's *Sketch*, p. 18.
[4] Sir A. Grant, *The Story of the University of Edinburgh*, vol. i, pp. 302-304.
[5] *Harveian Oration* (Edinburgh, 1780), pp. 16-17.

opinion, that it would be of great advantage to this college, city, and country, that medicine in all its branches be taught and professed here, by such a number of professors of that science as may by themselves promote students to their degrees, with as great solemnity as is done in any other college or university at home or abroad. The Council further considering, that the petitioners . . . have given the clearest proof of their capacity and ability to teach the above valuable ends and purposes . . . do therefore unanimously constitute, nominate, and appoint Andrew Sinclair and John Rutherford, doctors of medicine, professors of the theory and practice of medicine, and Andrew Plummer and John Innes, doctors of medicine, professors of medicine and chemistry in the college of Edinburgh." [1]   Dr. Innes appears to have disregarded his commission to teach chemistry, and to have taught practice of medicine conjointly with Dr. Rutherford. This Act of 1726, which established the Faculty of Medicine in the University, was passed under the Lord Provostship of George Drummond, Monro's " most powerful auxiliary in the conducting of all his transactions with the Town-Council ".[2] " Now for the first time the Town Council showed that they understood what is necessary to make a University Medical School—namely, a sufficient staff of Professors to instruct Students in all the main branches of Medical Science, and then conduct them to graduation with all the guarantees that the degree of any other University could give." [3]

The Act recognised, for the first time, the right of the whole body of professors to deliberate and vote " in the affairs of general concern to the College ". Accordingly, the Principal and professors met, in October 1726, as a Senatus Academicus, and having recognised the four newly-appointed medical professors, along with the Professor of Anatomy, as a Faculty of Medicine, " entered them as such in their minutes ".[4]

On the same day on which the four medical professors

[1] Bower, *History of the University of Edinburgh*, vol. ii, pp. 206-207.
[2] *Ibid.* p. 184.
[3] Sir A. Grant, *The Story of the University of Edinburgh*, vol. i, p. 311.
[4] *Ibid.* p. 314.

were added to the staff of the University, Mr. Joseph Gibson, one of the Surgeons, was appointed Professor of Midwifery for the City, but not for the College. " This institution, like every other connected with the history of medicine in Edinburgh, originated with the colleges of physicians and surgeons." [1] Mr. Gibson was a pioneer obstetrician in the days when practice was wholly in the hands of midwives. It is unlikely that any of the students were his pupils. Robert Smith, his successor in 1739, was appointed Professor in the College, but Thomas Young, who succeeded Smith in 1756, was the first occupant of the Chair to give regular instruction to students. In 1775 Dr. Young was elected an honorary member of the Royal Medical Society.

The next expansion in the Faculty of Medicine occurred in 1738, when the Chair of Botany was placed in the Faculty as the Chair of Medicine and Botany. The Town Council, as though they were creating a new Chair, " considering that, were a professor of medicine and botany elected and installed in the city's college, it would in a great measure contribute to the advancement of learning . . . they, therefore " appointed Dr. Charles Alston.[2] Dr. Alston was King's Botanist in connection with the garden of Holyrood, and was lecturing on materia medica before his election as Professor. He had begun his course of lectures at the request of John Monro.[3]

The professors " had no sooner opened their respective professorships, than many students of their own nation, some from England, from Ireland, and not long after from the Plantations likewise, flocked thither. This stimulated the professors to exert their great talents with the utmost energy." [4] A medical faculty at Edinburgh was a boon to nonconformists in England, who were barred from the universities there, and were willing to travel to Edinburgh, despite the bad roads and few stage-coaches. About 1750 students from the American Colonies began to arrive, and

[1] Bower, *History of the University of Edinburgh*, vol. ii, p. 257.
[2] *Ibid.* pp. 324-325.
[3] A. Duncan, M.D., *Harveian Oration* (Edinburgh, 1780), p. 16.
[4] J. Fothergill, *Works* (ed. J. C. Lettsom), vol. ii, p. 365.

their numbers grew steadily. The teaching at Edinburgh was far in advance of that in the English universities, where the scholastic traditions and methods lingered ; and the course, founded on the teaching of Boerhaave at Leyden, steadily increased the fame of the Edinburgh School.

In the early eighteenth century Boerhaave dominated medicine. Even in his lifetime he had become a myth. It was said that a letter from China, addressed to " Boerhaave, Europe ", was duly delivered, and that Peter, the Tsar of Russia, did not repent lying all night in his pleasure barge against Boerhaave's house, in order to have two hours' conversation with him on various points of learning, the next morning, before college time. His reputation depended upon his prodigious learning, his ability as a teacher, and his charming personality. We read of his fondness for music, and of his collection of shrubs at his country house. His early education at Leyden was in languages, mathematics, and divinity, as he intended to enter the Church, but a malicious representation of him as a Spinozist made him unwilling to risk being refused a licence to preach. He then devoted himself to medicine, which at first he had studied merely as a preliminary to ordination, and in which he had obtained a degree from the University of Harderwijk.

In 1701 he became lecturer on the institutes of physic at Leyden, and in his inaugural lecture urged a return to the Hippocratic method of enquiry and observation. His lectures often dealt with chemistry and its application to medicine, in which he followed the example of his predecessor, Sylvius ; but he also urged the use of mechanical reasoning in medicine, perhaps remembering the teaching of Dr. Archibald Pitcairne of Edinburgh who, while Professor of Medicine at Leyden in 1692, had Boerhaave as one of his students. Thus Boerhaave was aware that both chemistry and mechanics were useful in the understanding of medicine, and he seemed to be in a position to achieve a synthesis of the humoralism of the iatrochemists and the solidism of the iatromechanists. It must be remembered, however, that the chemistry of those days could make little positive contribution to medicine. It gave an impetus to the study of the doctrine of acrimonies, but its concepts were too vague to provide a safe foundation. It aroused controversy on the respective merits of galenical and chemical remedies, but it gave no proper grounds for decision. Thus it was most useful as a check to the excesses of the mechanists, whose mathematical ingenuities started from Harvey's demonstration of the circulation of the blood, and ended with the whole body as a hydraulic machine. Moreover, Boerhaave's philosophical training and temperament inclined him to quote authorities rather than reconcile them, and his wide reading made it easier for him to do this than to think or experiment. He gave praise to Harvey for the experiments by which he proved the necessity of a circulation of the blood before Leeuwenhoek saw the passage of the corpuscles along the capillaries from artery to vein, but he did not use experiment to provide facts. Where facts were wanting he turned to argument and speculation, and, in his writings, he " contented himself with a hashing up of the partial truths and the entire errors of his time ". It is evident that the matter of Boerhaave's teaching, so far as it has come down to us in his writings, does not account for his reputation. Boerhaave made no original contribution to medical science. His title of " father of modern medicine " rests on the part he played in developing *clinical* teaching.

In the fifth century B.C. Hippocrates had shown that it was possible to study medicine without philosophical preconceptions by making records of careful observations on sick people. From that time until the eighteenth century A.D. medical practitioners received clinical instruction by apprenticeship to a practising physician. In the school at Salerno (A.D. 800–1200) and in the Arabian Schools at Baghdad, Cairo, Damascus and Cordova (A.D. 800–1700) students were instructed in the hospitals, but, in the universities of Europe in mediaeval times, the scholastic spirit diverted medicine from the study of the sick to a textual criticism of the works of Hippocrates and Galen. The value of the results obtained by these great men obscured the far greater importance of the methods which they had used in order to obtain them. In the sixteenth century Vesalius showed the anatomists that they must study the human body and not the words of Galen and his commentators, and, in the seventeenth century, Harvey's discovery of the circulation, and Sydenham's clinical studies showed that the spirit of the renaissance was stirring in English medicine. Yet the medical courses in the universities remained a series of lectures on Galen and Hippocrates, and the Doctors of Medicine preserved the medical tradition in their debates on the authenticity of texts and the relative merits of commentators.

The credit for the introduction of clinical instruction to a university course in the seventeenth century belongs to Franciscus Sylvius, Boerhaave's predecessor at Leyden, who induced the University authorities to found a hospital entirely devoted to the use of the University. The Professors of Physic attended there, and the students had access to the patients. The hospital was provided with " a convenient amphitheatre where, in case any patients die of an extraordinary distemper, the necessary dissections are made with the greatest accuracy and decency, notice being always given to the students to attend ".[1] Boerhaave developed this clinical instruction ; and students from all over the world flocked to Leyden. The method of clinical teaching spread east to Vienna, with van Swieten, next, west to Edinburgh with Alexander Monro, *primus*, and thence to America. The establishment of clinical instruction, as part of the medical curriculum, was due to the enthusiasm for it which Boerhaave inspired in his pupils.

In 1721 after Alexander Monro was appointed Professor of Anatomy at Edinburgh, an appeal was issued for funds to establish an infirmary for the relief of the sick poor, and the provision for " students in Physic and Surgery " of " a better and easier Opportunity of Experience ". It is probable that this appeal was published by John and Alexander Monro.[2] The appeal was unsuccessful. The endeavour of the Royal

[1] W. Burton, *Life of Boerhaave* (London, 1746), p. 33.
[2] A. Logan Turner, M.D., *Story of a Great Hospital* (1937), pp. 39-40.

College of Physicians, five years later, was more fortunate ; and, in 1729, a hospital containing six beds was opened in Robertson's Close, on the south side of the Cowgate. In 1736 the Infirmary obtained a Royal Charter, and, in 1741, a large hospital, in place of the humble original one, was opened in Infirmary Street. Here, in 1748, Dr. John Rutherford, Professor of Practice of Physic, gave the first course of clinical lectures. It may be recalled that he was the maternal grandfather of Sir Walter Scott. " With the opening of the Royal Infirmary and the increased facilities for clinical instruction which the improved accommodation provided, the professional value of the training in medicine advanced steadily in public estimation." [1]

[1] A. Logan Turner, M.D., *The Royal Infirmary of Edinburgh* : Bicentenary Year, 1729–1929, p. 24.

CHAPTER II

Informal meetings in 1734—Archibald Taylor—William Cuming—
Alexander Russell—George Cleghorn—Alexander Hamilton—
James Kennedy—John Fothergill—William Cullen

THE story of the foundation of the Royal Medical Society is
told in the following letter written by Dr. William Cuming
of Dorchester on 14th October 1782 to Dr. John Coakley
Lettsom, who was then collecting materials for his Life of
Dr. John Fothergill.

" On one of the first days of August, 1734, an offer was
made to Dr. Russell, for a pecuniary gratification, of the body
of a young woman, a stranger, just then dead by a fever of
ten days standing. This he immediately communicated to
me, and we to four more of our fellow students, viz. :—George
Cleghorn ; Archibald Taylor . . . who died a few years after
in the East Indies ; Alexander Hamilton, son to the Professor
of Divinity in that University . . . ; and James Kennedy, a
young gentleman who, after having finished his studies at
Edinburgh, Paris, and Leyden . . . became the senior captain of dragoons in the service : he is still alive in Scotland.
. . . How it happened that Dr. Fothergill was not invited to
be one of this Society I cannot now recollect.

" As we had no proper place in which to lodge and dissect
the body, I waited on the Professor of Anatomy, and requested the use of the anatomical theatre, which he most
willingly and cheerfully granted me.

" After having finished our dissection in which we
employed the greatest part of that month, we agreed to spend
a social evening at a tavern. After supper, Archibald Taylor
proposed that we six . . . should meet once a fortnight,
early in the evening, at our respective lodgings ; and that a

Dissertation in English or Latin on some medical subject, at the choice of the Society, should be composed and read at each of those meetings. . . . I was appointed to prepare a Dissertation for their first meeting, on the signs, causes, and methods of cure of the *Rabies Canina*, which I accordingly did, and read on the 20th December following. Russell, I remember, followed me in one, *De Gonorrhoea Virulenta* ; then came Cleghorn, *De Epilepsia* ; Kennedy, *De Fluxu Mensium*, etc.

" This association continued during that winter and ensuing spring ; but in the summer of 1735 the members of this little society were dispersed and Cleghorn, I believe, alone remained, to continue, with his respected Fothergill, and some others, this Association, during the subsequent winter.

" This was the humble and fortuitous commencement of a Society, that has since become highly respectable . . . and is now incorporated by royal charter." [1]

A memorable feature of the origin of the Society is the association with it of the name of Alexander Monro, *primus*, father and founder of the Medical School of Edinburgh. Without Monro's consent to the use of the theatre within the University, Cuming and his friends might have failed to obtain a secure place in which to dissect the body. In those days, the possession by students of a body for dissection was a rare, if not unprecedented, stroke of fortune ; but it involved serious risks. The security which Monro afforded was needed, as popular prejudice at Edinburgh had rendered private dissection a hazardous undertaking.

Cuming suffered some ill effects from the historic dissection, and he described them in a letter, in 1783, to Dr. Lettsom. Considering the little opportunity of dissection afforded to students at that time, and the words in Cuming's letter " having finished our dissection in which we employed the greatest part of that month " the following passage clearly refers to the dissection in August 1734. " After a dissection during the month of August 1734, I was seized with feverish symptoms, and kept my bed for twenty-four

[1] T. J. Pettigrew, *Life and Writings of J. C. Lettsom*, vol. iii, pp. 288-291.

hours ; but since that time, with gratitude to the Almighty I recollect it, I have not been confined to my bed for the space of one entire day at a time." [1]

Cuming was the son of an eminent merchant in Edinburgh. After four years' study of medicine at Edinburgh, he went to France in the autumn of 1735, visiting the hospitals in Paris, and improving himself " by dissecting of bodies in anatomy ". In May 1736, he left Paris, in company with his friends, Robert Whytt, afterwards Professor of the Institutes of Medicine at Edinburgh, and James Kennedy, making a tour in Flanders on their way to Leyden. " During a stay of three days at Rheims, we took it into our heads to take out degrees there. We were separately examined in Latin for a considerable space, in anatomy, physiology, and the signs, causes and cure of diseases, besides delivering a commentary on an aphorism of Hippocrates. On our being asked of what country we were natives, and answering Scotland, one of the professors very politely said, *Qui se dicit Scotum dicit doctum.* We remained at Leyden for some time, listening to the lectures of the venerable Boerhaave." [2] Dr. Cuming ultimately settled in practice in Dorchester, where he remained to the last, notwithstanding pressing invitations from Dr. Fothergill to succeed their deceased friend, Dr. Russell, in London. He had a large practice among the county families, by whom he was regarded as a friend as well as a physician. In 1752 he intimated his desire to his friends in Edinburgh, " to have a degree from thence ", and was " adopted a fellow of the Royal College of Physicians at Edinburgh ".[3] His instructions to his executor regarding his interment suggest modern ideas of hygiene. A memorial was to be erected in the church, with the epitaph, " Near this place lie the remains of William Cuming, M.D. . . . who desired to be buried in the Church-yard, rather than in the Church, lest he who studied, while living, to promote the health of his fellow citizens, should prove detrimental to it, when dead." [4] He died in 1788.

---

[1] *Ibid.* vol. i, Correspondence, p. 14. [2] *Ibid.* pp. 4-7.
[3] *Ibid.* pp. 11-12. [4] *Ibid.* Memoirs, pp. 92-93.

Alexander Russell was a son of John Russell of Braidshaw, Writer to the Signet, " a gentleman of great eminence in the Law in Edinburgh ". One of his early friends was William Tytler of Woodhouselee, who acquired some fame as the author of an *Inquiry into the Evidence against Mary, Queen of Scots* in connection with the Casket Letters. After studying medicine at Edinburgh and a visit to London in 1735 Russell went to Turkey, and, about 1740, accepted a unanimous invitation from the English factory at Aleppo to be their medical adviser. His reputation as an accomplished physician and a man of imperturbable temper won him the confidence and esteem of the Asiatic inhabitants. Chiefly owing to the repeated requests of his intimate friend Fothergill, he wrote the *Natural History of Aleppo* which was published in 1756, and was soon regarded as a standard work. In the preface, he stated that his original intention was only to give an account of the epidemic diseases at Aleppo, particularly of the plague, which raged three years during his residence there. Russell possessed so thorough a knowledge of the plague that, when it broke out in Lisbon in 1757, the British Government consulted him about the measures to be taken to prevent it spreading to the United Kingdom. In 1755 he settled in London and later became physician to St. Thomas's Hospital, where Mark Akenside was one of his colleagues. His death in 1768, like that of Akenside in 1770, was caused by an attack of typhus fever.

George Cleghorn, while a student, was placed under the tuition of the Professor of Anatomy, in whose house he lived. For five years he continued to profit by the instruction of the great and good Monro, visiting patients along with him, and assisting at the dissections in the theatre. On Fothergill's arrival in Edinburgh in 1735, Cleghorn was introduced to him. The two students became inseparable companions and met frequently to compare notes. " Their moments of relaxation . . . were spent in a select society of fellow-students, of which Fothergill, Russell and Cuming were associates ; a society since incorporated under the name of the

Royal Medical Society of Edinburgh." [1] At the age of twenty, on the recommendation of Dr. St. Clair, Professor of Institutes of Medicine at Edinburgh, Cleghorn was appointed surgeon to the 22nd Regiment of Foot, then stationed in Minorca under the command of General St. Clair. During a residence of thirteen years there, he employed his spare time in investigating the nature of epidemic diseases. He was assisted by his correspondent Fothergill, and in 1751 he published his *Observations on the Epidemical Diseases in Minorca*, addressed to Fothergill, who had materially assisted him in the publication of the work. Soon afterwards he settled in Dublin, and later became Professor of Anatomy in the University there.[2]

In 1778 Cleghorn was elected an honorary member of the Society. A few years later he was greatly gratified by a present from Lettsom of two copies of his edition of Fothergill's *Works*, which contained an account of the origin of the Royal Medical Society.[3] In a letter of thanks to Lettsom, he complains of being no longer able to climb two or three pairs of stairs to bed-chambers and nurseries, supporting a weighty corporation of nineteen stone and a half on a pair of oedematous legs, and panting like a wind-broken horse before he gets half-way up : he has, therefore, retired from practice, though continuing his lectures on anatomy. In October 1908 Professor D. J. Cunningham, who then filled the Chair of Anatomy at Edinburgh, presented to the Society a signed portrait of Cleghorn.

In the summer of 1735 the members of the little association formed in 1734, save Cleghorn, left Edinburgh. In the autumn, however, Cleghorn, with Fothergill and some others, resumed similar meetings.

John Fothergill, like his biographer Lettsom, was a Quaker. He studied medicine at Edinburgh on the advice of Dr. John Rutty, also a Quaker, an old fellow-student with Alexander Monro in London.[4] He became a very successful

[1] *Medical Commentaries*, Decade Second, vol. v, p. 480.   [2] *Ibid.* pp. 478-482.
[3] J. Fothergill, *Works* (ed. J. C. Lettsom), vol. ii, pp. 367-369.
[4] Bower, *History of the University of Edinburgh*, vol. ii, p. 173, footnote.

practitioner in London. His *Account of the Sore Throat attended with Ulcers*, which appeared in 1748, is said to be the best of his publications, and to have greatly increased his reputation. This disease was apparently epidemic in Edinburgh in 1737, and in London in 1739. It was the subject of a dissertation, which was read before the Royal Medical Society in 1755, by Robert Ramsay, who found himself in some difficulty, as he had not seen a case during his medical course. Though some have claimed that this was the first description of diphtheria, it was almost certainly a severe form of scarlet fever. Cullen, Francis Home and others attempted to separate the two diseases, but there was much confusion until 1826 when Bretonneau defined diphtheria as a clinical entity. Loeffler's proof of the bacterial aetiology was published in 1884. Fothergill was an enthusiastic botanist ; and he had " a very complete botanic garden " on his estate at Upton in Essex. His notable collections of shells and insects were purchased, after his death in 1780, by his friend William Hunter, and his splendid collection of drawings of subjects in natural history was purchased, at the same time, for the Empress of Russia.[1] He was an original founder of a Society of Physicians in London, formed in 1752, which published at different periods, six volumes of *Medical Observations and Inquiries*. This Society has been sometimes confused with the Medical Society of London, founded in 1773. His name was commemorated in the latter Society by the Fothergillian Gold Medal, which was presented in 1784 by Dr. Lettsom, one of the original founders. The medal was to be given annually to the author of the best dissertation on a subject proposed by the Society, for which the learned of all countries should be invited as candidates. The first award was in 1787, when the medal was handed by Dr. Lettsom to Dr. William Falconer of Bath, a senior member of the Royal Medical Society, for a dissertation on " The Influence of the Passions upon Disorders of the Body ".[2]

In 1790 the Medal was awarded to Dr. Robert Willan,

---

[1] T. J. Pettigrew, *Life and Letters of J. C. Lettsom*, vol. i, Memoirs, pp. 88-89.
[2] *Memoirs of the Medical Society of London*, vol. i, pp. xiiii-xv.

another senior member of the Royal Medical Society, for a dissertation " On Cutaneous Diseases ", which " was the starting-point of modern dermatology ".[1]   The medal was awarded for the last time in 1805 : but, in 1813, on the death of Anthony Fothergill, the nephew of John Fothergill, the London Society came into possession of a sum of money to be paid out in gold medals ; and a Fothergillian Medal is now awarded every third year.

Fothergill, whose father had travelled extensively in America, was a particular friend of Benjamin Franklin, and a well-wisher to America.[2]   In 1765 he showed his strong desire for a reconciliation between the Mother Country and the American Colonies, by publishing his *Considerations relative to the North American Colonies*.   In 1774, when Franklin was in England, Fothergill and his friend, David Barclay of Youngsbury, requested him to draw up a plan for a reconciliation between the British Government and the Colonies.   Barclay was a descendant of Robert Barclay, the apologist of the Quakers, and he was the mutual friend of Benjamin Franklin and Fothergill.   In December 1774 the three friends met on two evenings to discuss the matter ; and Franklin, in his *Autobiography*, has left an account of both meetings.   " Dr. Fothergill, with his usual philanthropy, expatiated on the miseries of war ; that even a bad peace was preferable to the most successful war. . . ." [3] In 1783, three years after Fothergill's death, Franklin, then in Paris, wrote a letter to Lettsom in which he referred to the bid for peace.   " Our late excellent friend was always proposing something for the good of mankind. If we may estimate the goodness of a man by his disposition to do good, and his constant endeavours and success in doing it, I can hardly conceive that a better man has ever existed." [4]

William Cullen was another of those students who

---

[1] F. H. Garrison, *History of Medicine* (3rd ed.), p. 436.

[2] *The Autobiography of Benjamin Franklin*, vol. ii, p. 58.   Franklin's *Life* was completed by his grandson, W. T. Franklin.

[3] *Ibid.* p. 504.

[4] J. C. Lettsom, *Some Account of the Life of the late John Fothergill, M.D., F.R.S. etc.* (1783), pp. clxvii-clxviii.

attended the meetings in 1735. He had attended classes at the University of Glasgow and had served an apprenticeship to Mr. John Paisley, a surgeon in that city. He then went to London where, through the influence of Commissioner Cleland (Will Honeycomb of the *Spectator*) he obtained an appointment as ship's surgeon on a voyage to the West Indies. On his return to London he attended, for some time, the shop of an apothecary there, with great diligence. Two years (1732–34) he spent in the family of his relation, Captain Cleland of Auchinlee, in the parish of Shotts, Lanarkshire, wholly occupied in the study, and occasional practice, of his profession. On leaving Shotts, he spent some time studying general literature and philosophy under a dissenting clergyman at Rothbury in Northumberland. He then resolved to devote a certain period exclusively to the study of medicine. During the winter sessions 1734–35 and 1735–36 he attended the medical classes at Edinburgh, " where, even as a student, he signalised himself by being one of the founders of the Royal Medical Society ".[1] In 1788, when he was seventy-eight years of age, he gave an account of his membership in a letter written to James Cleghorn, who had succeeded his Uncle George as Professor of Anatomy in Dublin.

" Your Uncle and I are, I believe, the only surviving members of a society which existed at Edinburgh in the year 1735, and which laid the foundation of the Medical Society, which became more formally incorporated the year after, and as you know has flourished ever since, to the great advancement of medical science in this University. Tell your worthy uncle that I have what I consider, and I believe he would consider, as a curiosity. It is a manuscript book, in which the discourses of the society in 1735 are recorded ; and there are I believe some of his juvenile performances to be found in it. At our breaking up in the spring 1735, we drew lots for this book, and the fortunate lot fell upon Douglas, the surgeon of the Welsh Fusileers. This gentle-

[1] Sir A. Grant, *The Story of the University of Edinburgh*, vol. ii, p. 394.

man, after travelling about for some years, came at length to Glasgow, and died there, leaving me this book as a legacy." [1]

In 1736 Cullen commenced practice in Hamilton, his native town, in Lanarkshire. Soon afterwards he became acquainted with William Hunter. Hunter had been educated at the University of Glasgow, and was intended for the church. He began to feel strong objections to theological studies, and, influenced by Cullen's conversation, he decided to enter the medical profession. In 1737 he went to reside with Cullen, and remained there for two years. Cullen disliked the surgical part of his practice ; and it was agreed between him and Hunter that the latter should go, first to the University of Edinburgh, and then to London to see the practice of the hospitals, and improve himself in anatomy and surgery. On Hunter's return, a partnership was to take place between the two men. Hunter took with him to London a letter of introduction to Dr. James Douglas, an eminent physician there. Dr. Douglas advised Hunter to attend St. George's Hospital. At the end of the session, when Hunter was preparing to return to Hamilton, Dr. Douglas persuaded him to change his plan, and go to Paris with his son, a student of medicine, and thereafter settle in London and teach anatomy. Hunter communicated this proposal to Cullen who, considering that it gave his friend a better prospect in life, generously gave his consent to it. [2]

A picture of the thatched house in Hamilton, which Cullen occupied when he was in practice there, was presented to the Society in 1921 by Dr. Freeland Fergus of Glasgow, and is hung in the Society's rooms.

After several years' residence in Hamilton, Cullen removed to Glasgow, and, with the concurrence of the medical professors, commenced to deliver lectures in the University in the theory and practice of physic, in botany and materia medica, and in chemistry. As no lectures seem to have been delivered in any branch of medicine, except anatomy, Cullen was thus the chief founder of the Medical School of Glasgow

[1] John Thomson, *Life of William Cullen, M.D.*, vol. i, pp. 10-11.
[2] *Medical Commentaries* (Edinburgh, 1773–86), vol. viii, pp. 426-428.

even before his appointment, in 1751, as Regius Professor of Medicine. He was lecturer in chemistry there from 1746 to 1756. " Dr. Cullen was the true commencer of the study of scientific chemistry in Great Britain, and claims a conspicuous place in this historical sketch. . . . His singular talent for arrangement, his distinctness of enunciation, his vivacity of manner, and his knowledge of the science which he taught, rendered his lectures interesting to a degree which had been till then unknown in that university." [1] Joseph Black was one of his pupils. " Young Black was particularly delighted with a view which accorded so happily with those enlarged habits of thought which he had acquired ; and his great bias to this study was soon perceived by Dr. Cullen. No professor took a more lively interest in the progress of an emulous student than Dr. Cullen. It was his delight to encourage and assist their efforts, and therefore he was not long in attaching Mr. Black to himself, in the most intimate co-operation. . . . Thus began a mutual confidence and friend-ship, which did honour both to the professor and his pupil, and was always mentioned by the latter with gratitude and respect." [2]

The variety and distinction of the careers of those men who, in the days of their youth, laid the foundation of the Royal Medical Society, lend interest to their association as students. The story of the early meetings shows how the reading of a dissertation, which forms the main part of public business at most of the meetings at the present day, was at first a rehearsal of the exercises demanded of the candidates for the degree of Doctor of Medicine.

[1] Thomas Thomson, *History of Chemistry* (1830-31), vol. i, pp. 303-313 *passim*.
[2] Joseph Black, *Lectures on the Elements of Chemistry* (Edinburgh, 1803 ; ed. J. Robison), vol. i, Preface, p. xxii.

CHAPTER III

IN 1737 the Society was formally constituted with ten
members. The list of members is complete from the first
session, 1737–38, until the present day. One of the members
in 1737 was Stuart Threipland, son of Sir David Threipland,
Bart., of Fingask Castle, Perthshire, who served with the
Earl of Mar in 1715, and was attainted after the battle of
Sheriffmuir. He graduated M.D. at Edinburgh in 1742,
and, two years later, became a Fellow of the Royal College of
Physicians at Edinburgh. " Before he had been long in
practice, Prince Charles landed in the west of Scotland, and
Dr. Threipland, as an ardent Jacobite, joined him. He
accompanied the Prince on the march to Derby, and, after
Culloden, in the earlier part of his wanderings. He was in
hiding with the Prince and, along with Dr. Archibald
Cameron, he attended Lochiel, who was seriously wounded,
in a cave on the slopes of Ben Alder. After Lochiel had
recovered from his wounds, Dr. Threipland made his way
back to Edinburgh disguised as a presbyterian probationer.
He afterwards escaped to Rouen and joined Prince Charles for
a time in Paris. . . . The Royal College of Physicians at
Edinburgh preserves a small 18th Century travelling medicine
chest, which is traditionally called ' Prince Charlie's medicine
chest '. It appears to be of French origin and may have
been brought by Prince Charles Edward to Scotland in

1745. It certainly belonged to Sir Stuart Threipland." [1] In 1747 Dr. Threipland returned to Edinburgh, where he resumed practice. In 1766 he was elected president of the College of Physicians. He bought back the ancestral estate in 1783 : but the dignity of baronet was not restored to the family during his lifetime. He was known and addressed, however, by the title, as his name appears in the list of subscribers to the building of the Society's Hall in 1775, as " Sir Steuart Threipland ".

James Russell, the tenth name in the list of members, was a cousin of Joseph Black, the celebrated chemist. In 1747 he joined the Incorporation of Surgeons at Edinburgh. While studying medicine at Edinburgh, Black, " as well as Adam Ferguson, lived with their relation James Russell, whose singular correctness, and precision of thought, in various branches of science, could not fail to be of use to all who approached him ".[2] In 1764 Russell was appointed Professor of Natural Philosophy at Edinburgh in succession to his kinsman Adam Ferguson, who had resigned the Chair for the purpose of obtaining the Professorship of Moral Philosophy. As Black is always mentioned as having lived in the College Wynd during his student days in Edinburgh, Russell's residence must have been there ; and this circumstance may account for the friendship, in later years, of Russell's son, James, with Sir Walter Scott, who was born in 1771 in his father's house at the top of the College Wynd. James Russell, junior, was senior president of the Society in 1780–81, and was afterwards the first Professor of Clinical Surgery in the University of Edinburgh.

The study of botany in the University received a great stimulus in 1761 when Dr. John Hope was elected to the Chair rendered vacant by the death of Dr. Charles Alston in 1760. Hope was a son of Robert Hope, " one of the original six surgeons on the staff of the Infirmary in Robertson's Close ",[3] and a grandson of Sir Archibald Hope, Lord

---

[1] John D. Comrie, *History of Scottish Medicine*, 2nd ed., vol. ii, pp. 447-448.
[2] *Transactions of the Royal Society of Edinburgh*, vol. v, Part III, p. 103.
[3] A. Logan Turner, M.D., *Story of a Great Hospital* (1937), p. 120.

Rankeillor, a Senator of the College of Justice. He was admitted a member of the Royal Medical Society in 1745, and in 1748 he was the third early member to become an honorary member by rotation, a system which ceased in 1776 when honorary membership was conferred only upon distinguished scientific men. Nearly one hundred years afterwards, on the occasion of the Centenary Dinner of the Society in 1837, his son, Thomas Charles Hope, Professor of Chemistry in succession to Black, occupied the Chair.

After graduating M.D. at Glasgow, Hope became, in 1762, a Fellow of the Royal College of Physicians at Edinburgh. His appointment in 1761 was as Professor of Botany and Materia Medica. In 1768, having received a commission from the King appointing him Regius Professor of Botany, he resigned the Professorship of Materia Medica, which was erected into a separate Chair. By his exertions the Botanic Garden was removed from the ground east of the North Bridge to a more favourable site on the west of Leith Walk, where it remained until 1822 when it was removed to its present situation at Inverleith Row. At the time of his death in 1786, Dr. Hope was president of the College of Physicians.

Francis Home (1740)[1] was the first Professor of Materia Medica at Edinburgh. His father, James Home, a member of the Scottish Bar, was proprietor of Eccles, a well-known estate in Berwickshire. From the celebrated schoolmaster, Cruickshank, at the grammar school in Duns, he acquired a taste for classical literature which he retained throughout his long life. When he entered on the study of medicine at the University, he joined the Society, where he became the intimate friend of Mark Akenside. In 1742 he obtained an appointment as an army surgeon, and served in Flanders, when he had opportunities of studying at Leyden. In 1750 he graduated M.D. at Edinburgh, and later became a Fellow of the Royal College of Physicians there. His *Principia Medicinae*, published in 1758, brought him a European reputation.

[1] Here, as in subsequent pages, the date within brackets is the year during which the person concerned joined the Society.

The method of clinical teaching was introduced by Dr. Rutherford, Professor of Practice of Physic, who commenced delivering clinical lectures in the Infirmary in the winter session of 1746–47 ; and it was for a long time peculiar to Edinburgh among British schools. About this time the members of the Society set up a Clinical Board in order to gain clinical experience and to benefit the sick poor. In the first Obligation Book, that is, the book in which members signed their names on joining the Society, there is a minutely detailed set of regulations for the care of patients by two members, a senior and a junior, and for the supply of drugs and other necessaries at the Society's expense if the patient were destitute.

In January 1741 Mark Akenside was admitted a member of the Society. He had received his early education at the academy of the celebrated Dr. Doddridge in Northampton, where he contracted a lifelong friendship with his school-fellows John Roebuck and Jeremiah Dyson. Roebuck, like Akenside, afterwards studied medicine at Edinburgh, and joined the Society a week before he did : Dyson studied law. In the Obligation Book, Akenside spelt his name "Akinside" ; but in later years he adopted the form "Akenside". His intimate friends in the Society were Roebuck, Francis Home, Adam Austin (1739), Edward Archer (1740), Richard Brocklesby and John Gregory (1742). Dugald Stewart, Professor of Moral Philosophy at Edinburgh (1785–1810) has described Akenside's ability as a speaker in the Society, and the impression made by his eloquence on a contemporary student of divinity, William Robertson, afterwards Principal of the University of Edinburgh and a famous historian.

Akenside afterwards proceeded to Leyden and took the degree of M.D. there. Writing to his friend Dyson, shortly after his arrival there, he says : " I am now settled in Roebuck's chamber, the same house with Mr. Drew and Brocklesby. This last was the only one of my acquaintance I found here." And again : " I had not been above four days at Leyden before two of my Edinburgh acquaintances,

Mr. Austin and Mr. Home, came hither from their winter quarters at Ghent, to make the tour of Holland ". In 1747 Akenside commenced practice in London, where he was generously supported by Dyson, who had retired from the Bar on his appointment as Clerk to the House of Commons ; but he never really succeeded in practice. His manner was stiff and formal, and he acquired a propensity for wordy warfare which clouded his professional prospects. " At Tom's Coffee-house in Devereux Court, which he frequented in the winter evenings, and which was then the resort of various eminent men, he would engage in disputes, chiefly of literature and politics, that fixed on his character the stamp of haughtiness and self-conceit." However, he received the degree of M.D. from the University of Cambridge, and became a Fellow of the Royal College of Physicians. In 1759 he was appointed Physician to St. Thomas's Hospital ; and two years later, by Dyson's influence, he became Physician to the Queen. In 1764 Akenside published his medical work, written in Latin, *De Dysenteria*, which was praised for the purity of its style. A copy of the work, bearing the inscription on the title-page, " For Dr. Cullen Edin. From Dr. Wm. Hunter ", is in the Society's library.

Dr. John Roebuck became the founder of the Carron Iron Company. While studying medicine at Edinburgh, he formed an intimate acquaintance with William Robertson, a student of divinity, afterwards Principal Robertson, and David Hume, who had published his treatise *On Human Nature*. In later years he became an intimate friend of Dr. Black. He graduated M.D. at Leyden, and afterwards practised for a few years in Birmingham. He then forsook medical practice, and applied his mind and energy entirely to the rapidly developing science of chemistry. In 1749 he commenced the manufacture of oil of vitriol at Prestonpans. A neighbouring gentleman, Mr. William Cadell of Cockenzie, having endeavoured, with indifferent success, to found a manufactory of iron, Dr. Roebuck was led to make some experiments which were very successful ; and the doctor and his partner, Mr. Garbet, resolved to establish an extensive manufactory. Roebuck chose a spot on the banks of the river Carron which flows into the Firth of Forth at Grange-mouth, and he engaged Smeaton and James Watt as engineers. On 1st January 1760 the first furnace was blown. Thus " he introduced a spirit of enterprise and industry before that time little known in Scotland ".

Richard Brocklesby, like Roebuck, graduated at Leyden. He became a physician of great eminence in London, and was intimate with many most distinguished men, including Sir Joshua Reynolds and Burke. " Among those who loved Burke best was Doctor Brocklesby, the tender physician who watched and soothed the last hours of Johnson." [1]

John Gregory joined the Society a few months after Brocklesby. On leaving Edinburgh he studied at Leyden and Paris. He obtained the degree of M.D. at Aberdeen, and later became Professor of Medicine, though apparently he delivered no lectures, at King's College there. In 1766 he succeeded Dr. Rutherford in the Chair of Practice of Physic at Edinburgh. " From his great-grandfather, David Gregory, Esquire, of Kinairdy, in Aberdeen-shire, he was the fifteenth descendant, who had held a professorship in a British university." [2] He is the authority for the statement which Dr. Andrew Duncan made in his Address to the Society at the commencement of the session 1771–72 : " At the establishment of this Society, the system of Boerhaave maintained in Europe a sway as universal as ever that of Galen had done before. But the founders of this institution, while they were far from being the least sensible of the high merit of so great a master, did not hesitate to shake off a blind veneration for his errors. Reason, philosophy, and experiment were their constant and their only guides. By these means, by such men, and in this place, were the founda-tions of the Boerhaavian doctrine first shaken."

At the outset, the Society met once a week, in a tavern, as was the custom of clubs in Edinburgh at the time ; and there is a tradition that the tavern was in the vicinity of the

---

[1] Lord Morley, *Burke* (English Men of Letters Series).
[2] *Medical and Philosophical Commentaries*, vol. i (London, 1773), p. 211.

University. A President was appointed each week to superintend the business which was a Discourse on a professional subject of the member's own selection, a Consultation on an actual case of disease, and an Answer to a medical question : " the feast of reason concluded with a more substantial but equally temperate repast ". After the fines had been collected, each member paid sixpence to defray his part of the expense. If he called for anything from the house without the Secretary's permission, he had to pay for it himself. A later rule was that if a member were absent from the Society, the President could, if he thought proper, without giving any reason, accuse him of having been at the play. The member was obliged under a penalty of half a crown to answer whether or not he had been there. The dues were collected from the members by one of them appointed to be Secretary and Treasurer for a month.

At this time a single negative to a petition for a seat was sufficient for its rejection. This exclusiveness in the choice of members made membership an honour, and ensured a spirit of friendship which was valuable in the young Society.

Some time after 1741, when the Infirmary, which had obtained a Royal Charter in 1736, moved to a large new building in Infirmary Street, the Managers granted permission to the Society to hold its meetings in one of the vacant rooms ; and an entry in the Infirmary minutes of the year 1753 shows that a library was being accumulated there with the funds which had previously paid for the tavern accommodation.

Debate in a student society perforce reflects the teachings of the professors ; but the Society, imbued with the freedom of spirit for which the University of Edinburgh has always been distinguished, early showed a disposition to criticise them. The original professors had studied at Leyden, and it was natural that they should base their teaching on that of Boerhaave : but it was unfortunate that they failed to appreciate the value of work done by others after his death ; and that they built his teaching, as he had not done, into a system as unassailable in Edinburgh as Galen's had been

31

throughout Europe. Thus the *Boerhaavian System* required criticism and, as Dr. Andrew Duncan stated in 1771, it was the Society which began that criticism. It is probable that William Cullen, while a student, took part in these debates.

In 1780 the Society paid a tribute to the service to medicine rendered by the University of Leyden, by electing to honorary membership the Rector, Walter van Doevern, a distinguished teacher of medicine and medical author.

When Cullen moved to Edinburgh on his appointment, in 1755, as joint Professor of Chemistry with Plummer, who died shortly afterwards, he found the system of Boerhaave taught exactly as it had been twenty years before, when he was a student at Edinburgh, and he set himself to criticise it. In 1766 Cullen became Professor of the Institutes of Medicine, as physiology was then called, and in 1773, at the age of sixty-three, he became Professor of Medicine. Two of his sons were members of the Society about this time, when their father was one of the most celebrated physicians in the world. Henry (1771) was admitted a Fellow of the Royal College of Physicians at Edinburgh and was appointed a physician to the Royal Infirmary there. Archibald (1774), who was a president of the Society in 1780, gave up medicine, and studied law in London, where he attained some eminence at the Chancery Bar. Professor William Cullen published in 1769 a *Synopsis Nosologiae Methodicae*, in which he attempted to classify diseases on the system adopted by Linnaeus for plants. Dissertations read before the Society at this time were often in the form of commentaries on a case. Many of these descriptions of cases written by the dissertator, or set for him by another member, are excellent short case reports. The dissertator was asked, " Quis morbus, quae causae, quae ratio symptomatum, quae prognosis, et quae ratio medendi ? " In deciding " Quis Morbus ? " it was common to quote Cullen and discard two of his three chief classes— say, pyrexiae because there was no fever, and neuroses because there was no disturbance of sensibility or motion— and then apply the same process of exclusion to the genera and species of the third class—cachexiae. A fourth class—

Locales—is found in Cullen's book. The importance which classification assumed at this time was an expression of the hope that some principle would be found to set in order, as Newton's generalisation had ordered physics, the mass of facts established by the generation of Harvey and Sydenham, Malpighi and Sylvius.

Thus Cullen appears as a systematist who taught solidism, but his sagacity prevented his being led away by theory, and brought him back constantly to the individual patient. He was a great teacher and a great consultant, but like Boerhaave, he tried to fill the deficiencies of contemporary physiology and pathology by speculation. His physiological teaching was largely unaffected by Haller's ideas, though he published in 1786 an English translation of the *Elementa Physiologiae*; and Morgagni's publication of his *De Sedibus et Causis Morborum* in 1761 made equally little impression on his pathology.

Cullen's failure to use the experimental method is the more remarkable in that his predecessor in the Chair of the Institutes of Medicine was Robert Whytt, who has been claimed as the first neurologist, and one of the first to devote himself to clinical research. Whytt performed laboratory and clinical experiments on the solution of vesical calculi ; on reflex action, and on referred pain. It was only some fifty years later that Charles Bell and Claude Bernard followed his example to any purpose. Whytt's description of tuberculous meningitis has never been surpassed.[1]

In the judgment of Sir Clifford Allbutt, Cullen actually made no real additions to medical knowledge, and his contemporary reputation rested on the soundness of his judgments in which he was a model of good sense.

It was fortunate for chemical science that about the middle of the eighteenth century the search for a solvent of urinary calculi was exciting great public interest. The numbers of the *Gentleman's Magazine*, which contained Johnson's " Life of Boerhaave ", published lists of subscriptions to a fund for the purchase of a secret remedy purveyed

[1] *Observations on the Dropsy in the Brain* (Edinburgh, 1768).

33

by a Mrs. Joanna Stephens, who asked for five thousand pounds. When the money was not raised, Cheselden, Hawkins and Sharp were appointed by Parliament to examine her claims. They pronounced the remedy effective ; and Walpole's government paid the money. The prescriptions were for a decoction of boiled herbs, wild carrot and burdock seeds, soap, honey, and powders of roasted eggshells crushed with garden snails in the month of May.

Studying the same problem in Edinburgh, Joseph Black, Cullen's zealous chemistry pupil, made the first isolation and study of a gas (carbon dioxide) which he called fixed air. He described this discovery in his graduation thesis in 1754, and in the following year he read, before the Philosophical Society of Edinburgh, an account of his experiments.[1] His results were obtained by careful quantitative methods ; [2] and they led to the overthrow of Stahl's phlogiston theory. They might also have led to an understanding of respiration, for in 1674 Mayow had isolated oxygen, calling it *spiritus nitroaereus*, but his work had been forgotten, and it was not till the work of Priestley in 1770, and Lavoisier's extension of Black's work in 1775, that chemistry gave an adequate description of the gaseous phenomena of respiration.

Black was elected an honorary member of the Society in 1767, the year after he succeeded Cullen in the Chair of Chemistry at Edinburgh. A portrait of him, painted by David Martin in 1787, is in the Society's Hall.

During Black's student days in Edinburgh, Oliver Goldsmith arrived there, from Ireland, to study medicine at the University. And the tradition is that he lodged in the wynd in which Black was then residing. This was the College Wynd, a " picturesque medieval lane, with its jutting balconies, battlemented roofs and charming old windows " which " had for nearly two centuries been a kind of University or College ' Close ', practically reserved for the residence of the learned Regents or Professors from generation to

[1] *Essays and Observations, Physical and Literary* (Edinburgh, 1756), vol. ii, p. 157.
[2] Sir William Ramsay, K.C.B., *Life and Letters of Joseph Black, M.D.* (London, 1918).

generation ".[1] The Wynd, now known as Guthrie Street, leading from the Cowgate to Chambers Street, was demolished, about 1790, to make way for the north front of the University buildings which were taking the place of the old College buildings.[2] Black was a fellow-student with Goldsmith, and he remembered him well. It is certain that Goldsmith was genuinely fond of chemistry, and that Black, at the height of his fame, " remembered him favourably ".[3]

At the time when Goldsmith arrived, Edinburgh was still confined within the city walls. And, with regard to transport facilities, it was much in the same situation as a city-state of the ancient Greeks. Even in 1763, " There were two stage-coaches, with three horses, a coachman, and postilion to each coach which went to the port of Leith (a mile and a half distant) every hour from eight in the morning till eight at night, and consumed a full hour upon the road. There were no other stage-coaches in Scotland, except one, which set out once a month from London, and it was from twelve to sixteen days upon the journey. . . . The hackney-coaches were few in number, and perhaps the worst of the kind in Britain." [4] Hotels were unknown. " A stranger coming to Edinburgh was obliged to put up at a dirty uncomfortable inn or to remove to private lodgings. There was no such place as an hotel ; the word, indeed, was not known or was only intelligible to persons acquainted with French." [5] And the old College buildings, where celebrated professors lectured to students from all parts of the world, were in a woeful state. As late as 1768, Dr. Robertson, Principal of the University, said : " A stranger, when conducted to view the University of Edinburgh, might, on seeing such courts and buildings, naturally enough imagine them to be almshouses for the reception of the poor ; but would never imagine that he was entering within the precincts of a noted and flourishing seat of learning ".[5]

[1] W. T. Fyfe, *Edinburgh under Sir Walter Scott* (London, 1906), pp. 5-6.
[2] J. Forster, *Life and Adventures of Oliver Goldsmith*, vol. i, p. 50.
[3] W. Creech, *Edinburgh Fugitive Pieces* (Edinburgh, 1815), pp. 67-69.
[4] *Ibid.* p. 92.
[5] Sir A. Grant, *The Story of the University of Edinburgh*, vol. ii, p. 193.

Amidst these surroundings Goldsmith commenced the study of medicine. On 13th January 1753 he was admitted a member of the Society and his signature appears in the first Obligation Book. He did not read a dissertation before the Society. The earliest dissertation extant in the Society's library is dated 1751. From that year onwards, the list of authors of dissertations is complete and his name is not on the list. His period of study at Edinburgh was too brief to equip him for such a test. His estimate of his teachers, with the exception of Monro, was not high ; but against that must be placed his indolence as a student. He has left a valuable description of Monro's great powers. " 'Tis he [Monro] I may venture to say, that draws hither such a number of students from most parts of the world, even from Russia. He is not only a skilful physician, but an able orator, and delivers things in their nature obscure in so easy a manner, that the most unlearned may understand him." [1]

A leaf from an Edinburgh ledger of 1753 affords a glimpse of Goldsmith's colourful appearance in the dingy classrooms of the College. Entries in the ledger show that he purchased, among other articles, " Sky-Blew Sattin . . . Sky-Blew Shalloon . . . silver Hatt-Lace . . . a s'fine small Hatt . . . and best s'fine high Clarett-colour'd Cloth ".[2] But this bright student of medicine had powers of description as enlivening as his apparel ; and despite his opinion " that an Edinburgh ball and a deserted village were about upon a par as to liveliness ",[3] his account of one is amusing.

" When a stranger enters the dancing-hall, he sees one end of the room taken up by the ladies, who sit dismally in a group by themselves ;—in the other end stand their pensive partners that are to be ;—but no more intercourse between the sexes than there is between two countries at war. The ladies indeed may ogle, and the gentlemen sigh ; but an embargo is laid on any closer commerce. At length, to interrupt hostilities, the lady directress, or intendant, or

[1] J. Prior, *Life of Oliver Goldsmith*, vol. i, p. 146.
[2] J. Forster, *Life and Adventures of Oliver Goldsmith*, vol. i, pp. 53-54.
[3] Lieut.-Col. A. Fergusson, *The Hon. Henry Erskine* (Edinburgh, 1882), p. 111.

what you will, pitches upon a lady and gentleman to walk a minuet ; which they perform with a formality that approaches to despondence.   After five or six couples have thus walked the gauntlet, all stand up to country dances ; each gentleman furnished with a partner from the aforesaid lady directress ; so they dance much, say nothing, and thus concludes our assembly.   I told a Scotch gentleman that such profound silence resembled the ancient procession of the Roman matrons in honour of Ceres ; and the Scotch gentleman told me, that I was a very great pedant for my pains." [1]

Goldsmith had not resided long in Edinburgh before the unbounded benevolence of his disposition involved him in financial trouble.   He was obliged to flee to avoid imprisonment, for he had bound himself to pay a larger sum of money for a fellow-member of the Society, Hugh Kennedy by name, than he could afford.   He left Edinburgh in the beginning of 1754, but he had only reached Sunderland when he was arrested for debt.   From this situation he was rescued by the generosity of two friends, Laughlan M'Leane, a fellow-member in the Society, and Dr. Joseph Fenn Sleigh.   On being restored to liberty he took ship to Rotterdam.   During his travels on the Continent he obtained the degree of Bachelor of Medicine at Louvain.   He never commenced practice.   In later years some of his friends proposed that he should follow Akenside's example by deriving a more certain income as a physician than he could possibly earn solely as a man of letters.   The project did not advance further than the purchase of a cane, a professional wig and a smart scarlet cape.   Nevertheless Goldsmith rendered signal service to humanity, for he was an original founder of the Royal Humane Society.   " Dr. Goldsmith's natural disposition led him to covet a life of learned leisure ; but this was too often interrupted by that want of money to which the benevolence of his disposition frequently reduced him." [2]

Dr. Johnson, who knew Goldsmith early, and who wrote

[1] Prior, *Life of Oliver Goldsmith*, vol. i, p. 141.
[2] *The Percy Memoir*, p. 12.

the epitaph for the monument to him in Westminster Abbey, said : " He was a very great man ".

Goldsmith's friend, Laughlan M'Leane, joined the Society in 1754. After studying medicine at Edinburgh, he went to America where he acquired a great professional reputation. Returning to England, he gave up medicine and, by means of patronage, secured a series of lucrative government appointments. Ultimately he became an agent to Warren Hastings in India ; and, in that capacity, he brought home the Governor-General's conditional resignation of office. When Hastings disavowed the resignation, and disowned his agent, M'Leane embarked for India to obtain an explanation. The ship foundered with the loss of all on board.[1]

Two other prominent members of the Society about this time were Gregory Grant (1751), and Robert Ramsay (1755). The former became a celebrated physician in Edinburgh. He was interested in chemistry and had a room in his house fitted as a laboratory. In 1770 he gave a course of lectures on Practice of Physic, which increased his reputation. His house was the scene of many fashionable parties ; and he entertained Mrs. Siddons when she visited Edinburgh. He was known for his interest in piping and Gaelic, and for his skill as a dancer of reels.[2] Robert Ramsay became the first Professor of Natural History at Edinburgh.

Whatever benefit the poet Goldsmith and " medical truants " like Roebuck and M'Leane derived from membership of the Society, it was a great advantage to those who later practised medicine to discuss the latest medical ideas during the criticism of dissertations. When Black became Professor of Chemistry at Edinburgh in 1766 he continued experiments on the subject of latent heat. He made the discovery in 1762, while Professor of Medicine at Glasgow, but did not publish it until 1803. In 1775 Nathaniel Tucker read a dissertation on the question—" Is the Doctrine of Latent Heat well founded ? "—beginning thus : " Engaged in a general course of medical studies we regret that we have

[1] Prior, *Life of Oliver Goldsmith*, vol. i, pp. 148-152.
[2] Kay's *Portraits* (Edinburgh, 1877), vol. ii, pp. 110-111.

neither time nor abilities to enter into minute investigation of our subject ''. Modern medical students are not the first to complain of an overcrowded curriculum.

While Black was in Glasgow he had James Watt as a pupil. Watt was engaged in fitting up the instruments in the McFarlane Observatory, and there is no doubt that Black's discoveries inspired Watt's improvements in the steam engine. The professor and the engineer corresponded regularly and their friendship is proof of the fine characters of both men.

Sir Walter Scott records an incident in Black's practice on his return to Edinburgh. Scott's nurse was '' ill of a consumption . . . which she chose to conceal. . . . She went privately to consult Dr. Black, the celebrated professor of chemistry, who put my father on his guard. The woman was dismissed, and I was consigned to a healthy peasant.'' [1]

Black was a most successful teacher. His striking appearance, captivating voice, attractive manner, and power of exposition aided him, and he made chemistry a fashionable study in Edinburgh. When he was a little over sixty he was obliged to employ an assistant, and he chose a senior member of the Society, Dr. John Rotheram (1742), who afterwards became Professor of Natural Philosophy at St. Andrews.

With the growth in numbers, the accommodation in the Royal Infirmary became insufficient for the meetings, and the library was '' not in such a situation as could be desired either with regard to conveniency or preservation ''. It was clear that the Society would benefit from a building of its own. In 1771 a committee was appointed consisting of the four Presidents, with Drs. Cullen, John Gregory and Andrew Duncan, senior, to take the matter in hand. A subscription list was opened, and by 1775 sufficient funds were available to allow the Society to begin building a Hall on an area of ground granted by the College of Surgeons near their Hall, and on the west side of Surgeons' Square, adjoining the ground afterwards occupied by the old High School at the foot of Infirmary Street.

[1] J. G. Lockhart, *Life of Sir Walter Scott* (2nd ed.), vol. i, p. 19.

The subscription list was headed by six members of the Faculty of Medicine, Drs. Cullen, Black, Monro, *secundus*, Dr. John Gregory, Professor of Practice of Physic, and Drs. John Hope and Francis Home, Professors of Botany and Materia Medica, respectively; and Thomas Young, Professor of Midwifery, and Robert Ramsay, Professor of Natural History also subscribed. Dr. Foart Simmons, Dr. William Hunter's biographer, was a subscriber. Among the subscribers from the American Colonies were Dr. Peter Middleton (1749) of New York, the earliest American historian of medicine; and Dr. Samuel Bard (1763) also of New York, whose essay on diphtheria or " angina suffocativa " is described by Osler as " an American classic of the first rank ".[1] The subscription was not confined to members of the medical profession. Andrew Duncan, senior, was indefatigable in collecting subscriptions, and many eminent men outside the profession responded to his appeal. On 21st April 1775 the foundation stone was laid by Dr. Cullen, who was President of the Royal College of Physicians at the time, and who had suggested the site and plan of the building. The medical professors, and all the members of the Society who were in Edinburgh, were present.[2] The stone bore the inscription, " Sacred to Medicine; Founded April 21st 1775 by Thos. McInnes *Mason* ".

Before the ceremony an extraordinary meeting was held in the Hall of the Royal College of Surgeons, at which Gilbert Blane, one of the Medical Society's presidents, delivered an oration. The extracts which follow show how well the classical model of his eloquence lent itself to a eulogy of the Society's history and aims.[3]

" As this is one of the most important and joyful occasions on which the Medical Society ever assembled, it is with pleasure I endeavour, in compliance with your appointment, to call your attention to the utility of the present undertaking,

---

[1] Garrison, *History of Medicine* (3rd ed.), pp. 390-391.
[2] *Medical and Philosophical Commentaries* (London, 1775), vol. iii, p. 217.
[3] Address to the Medical Society of Students at Edinburgh, upon laying the Foundation of their Hall, 21st April 1775, by G. Blane.

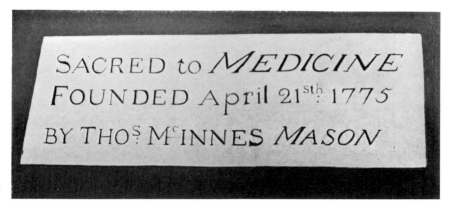

THE FOUNDATION STONE OF THE SOCIETY'S FIRST HALL

This stone is now incorporated in the wall of the staircase at 7 Melbourne Place. It was originally laid on Friday April 21st 1775 by the venerable Dr. Cullen. In June 1853, during the demolition of the Old Hall, the stone was found to contain a glass bottle and a leaden case. In the bottle was a silver medal which is still in the Society's possession

and congratulate you on this auspicious event. It is not my purpose to enlarge on the advantages of our Institution, nor to recommend to you a becoming zeal and attention to its interest. It would be insulting you to suppose that your own experience had not rendered you sensible of the many benefits to be derived from it ; or that any suggestions of mine could enlighten or animate you in your duty.

" The laudable and liberal views of the venerable founders of this Institution can never be enough admired ; and let us not fail, on this occasion, to pay them our tribute of gratitude and applause. Our predecessors perceived that it was not merely the frigid plodding on books, nor the doctrines and precepts of age and authority ; nor the little detail of an empirical practice, that could inspire that taste and spirit, and give that manly turn to our inquiries, which alone can render study agreeable, vigorous and successful. They perceived, that it was in Society alone, by the mutual communication and reflection of the lights of reason and knowledge, that the intellectual as well as the moral powers of man are exalted and perfected.

" Such were the feelings and reflections of the founders of this Society. Here they learned to reason and think for themselves ; here they combated prejudice and error, however sanctified by antiquity and authority, and it was here they learned to love and esteem each other, and to cement the bonds of true friendship ; a friendship sincere and durable, inasmuch as it was founded on a virtuous and liberal intercourse.

" These advantages have descended through a series of successors for near forty years, and have at length devolved upon us. During all this time, one thing was wanting to complete the utility of this establishment, and to give it all the advantages of which it was capable. A place of meeting which should be our own property, was long and ardently wished for, by those who meant well to the Society ; and a scheme for this purpose was at length set on foot by Drs. Duncan and Goulding, who have long adorned it by their uncommon medical and literary accomplishments. They

41

were seconded with liberality and zeal both by present and former members ; and, with reliance on some farther aid, we have now the prospect of seeing their plan accomplished. Let us reflect, that as we are now more the objects of public notice, so a strict attention to the proper end of the Institution is the more indispensable. It is only by inspiring a taste for inquiry and study, by awakening a zeal for our own improvement, and the reputation of the Society, that this undertaking can fulfil its intention. Allow me only to express a wish, that, as virtue and the generous thirst of knowledge have prompted to this undertaking, may science, candour, and liberality of sentiment for ever reign within its walls, and distinguish it to the latest ages."

CHAPTER IV

Cullen's pupils — Gilbert Blane — William Withering — Early American members—John Moultrie—John Morgan—Adam Kuhn —Benjamin Rush—Caspar Wistar—The Brunonian Theory— Cullenians and Brunonians—The Royal Charter—Expulsion of Dr. Martyn and the law against duelling—The Action against the *Edinburgh Evening Post*—Thomas Addis Emmet—The Apparatus Committee—Physiological Experiments in 1785—Thomas Beddoes —Death of Dr. Cullen

THE Medical Hall was opened in 1776. " Besides small apartments, it contains three rooms of thirty feet by twenty each. One of these serves as a hall for their weekly meetings, another as a repository for their valuable collection of medical books, of natural curiosities, and anatomical preparations ; and the third is to be fitted up for chemical experiments. . . . The building has a plain handsome front ; and the roof terminates in a cupola, intended for an observatory, and adorned with the ensigns of the Aesculapian art." [1] The first meeting in the Hall was held on the 26th April 1776. Robert Freer was in the Chair. He was six times a president, and later became Professor of Medicine at Glasgow. On this occasion he delivered an address in which he extolled the generosity of the contributors to the building of the Hall. A list of contributors was hung in the Hall, and the first name on the list was that of Dr. Cullen.

Many of Cullen's pupils, who attained eminence in the profession, were members of the Society. Gilbert Blane was a president only for the one year in which he delivered his address at the foundation of the Hall. In 1775 he read a dissertation before the Society : it was, " What is the Nature

[1] Hugo Arnot, *History of Edinburgh* (1779), p. 430.

of Antiseptics, and how do they Operate ? " [1] In the same year he was President of the Speculative Society of Edinburgh, then in its eleventh session. In 1780 he was appointed Physician to the Fleet under Rodney, and saw service at Gibraltar and in the West Indies. " As the Admiral on these occasions allowed me the honour of being at his side, I carried in my pocket several tourniquets of a simple construction, in case accidents to any person on the quarter deck should have required their use." [2] He rendered great service to his country when, in 1795, he succeeded in reforming the hygiene of the Navy by the introduction of the use of lemon juice for the prevention of scurvy. In 1793 he was appointed Physician to St. Thomas's Hospital, and in 1812 he was made a baronet. Sir Astley Cooper said that he was a painstaking physician, but so cold in his temperament that his junior officers nicknamed him " Chilblaine ". In 1830 Blane established a fund to encourage naval medical science by awarding gold medals ; and a Gilbert Blane medal is still awarded annually to the officer obtaining the highest aggregate marks in the examinations for promotion to Surgeon Commander.

Other distinguished pupils were Thomas Smith (1758), who was the first senior president of the Society, and who won fame on the publication of his Thesis, *De Actione Musculari*, when he graduated M.D. in 1767 ; Matthew Dobson (1755), who assisted Dr. Cullen in his notable experiments on the Cold produced by Evaporation ; Sir Walter Farquhar (1760), who attended Gibbon during his last illness, and who became " the attached friend and physician " [3] to William Pitt, whose first testamentary injunction, dictated on his deathbed, was, " I owe Sir Walter Farquhar one thousand guineas from October 1805, as a professional debt " ; [4] Alexander Monro Drummond (1760), who was six times a president of the Society, and was nominated successor to Dr. Cullen in the Chair of the Institutes of Medicine, but who

[1] *Dissertations of Royal Medical Society* (1892), pp. 15-31.
[2] Blane, *Observations on the Diseases incident to Seamen*, p. 499 (Pt. III, chap. iv, " Of the Wounds received in the Actions of April 1782 ").
[3] Earl Stanhope, *Life of William Pitt* (London, 1861), vol. iv, p. 369.
[4] *Ibid.* p. 384.

did not avail himself of the appointment ; James Carmichael-Smyth in 1765, along with Thomas Smith and Drummond, one of the first four annual presidents of the Society, who was rewarded by Parliament for his recommendation of nitrous fumigation as a means of destroying contagion ; and William Withering (1763), celebrated medical botanist and author of an *Account of the Fox Glove and some of its Medical Uses*, which introduced the right use of digitalis, and showed that valuable drugs might be discovered by the scientific investigation of quack remedies. In 1779 Dr. Jonathan Stokes, " then a student of medicine at Edinburgh, communicated to the Medical Society of that place, the result of Dr. Withering's experience, in the use of this medicine. And, upon this, it was afterwards tried with success in the Royal Infirmary at Edinburgh." [1] John Rogerson (1763) became Physician to the Empress Catherine II of Russia. John Haygarth (1763), who settled in Bath, supplied the cowpox virus to Benjamin Waterhouse, the pioneer of vaccination in the United States of America. Waterhouse wrote to Haygarth : " Accept my best thanks for the phial of vaccine poison. I have inoculated five of my own family, and roused the public attention even beyond what I had imagined. I shall try the variolous matter on them in a week or two. I consider this as a very important thing to my country, where the dread of the smallpox is still great." [2]

The associations of the Society with the American Colonies are a very prominent feature in its history at the time when Dr. Cullen was at the zenith of his great career in the University of Edinburgh. But even before that period, American students arrived in Edinburgh to study medicine, and joined the Society. The earliest was John Moultrie, of South Carolina, who was admitted a member in 1747, during the eleventh session of the Society. His signature is in the first Obligation Book. He graduated M.D. at Edinburgh in 1749, with a Thesis, *De Febre Maligna*. He was " the first American to graduate in medicine

---

[1] *Medical Commentaries for . . . 1785*, vol. x, p. 135.
[2] *Annals of Medicine* (Edinburgh, 1800), vol. v, p. 478.

abroad ".[1]   In a letter, dated 16th July 1746, to his parents, Moultrie gives a picture of student life at that time, and comments on the introduction of clinical lectures.

" I lodge in a house where is seven sober young students, we all breakfast and supp in our rooms and dine at one table in our lodging where there is nothing drank stronger than twopenny . . . we take it by turns to give tea . . . so that I am very little out, unless on Saturday evening I take a walk to Leith to see good Mrs. Seaman.

" My expenses for Chamber £1 : 10s. per Quarter, for dinner £4 per Quarter.   I began with my Latin master the week I came at £2 : 2s. per Quarter, coal, candle, washing and c. unknown.   I shall attend the Lectures of Anatomy and Materia Medica this season at £3 : 3s. each, which is Dr. St. Clair's advice to me who takes some pains about me."

The next American student who joined the Society was Peter Middleton (1749), afterwards of New York, author of the earliest American history of medicine.[2]   Samuel Bard, who afterwards became Professor of Practice of Physic at King's College, New York, joined the Society in 1763.   His notable essay, entitled " An Enquiry into the Nature, Cause, and Cure of the Angina Suffocativa, or Sore Throat Distemper, as it is commonly called by the Inhabitants of the City and Colony of New York ", etc., was communicated to another former member of the Society, Dr. John Morgan ; and by him was laid before the American Philosophical Society, Philadelphia.[3]   Both those men sent their subscriptions towards the building of the Medical Hall to Dr. Andrew Duncan, senior, who took a kindly interest in students from abroad.

John Morgan of Philadelphia joined the Society in 1762. He was introduced to Dr. Cullen in a letter, dated 21st October 1761, from Benjamin Franklin, who was then residing in London.   Dr. Cullen had become personally acquainted with Dr. Franklin, when the latter visited Edinburgh in the

---

[1] Garrison, *History of Medicine* (3rd ed.), p. 422.   [2] *Ibid.* p. 715.
[3] *Transactions*, vol. i, p. 322.

autumn of 1759.   The letter ran: ". . . . thank you for the civilities you were so good as to shew my friend Mr. Shippen.   The bearer, Mr. Morgan, who purposes to reside some time in Edinburgh for the completion of his studies in Physic, is a young gentleman of Philadelphia, whom I have long known and greatly esteem ; and as I interest myself in what relates to him, I cannot but wish him the advantage of your conversation and instructions."

Morgan graduated M.D. at Edinburgh in 1763 : his Thesis was, *De Puris confectione*.   He dedicated his Thesis, which he published, *Societati Medicinae Studiosorum in Academia Edinburgena dudum institutae*.

In a letter, dated November 1764, which Morgan wrote to Dr. Cullen, shortly after he had returned to London from a tour through France and Italy, there is a passage which shows that he was already contemplating the establishment of a medical faculty at the College of his native town.   " My scheme of instituting lectures you will hereafter know more of.   It is not prudent to broach designs prematurely, and mine are not yet fully ripe for execution." [1]

Morgan was afterwards, with William Shippen, the principal founder of the Medical Department of the University of Pennsylvania, which was organised at the College of Philadelphia, and in which he was the first Professor of Practice of Physic.

Adam Kuhn of Pennsylvania joined the Society in 1766. He had been a pupil of Linnaeus before he graduated M.D. at Edinburgh in 1767.   His Thesis was *De Lavatione frigida*. He became Professor of Botany and Materia Medica in the College of Philadelphia.   In the first volume of *Transactions of the American Philosophical Society held at Philadelphia*, which was published in 1771, Kuhn's name appears, along with the names of Benjamin Rush and William Shippen, as a curator ; and the name of Dr. Cullen appears as a European member.   Benjamin Franklin was the founder and first president of the Society.

Benjamin Rush of Pennsylvania joined the Society in 1767.

[1] John Thomson, *Life of William Cullen, M.D.*, vol. i, pp. 634-635.

He graduated M.D. at Edinburgh in 1768. His Thesis was *De Ciborum concoctione*. A year later, he was elected Professor of Chemistry in the College of Philadelphia, where, in 1789, he succeeded Morgan in the Chair of Practice of Physic. When the Medical College of Philadelphia was incorporated into the University of Pennsylvania in 1791, Rush was appointed Professor of the Institutes of Medicine.[1] In the political history of his country, he figures as a signatory of the Declaration of Independence. Rush was elected an honorary member of the Society in 1785.

William Shippen graduated M.D. at Edinburgh in 1761. His Thesis was *De Placentae cum Utero nexu*. He was not an ordinary member of the Society, but he was elected an honorary member in 1787. In the same year, and only a week later, Benjamin Franklin was elected an honorary member for his services to medicine.

Caspar Wistar of Philadelphia joined the Society in 1784, and became a president in the following year. He was appointed Professor of Anatomy in the University of Pennsylvania in 1791, and has given his name to the Wistar Institute of Philadelphia and to the shrub " wistaria ".

During the Tercentenary Festival of the University of Edinburgh, which was celebrated in April 1884, Dr. Billings, the representative of the University of Pennsylvania, speaking at a luncheon in the University New Buildings, said : " It is now about one hundred and thirty-five years since the first American received his degree of Doctor of Medicine at the University of Edinburgh, and Dr. John Moultray returned to Charleston to fight the yellow fever on the methods and principles which he had here acquired. Sixteen years afterwards, four or five graduates of the University of Edinburgh became the first medical faculty in America—the faculty of the University of Pennsylvania—which adopted the organisation and the methods of work of this University, their *Alma Mater* ".[2] In the Congratulatory Address from the Uni-

---

[1] Garrison, *History of Medicine* (3rd ed.), p. 393.
[2] *Records of the Tercentenary Festival*, p. 72. Presented to the Society by the University of Edinburgh.

versity of Pennsylvania to the University of Edinburgh, a tribute was paid to the memory of Dr. Cullen : " Of the five founders and first Professors of our Medical School, four were graduated from the Edinburgh University during 1761 to 1768. To them, their idolised teacher, your great Cullen, stood as sponsor ; he deemed himself ' happy ', as he said, ' in educating those young men to whom so important a Medical College as that in Philadelphia will owe its foundation and future credit '." [1]

These early associations of the Society with the American Colonies survive, with undiminished mutual regard, in the Society's relations to the medical profession in the United States of America. Within recent years, two distinguished senior members of the Society have appeared on important occasions there. In January 1921, Sir Harold Stiles, formerly Professor of Clinical Surgery in the University of Edinburgh, delivered an address before the Society on a visit which he had paid to America. At the invitation of the American College of Surgeons, he had delivered the Convocation Address to the Annual Congress at Philadelphia. In 1936 the U.S.A. Army Medical Service sent an invitation to the president, or other representative of the Society, to attend the Celebration in connection with the One Hundredth Anniversary of the U.S.A. Army Medical Library at Washington. At the request of the Society, Professor B. P. Watson of New York, formerly Professor of Midwifery and Gynaecology in the University of Edinburgh, and a past president of the Society, consented to represent the Society. A message of greeting to the Service was sent.

To return to the eighteenth century, it was in 1767 that Dr. Cullen drew up the first *Statuta Solennia* for medical degrees in the University. The need of those regulations was made apparent by the imposture of Samuel Leeds. Leeds, who was a member of the Society, had attended the University lectures, which were then delivered in Latin, without knowing any Latin, and had obtained the degree of M.D. by presenting a thesis of which he was not the author.

[1] *Records of the Tercentenary Festival*, pp. 266-267.

Exposure followed, and the *Statuta Solennia* were the result.

Another member, who ultimately brought discredit on himself, was John Brown, who became known as the author of the Brunonian System. He was admitted a member of the Society in 1761.

Brown[1] was born in 1736 at Preston, Bunkle, in Berwickshire. His father, a weaver in poor circumstances and a member of the Antiburgher (Secession) Congregation, died while the son was a schoolboy. The boy, however, showed such promise that the Antiburghers contributed funds to keep him at the Latin school at Duns to which his father had sent him, with the intention that he should afterwards study for the ministry. The mastery of Latin which the boy gained there from Mr. Cruickshank, one of the famous dominies of the time, was of great value to him in later life. In 1754 Brown attended a sermon preached before the synod of Merse and Teviotdale in the Established Church at Duns ; and his appearance there was regarded as so serious an offence by the Antiburghers, that he was rebuked for it. Thereupon he broke off all connection with them. In 1756 he entered the University of Edinburgh to study for the Church. About this time David Hume published his *Philosophical Essays*. Brown became an admirer of Hume's philosophy, and to his intimate friends " he declared himself a convert to scepticism, from which he never was reclaimed ". As a student he was more distinguished as a pugilist than as a scholar. His odd figure and deportment, and eccentricities of dress excited the derision of the students, and led to frequent encounters.

At this critical point in his life, he was introduced by his old school friend, Thomas Somerville, to William Elliot of Arkleton, a member of the Royal Medical Society, who was a candidate for the degree of M.D. The purpose of the introduction was the employment of Brown, as an excellent Latin scholar, to translate Elliot's thesis. This task altered his views, and Brown turned to the study of medicine. The medical professors waived their fees in consideration of his

[1] T. Somerville, D.D., Minister of Jedburgh, *My Own Life and Times, 1741–1814*, pp. 134-140.

circumstances ; and he derived an income from giving instruction in Latin to students of medicine, and translating theses.[1]   Dr. Cullen kindly employed him as a tutor to his children.[2]

Brown had shown remarkable aptitude and industry in the acquirement of knowledge.   Unhappily for himself, however, he was suspicious even of his benefactors, and he lacked any sense of gratitude to correct his idea that they were thwarting his ambitions.   This suspicious streak was doubtless fostered by an intemperance which excited remark in an age when sobriety was not commonly held to be a virtue. Yet his qualities as a boon companion made an appeal to students.   Brown was elected a president of the Society in 1773, senior president in 1776, and again senior president in 1779.

Although Brown somewhere condescends to speak of his " very large practice ", and expressed a wish " to ride in his own carriage ",[3] he does not appear to have practised.   The theory which he evolved during his years as tutor was the more remarkable in that while it was the most complete metaphysical theory of medicine ever evolved, it seemed to justify itself in practice.   It was based on the phenomenon of excitability which derived from the spasm and atony of Hoffmann and Cullen and the irritability of Haller and Whytt. Brown postulated that life was due to excitability.   Health was maintained when stimuli evoked the correct degree of excitability.   Diseases were sthenic when stimulation was strong, and asthenic when it was weak or when excessive stimulation had led to exhaustion.   The important thing in diagnosis was to decide whether the disease was sthenic or asthenic. This simplification of diagnosis resolved treatment also into a choice between depressants or stimulants.   Brown used alcohol and opium most frequently, and opium most of all since he considered that it was the strongest stimulant, and that the majority of diseases were asthenic.

Brown's theory found support among the students.

[1] *Ibid.*

[2] John Thomson, *Life of William Cullen, M.D.*, vol. ii, p. 711.

[3] J. Brown, *Elementa Medicinae*, trans. by Author (ed. by T. Beddoes), 2 vols. ; vol. i, Biographical Preface, p. civ.

Cullen used to tell his students in a lecture early in his course that he would have a poor opinion of any of them who took the doctrines of his master as the only just ones without examining those of others. He told them that advance in medicine would come from a generalisation that would reconcile all the facts which he classified in his lists of diseases and explained in terms of spasm and atony and acrimony. Thus the students were encouraged to be sceptical, and their minds were prepared for just such an advance and simplification as Brown's theory seemed to offer. It was, unfortunately, the premature generalisation of a coarser mind rushing in where a finer intellect held back. Brown's theory stood in the same relationship to the teaching of Cullen as did the rigid atomism of Themison to the more enlightened dogmatism of his master Asklepiades. The students could hardly be blamed for being attracted by the simplicity of Brown's theory. When his application for the Chair of the Institutes of Medicine proved unsuccessful, he began, in 1778, to deliver lectures on his new system, using the manuscript of his *Elementa Medicinae* as his text-book. The students formed two parties, the Cullenians and Brunonians, and debated the points at issue with partisan heat ; the latter, as rebels against authority, showed the greater vehemence in the very lively debates at the meetings of the Royal Medical Society.

Meantime the Society was considering the precarious position in regard to its property, heritable and moveable. In 1777 a petition for a charter of incorporation, signed by seven professors and many prominent medical practitioners in the city, was presented to the Town Council. But in 1778 it was clear that the University was resolved to oppose the petition. An endeavour was made by the Society to ascertain the attitude of the whole Senatus, but it was met by a policy of evasion in which Principal Robertson figured. In this connection, it may be mentioned that the proposal, which was made in 1782, to incorporate, under a Royal Charter, the Society of Antiquaries of Scotland, met with similar opposition from the same quarter. The reasons put forward by the Principal and a number of the professors were " a little far-fetched ". " They pointed out, that though there were two literary societies in England, Scotland was ' too narrow a country ' for more than one, as every one must allow ; and that the formation of a Royal Society, including every branch of literature and science, would be better." [1] It was evident that the Medical Society would not obtain a charter from the Town Council. Before the close of the summer session in 1778 the Society appointed Drs. Andrew Duncan, senior, and Andrew Wardrop, and Mr. Robert Freer, a committee, to obtain legal advice as to the best method of seeking incorporation. The Society had passed an astute proposal by Dr. Duncan that application should be made to the Surgeons to grant a Disposition of the ground feued to the Society in favour of the presidents in office, and their successors in office, on behalf of the Society, in terms of the missive which had passed between Mr. Robert Walker on the part of the Surgeons, and Dr. Andrew Duncan and Mr. Aitken on the part of the Society ; and that measures should be taken to obtain for the Society the rights and privileges of an incorporated body.

Two leading members of the Scottish Bar, the Lord Advocate, Henry Dundas, and the Hon. Henry Erskine, were consulted. Dundas, afterwards Viscount Melville, became, under Pitt, the Tory dictator of Scotland. Henry Erskine declared himself a Whig. He was dismissed from the office of Dean of the Faculty of Advocates because he had presided over a public meeting which protested against the war with France. Dr. Andrew Duncan was an intimate friend of Henry Erskine, and Erskine's brother, the Earl of Buchan, was in the favoured position of a correspondent of George III in matters connected with the Earl's estate of Dryburgh, which included the Abbey, a correspondence which the King evidently enjoyed. Dr. Duncan no doubt consulted his friend, and framed the Memorial which the committee presented to Counsel. Counsel gave it as their Opinion that a Charter from the Crown would answer the purposes of the Society, and that an application through the

[1] Lieut.-Col. A. Fergusson, *The Hon. Henry Erskine* (1882), p. 206.

Secretary of State to be laid before the Crown would have the effect of procuring a Charter. They considered that the petition could not proceed upon better grounds than those set forth in the Memorial. The Society, after considering the Opinion of Counsel, decided to petition the Crown, and appointed Drs. Andrew Duncan, Maitland, and Wardrop to draw up the Petition and take the necessary steps to obtain the Charter. They were given full powers to raise, by loan or otherwise, money to defray the expense. In this matter the Society was aided, as so often, by the generosity of the medical professors.

At a meeting of the Society on 4th August 1778, with Dr. Wardrop in the chair, a draft of the Petition was submitted and unanimously approved. Dr. Wardrop was authorised to sign the Petition in the name of the Society, and transmit it to Mr. Chalmer, Solicitor in London, with instructions for taking the steps necessary to procure the Charter. The Petition ran :

" To the King's Most Excellent Majesty,
 " The Humble Petition of the Presidents and Members
  of the Medical Society of Edinburgh
 " Sheweth
 " That in the year 1737, certain Persons, Students and Practitioners of Physick at Edinburgh, formed themselves into a Society for the laudable purpose of promoting an Ardour for Medical Enquiries, and since that time the Society has continued under the title of the Medical Society of Edinburgh, having regular meetings, admitting into their number, Persons engaged in the Study and Profession of Physick, and in the month of November annually electing four of the members to preside by turns.

 " That the Society, by contributions of the Members, have gradually made a collection of Medical Books, which is daily increasing, and of the Chemical and Philosophical Instruments, and the like, to a considerable value. They likewise have purchased ground within the City of Edinburgh, and thereupon erected a building in which is their Hall or place of Meeting, and their Library.

" The Petitioners beg leave to represent to Your Majesty that, from their not being a Body Corporate, they find themselves under difficulties in obtaining compleat Titles to their real property, and in securing and managing both it and their moveable effects, so that they may remain with the Society in perpetual succession, agreeable to the design of the contributors ; for remedy whereof they are advised to apply to Your Majesty, and do most humbly pray,

" That Your Majesty will be graciously pleased to grant Your Royal Charter or Letters Patent under the Seal appointed by the Treaty of Union to be kept and used in Scotland, in place of the Great Seal formerly used there, constituting and erecting Robert Freer of Edinburgh, Surgeon, James Melliar of Taunton in the County of Somerset, Andrew Wardrop of Edinburgh, and Caleb Parry of Cirencester, in the County of Gloucester, Doctors of Medicine, present Presidents of said Society, and their successors, and the other Persons who are or hereafter shall be Members of said Society into one Body Politic and Corporate, or Legal Incorporation, under the name and title of the Medical Society of Edinburgh.

" And Your Majesty's Petitioners shall ever pray etc. Signed by desire and in presence of a General Meeting of the Members of said Society held at Edinburgh this fourth day of August 1778 by,

" ANDW. WARDROP, Prest."

A Royal Charter of Incorporation was granted by King George III. At a meeting of the Society, held on 2nd January 1779, Mr. John Ford, President, in the Chair, read the Royal Warrant dated at St. James's, the 14th day of December 1778. The original is in Latin. The following translation of part of it appeared in *Medical Commentaries* : Edinburgh, vol. vi, 1779.

" His Majesty being satisfied that the design of the petitioners is laudable, and that they deserve encouragement, does therefore ordain a Patent or Charter, to be passed, or expede under the Seal appointed by the Treaty of Union, to be kept and used in Scotland, in place of the Great Seal formerly used there, constituting, erecting, and incorporating, as His Majesty, by his prerogative royal, and special grace, for himself, and his royal successors, hereby constitutes, erects, and incorporates, and perpetually establishes and confirms, the said Robert Freer, James Melliar, Andrew Wardrop, and Caleb Parry, and their successors, presidents of the Society for the time being, and other persons, who now are, or hereafter shall be, members of the said Society, into one body, politic and corporate, or legal incorporation, under the name and title of *The Medical Society of Edinburgh*; and as such, and by such name, to have perpetual endurance and succession ; and to be able and capable to take and hold property, real and personal, and to sue, plead, defend and answer ; and to be sued, impleaded, defended, and answered, in all, or any of His Majesty's Courts of Justice, and in other respects to act, or do, agreeable to the law and practice of His Majesty's Kingdoms in like cases."

On 12th January 1779 the Charter was sealed at Edinburgh. The Charter and Seal are now displayed in the Society's Hall in a case on the left of the Chair. They were placed there in 1923 with the aid of a donation given for the purpose by E. A. Carmichael, F.R.C.S.E.

Caleb Parry, whose name appears in the Charter, became " a highly esteemed practitioner of Bath, who, like Heberden, acquired a lifelong habit of taking notes, described the first recorded cases of facial hemiatrophy (1814), and of congenital idiopathic dilatation of the colon (1825), and, in 1786, left an account of exophthalmic goitre so complete and original that it more justly entitles him to the honour of its discovery than either Flajani (1800), Graves (1835), or Basedow (1840)." [1]

In the year that the Charter was granted, John Brown graduated M.D. at St. Andrews. In 1780, when he was a president of the Society for the third time, he published his *Elementa Medicinae*, which expounded his system and

---

[1] Garrison, *History of Medicine* (3rd ed.), p. 372.

THE ROYAL CHARTER

Charter of incorporation granted by King George III to the Presidents and Associates of the Medical Society of Edinburgh; reciting their petition, granting privileges, and confirming Robert Freer, James Melliar, Andrew Wardrop, and Caleb Parry in their office as Presidents. Dated at St. James's, 14th December 1778. Written to the seal, registered, and sealed with the King's great seal for Scotland at Edinburgh, 12th January 1779

inveighed against the Edinburgh medical professors. Among the profession in Great Britain the theory did not have any great following, for Lettsom in London, and James Gregory in Edinburgh were enunciating a critical empiricism to which a speculative theory, such as Brown's, was irrelevant. In Italy and Germany it met with more success, since the philosophical atmosphere was more propitious. Later, in France, Broussais developed his theory from it, and Benjamin Rush in America taught an exaggerated form of it. Rush was a student in Edinburgh at the same time as Brown. He taught that only one disease existed, and that the proximate cause of disease was irregular, convulsive, or wrong action in the system affected. When yellow fever broke out in 1793, he read all that the authorities had to say, and announced that bleeding and purging offered the only cure. His system was for long unquestioned. Eventually it collapsed completely.

Brown's theory appealed to students in Germany, and in Göttingen a troop of Hanoverian horse had to disperse a riot between opposing factions. In Edinburgh also feeling ran high among the students, and the Society found itself compelled to pass a law against duelling.

At an ordinary meeting of the Society, on 10th February 1781, the expulsion of Dr. John Richard Martyn was proposed. The reasons given for the proposal were that he had introduced anarchy and confusion into the Society by blending private with public business, and had thereby materially injured the Society by exposing it to the ridicule of strangers ; that he had endeavoured to take away the freedom of debate which was essential to the well-being of the Society, and had attempted to introduce new modes of settling differences in debate by appeals to the sword ; that he had made use of expressions reflecting upon the honour of the Society ; and that he had put an effectual check to the growth of the Society by declaring publicly that he would reject every candidate whose sentiments differed from his own. The last item of the accusation was especially serious, as two negatives were sufficient, at the time, to reject a petition for a seat in the Society.

An extraordinary meeting was held to consider the proposal of expulsion, but Dr. Martyn forestalled discussion by resigning his seat. His speech on the occasion was a bitter denunciation of the Cullenians and their teachers. He said that the proposal against him was set on foot by some despotic teachers ; that the original intention of the Society was counteracted by a prejudice that debarred the opportunity of liberal enquiry ; and that he resigned his seat with the greater pleasure, as he was convinced that the good wishes of every gentleman in the Society, who really deserved the name, attended him in his principle and conduct, and in a thorough contempt for the behaviour of a party in the Society, who had not the spirit to think for themselves, and were only the tools of a set of teachers, who, by their ungenerous proceedings, were bringing disgrace on a medical school, once the most famous in Europe, but now likely to decline.

The Society took prompt action to prevent similar defiance of order in the future. Nine days after Dr. Martyn's speech, an extraordinary meeting was held to receive proposals for new laws. Charles Stuart, a pupil and friend of Dr. Cullen, and afterwards P.R.C.P.E., moved " That it shall be enacted that the president shall censure every personal, impolite, or disorderly expression, which may occur in the warmth of debate ; that it shall be his right to stop the speaker for that purpose ; that if the president shall be inattentive to this, every member shall be entitled to call his attention to it, and, if necessary, the sense of the Society shall be taken directly on the business ; that such concessions shall be made, and such satisfaction given by the member who has offended, as the Society may judge to be necessary, in case of refusal of which, the offending member shall be *ipso facto* expelled." The proposal was admitted as a law at the legislative meeting held on 7th April 1781.

The next threat to freedom of debate in the Society, arising out of the Brunonian controversy, was met with equal vigour and decision. An anonymous Brunonian had communicated to the *Edinburgh Evening Post* certain proceedings of the Society, which were published forthwith in that paper. Such an encroachment upon the rights of the Society, if not repressed, and secured against in time coming, would have counteracted the very purposes of the Society.

Campbell Denovan, the printer and publisher of the newspaper, inserted the communications in a series of articles, under the title of " Medical Intelligence ". It was clear that the intention of the publications was to communicate a depreciatory account of the papers read and the discussions held in the Society. The purpose was to misrepresent, and to expose them to ridicule and contempt ; and they were evidently the production of some mean, illiberal person, who maliciously wished to injure the Society. But the urgent necessity of putting a stop to the publications was that members would neither read papers nor attempt discussions, if they knew that these would be exhibited next day in a public newspaper.

The Society adopted measures to detect the culprit and prevent further leakage of information. At the time, there was a law entitling four members, at the private business of every ordinary meeting, to nominate, according to seniority, each, one visitor, to be admitted at the public business of the next ordinary meeting. The law was temporarily suspended. It was resolved that no visitors should be admitted until the publications of the debates in the *Edinburgh Evening Post* were stopped, or the author of those formerly published was detected. A committee was appointed to draw up a Case for the Opinion of Counsel, enquiring what legal means ought to be pursued to prevent such publications in future, and to bring to justice the author and abettors of the articles already published. Counsel consulted were the Hon. Henry Erskine and Robert Cullen, eldest son of Dr. Cullen. Their Opinion was asked whether the publications could be considered as a libel upon the Society at large, or on any individuals in it ; if libellous, what were the proper steps to be taken to punish the author, and whether the publisher could be considered as the author, or obliged to produce his author or authors.

The Opinion of Counsel was that even though the articles

had been faithful representations of the proceedings, they were an encroachment on the Society's exclusive right of publication ; that their defamatory character gave a right to prosecute both author and publisher for redress, but that it was advisable, if an action were raised, to found chiefly on the right of publication ; that there should be a conclusion, in the summons, not only for damages, but for having the Society's sole right to publish any account of their proceedings declared and established by a judgment of the Court, and for prohibiting such encroachments in future ; and that it would be proper to conclude for damages against the printer as well as the author.

Campbell Denovan having refused to discover the author, an Action was brought against him alone. The Lord Ordinary, Lord Hailes, gave judgment that it was lawful for every one to publish an account of the enquiries and debates of a Society instituted for the purpose of free enquiry and debate, concerning matters of science, unless such account were libellous or contrary to law ; and that the articles libelled on and said to be medical intelligence consisted of unmeaning declamation, and of things altogether unintelligible ; and therefore were not actionable. A Petition to the Lords of Council and Session—i.e. an Appeal to the Inner House, which was not separated into two Divisions until 1808—was framed a fortnight later, but there is no evidence that it was acted upon. The Society probably thought that there was no justification for going further on the abstract question of right, as the firm attitude of the Society had already put an end to the offending publications.

The sequel to these legal proceedings in 1783 was a proposal by Thomas Addis Emmet, which was admitted as a law at the legislative meeting held in the first week of March 1784. Emmet's proposal was: " That every person, who shall be hereafter admitted to the Society, shall be obliged to declare upon his honour, as part of his obligation when signing the laws, that he will not at any time hereafter communicate any things that shall pass in the Society, with a view to their publication, directly or indirectly, to any printer or publisher ".

Emmet was elected a president of the Society in 1784. He graduated M.D. at Edinburgh in 1783. His academic career in Edinburgh, outwith professional studies, was remarkable in that he was president of the Speculative Society for three years in succession, 1783–84–85. After leaving Edinburgh he settled in practice in Dublin, where his father, Robert Emmet, who was unanimously elected an honorary member of the Royal Medical Society of Edinburgh in 1783, was physician to the Viceroy. Shortly afterwards he relinquished medicine for the Irish Bar, where he acquired a large practice, but the Irish Rebellion of 1798 put a stop to his success. As a chief of the United Irish Party he was implicated in the outbreak, arrested, and detained as a political prisoner for three years at Fort George, in Scotland. On his release he went eventually to the United States of America, where he became leading Counsel at the New York Bar. He was an accomplished man of high character, and an eloquent speaker. His younger brother Robert was hanged for his share in the Irish Conspiracy of 1803.

The loss of the minute books for this period makes it necessary to rely on external evidence ; and from that it is certain that, after 1784, the passions aroused by the Brunonian controversy subsided rapidly. Brown's brief spell of eminence did him no good, morally or materially. Brown continued his lectures with his bottles of whisky and phials of laudanum to stimulate his natural eloquence to frenzied declamation.[1] He fell into debt, and for a time his pupils attended his lectures in prison.[2] Finding his supporters dwindling, he left Edinburgh in 1786 ; and two years later he died in London at the age of 52.

The Society gained from the controversy the law (now Law 53) by which the president asks for an assurance that no hostile meeting will take place if, in the heat of debate, one member utters a personality against another.

About this time great interest was shown by the Society in physiological experiments. Only a few years before, in

---

[1] J. Brown, *Elementa Medicinae*, trans. by Author (ed. by T. Beddoes), Biographical Preface, p. lxxxvii.　　　　　[2] *Ibid.* p. lxxxix.

the winter session 1777–78, Dr. Adair Crawford had described, for the first time, at a meeting of the Society, his experiments on animal calorimetry. His paper doubtless acted as a stimulus to investigation. In 1785 a committee was appointed to supervise the fitting up of a laboratory for chemical experiments, and " to purchase different philosophical instruments, particularly an electrical machine, thermometers, barometers, and other instruments for meteorological observations ". In 1786 the Society announced that several rooms in the Hall were available to members for the purpose of private dissection and chemical experiments. It was agreed to appoint annually an experiment committee, and to allow them a certain sum from the Society's funds to defray the expense of such experiments as the Society should think proper to direct on particular subjects. The use of these rooms was allowed, under proper regulations, to members who chose to conduct experiments at their own expense.[1] The records show that Andrew Fyfe, dissector to Dr. Monro, *secundus*, assisted at several experiments in 1785. Rabbits were used to study the effects of heat and cold on the body, and the state of the stomach during vomiting. Dogs and calves were used for transfusion experiments, which sometimes failed owing to clots in the cannula, but some succeeded, and allowed the investigation of plethora in the recipient and anaemia in the donor. Fowls as well as rabbits were used to study the fatal effect of respiring fixed air. The discussions on these experiments were keen.

In 1796 an Apparatus Committee is mentioned in the records for the first time. A great stimulus to chemical investigation was given about this time by the very successful large-scale experiments which Dr. Thomas Charles Hope, Professor of Chemistry, performed before his class. The Apparatus Committee continued until 1835, when it was combined with the Museum Committee under the latter name. At different times it included among its members Marshall Hall, John Davy, Thomas Addison, Bransby Blake Cooper, Charles Hastings and Allen Thomson.

[1] *Medical Commentaries* (Edinburgh, 1787–95), vol. i, p. 430.

Thomas Beddoes, who later edited Brown's translation of the *Elementa Medicinae*, and prefaced it with a biography of the author, joined the Society in 1785 and became a president in the same year. " He took an active part in the extensive series of physiological experiments in which some members of the Society were at that period engaged." [1] Caspar Wistar of Philadelphia was a president along with him. Beddoes graduated M.D. at Oxford in 1786. He is noteworthy as the founder of the Pneumatic Institution at Clifton, where, on the recommendation of Gregory Watt, youngest son of James Watt, the celebrated engineer, seconded by Mr. Davis Gilbert, afterwards president of the Royal Society, he engaged a young Cornishman to superintend the institution. The young man was Humphry Davy, who " was employed for about a year in investigating the effects of the gases when employed in respiration ".[2] There Davy discovered the anaesthetic properties of nitrous oxide. Beddoes' comment on the results of the experiments was prophetic. He wrote : " Man may sometime come to rule over the causes of pain or pleasure, with a dominion as absolute as that which he at present exercises over the instruments of his convenience ".[3] The constructor of the apparatus for the Institution was James Watt. Interesting but less happy was the attempt to show that all disease was the result of excess or deficiency of the recently discovered oxygen. With this, Louis Odier was associated. He was a president of the Society in 1770.

Beddoes was the author of a Memoir of John Brown, which incensed the latter's eldest son, William Cullen Brown, who wrote a Memoir of his father in order that, as he declared, justice should be done to his father's memory. William Cullen Brown studied medicine at Edinburgh, where he received generous treatment from the professors. He joined the Society in 1793, and became a president in 1801. In 1802 he graduated M.D. at Edinburgh.

The names of three other pupils of Dr. Cullen, who were

---

[1] J. E. Stock, M.D., *Life of Thomas Beddoes, M.D.*, p. 14.
[2] Thomas Thomson, *History of Chemistry* (1830-31), vol. ii, p. 257.
[3] J. E. Stock, M.D., *Life of Thomas Beddoes, M.D.*, p. 179.

members of the Society, may be mentioned. Thomas Fowler (1776) introduced his solution of arsenic in *Medical Reports of the Effects of Arsenic* (1786), which he dedicated to Dr. Andrew Duncan, senior : " As neither Time nor Distance can ever efface from my Memory the Kindness and Friendship with which you honoured me during my Residence at Edinburgh ; I beg leave to inscribe to you these medical Reports, as a Testimony of my great Respect for your Abilities and Virtues ". James Currie (1778) became an eminent physician in Liverpool, and published, in 1797, the first important work on hydrotherapy, basing his treatment of fevers on careful thermometry. This was an excellent piece of clinical research. It originated in the dissertation, " On the effects of cold on the Animal Body ". Currie was the first editor of the works of Robert Burns. The third, Robert Willan, has been mentioned previously.

In 1789 Dr. Cullen resigned from the Chair of Practice of Medicine. A meeting of his pupils and admirers was held in the Society's Hall to consider a suitable form for a memorial of his great services to medicine, to be placed in the University Buildings, which were then being erected. The four presidents of the Society were members of the Committee appointed to receive subscriptions. The bust of Dr. Cullen, which was executed at the time, is in the library of the University. A portrait executed by David Martin, in 1776, for the Society is in their Hall.

In 1790 Dr. Cullen died. As a student, he had attended the informal meetings which laid the foundation of the Society. As a celebrated teacher and physician he had been elected an honorary member of the Society in 1764. As a professor in the University of Edinburgh the Society's debt to him was as great : indirectly on account of his encouragement of independent thought among his students ; as it was directly for his many activities on behalf of the Society.

CHAPTER V

DR. ANDREW DUNCAN's friendship with Henry Erskine was
doubtless an important factor in the success which attended
the Society's petition for a Royal Charter. The friendship
commenced at school. " On the Erskine family settling
at St. Andrews, Henry and his younger brother, being too
young to attend any of the college classes, were sent to learn
the rudiments of the Latin tongue at the school of a very
worthy man, Richard Dick by name. This fact is recorded
by a schoolfellow of theirs, and an especial friend of Henry
Erskine, Andrew Duncan, who became afterwards a professor
at the University of Edinburgh, and somewhat a ' character '.
. . . Under the title of *Ludi Apollinares*, Professor Duncan
instituted certain gymnastic sports, consisting of golf on
Leith Links, swimming, etc., amongst his medical brethren
in Edinburgh. In the capacity of scribe to these ' filii
Aesculapii ', he produced from time to time *Carmina Rari-
orum Macaronicorum*, as he styled them, one of which is a
history of his own life, in doggerel rhyme." [1] In this poem
Dr. Duncan mentions—

> Good Dick, a teacher much respected,
> Boys from all quarters had collected ;
> And by the powerful aid of taws ;
> Enforcing pedagogic laws

[1] Lieut.-Col. A. Fergusson, *The Hon. Henry Erskine* (1882), p. 63.

. . . 'Twill then suffice
To name a few whom much I prize . . .
Erskines, a couple precious more,
Than ever Britons saw before.[1]

Dr. Duncan was the founder of the Public Dispensary in West Richmond Street, Edinburgh, and of the Edinburgh Asylum for the Insane, and he was successful in obtaining Royal Charters for both institutions. His interest in the treatment of the insane was aroused when, " as a young practitioner, he was called upon to attend the poet Fergusson in the local madhouse. The scene he encountered was never forgotten by him ; and, when he finally attained power at the top of his profession in Edinburgh, he laid the foundations of Morningside Asylum and the Chair of Psychiatry in the University of Edinburgh." [2] He presided at the first meeting of the Harveian Society, which he founded in 1782 ; and he was the first president of the Medico-Chirurgical Society of Edinburgh at its institution in 1821. In 1790 he was appointed to the Chair of the Institutes of Medicine ; and in the same year, and again in 1824, he was elected P.R.C.P.E. He was the founder of the Caledonian Horticultural Society, which was later incorporated by Royal Charter. In 1808 he was presented with the Freedom of the City of Edinburgh in recognition of the benefits he had conferred on the community.

In January 1779 Dr. Duncan put forward a proposal that the Royal Medical Society should exercise its right of publication. He proposed that at regular monthly meetings, communications intended for publication should be read and considered ; and that all the papers should be referred to the future consideration of a printing committee, who should superintend the printing of these, as the transactions of the Society. Papers on medical subjects, or such parts of philosophy as were connected with medicine were to be accepted from practitioners outside the Society, as well as from members.

[1] A. Duncan, sen., M.D., *Miscellaneous Poems, extracted from the Records of the Circulation Club at Edinburgh* (1818), pp. 19-22.

[2] Inaugural Address to the Society by the Professor of Psychiatry (the late G. M. Robertson), 15th October 1920.

A circular letter, dated 1st March 1779, which explained the nature of the Society's intention, was addressed to absent members, many of whom were practitioners of high reputation in every part of the British Dominions, requesting communications for the Society's transactions. The project did not progress beyond an announcement, in the *Medical Commentaries*, of the forthcoming publication of the first volume of *Transactions*, which was to contain an article on the Sigaultian Operation, communicated by Dr. John Purcell, Professor of Anatomy in Trinity College, Dublin.[1] Dr. Purcell, a non-member, was the first distinguished man of science to be elected an honorary member of the Society. Dr. Cullen was the second. Hitherto, honorary members were simply ordinary members who became such by rotation.

At the beginning of 1782 fresh regulations were introduced for the guidance of the committee, and two years later the forthcoming publication of the *Transactions* was once more announced. There the activities of the committee ceased ; and the plan is not mentioned again in the minutes until 1814, when it was renewed in a modified form, but without success. From the outset its success was doubtful. The field was already occupied by the *Medical and Philosophical Commentaries* edited by Dr. Andrew Duncan, senior. These were published from 1773 till 1795. They succeeded the *Medical Essays and Observations* and *Essays and Observations, Physical and Literary* published by Monro's Society and the Philosophical Society respectively, and were continued as the *Annals of Medicine*, conducted by Dr. Duncan and his son, Dr. Andrew Duncan, junior. In 1805 the latter became the first editor of the *Edinburgh Medical and Surgical Journal*, which, in 1855, became incorporated with the *Edinburgh Monthly Journal of Medical Science* and assumed the title *Edinburgh Medical Journal*. Thus it was one of the earliest periodicals to be devoted entirely to medicine. The Medical Society, founded by Monro, in 1731, for the purpose of publishing medical essays had declined rapidly. After the first year of the institution, the members

[1] *Medical Commentaries*, vol. vi, pp. 350-351.

neglected their duty, so that the work of compiling the essays fell almost entirely on Monro. Still less, therefore, was it likely that Dr. Duncan's plan of publication for the Royal Medical Society, whose active members were undergraduates and recent graduates, would be a success. Without the regular support of the senior members, the active members could not supply the material for publication.

Dr. Duncan, senior, was six times a president of the Society, and was treasurer from 1771 to 1786, during the time when money was being raised for the building and fitting up of the Hall. The Society recognised the value of his unceasing activity on its behalf, particularly with regard to the building of the Hall, and the obtaining of the Royal Charter, by presenting him with a gold medal.

The creation of an Order of Corresponding Members, on 1st March 1784, was a logical development of the plan to publish the *Transactions* of the Society. The Order shared, to some extent, the fortunes of the plan of publication. It was relinquished in 1796, and resumed in 1817. Two years later, a committee appointed to prepare a diploma reported that the Order was not sufficiently defined to enable them to arrange a diploma applicable to the various descriptions of its members. They were authorised to examine the laws relating to the Order. The investigation revealed that a corresponding member, who might be an ordinary or extra-ordinary member, forfeited his privileges if he came to reside within ten miles of Edinburgh, so that any distinguished foreigner elected to the Order, on coming within ten miles of the city, would forfeit not only his privileges but also his membership. The committee also pointed out that on the Continent the title was regarded as inferior to that of ordinary member, to which it was regarded merely as a step ; and that it was needless to bestow the title on ordinary or extra-ordinary members who, without it, enjoyed all the privileges of the Society. They recommended the abolition of the title and plan. The recommendation was not accepted, and, at the legislative meeting in 1820, the offending anomalies were removed. The Order was made to consist of any practitioner eminent in medicine or surgery, whether previously a member of the Society or not, provided he was not permanently resident in Edinburgh. No dissertation was to be required from the corresponding member, who was to enjoy all the privileges of an extraordinary member, subject to the same restrictions. A suitable diploma was arranged.

Complementary also to the plan of publication was the institution in March 1784 of an annual Prize Question. It was resolved that the Society should annually propose, at the beginning of January, experimental enquiries concerning different subjects in medicine and medical philosophy. The essays, written in Latin, were to be transmitted to the secretaries of the printing committee, and the adjudicators were to be the members of the printing committee. At the first meeting in the ensuing April a medal of twenty guineas value was to be given to the author of the best essay, if such essay were judged to have sufficient merit. The Society reserved to itself the right of publishing the prize essay in any form it might think proper. Each dissertation was to bear a motto which was likewise to appear on the outside of a sealed packet containing the name and address of the author. The enquiry proposed by the Society in 1784 was " On the General and Medical Properties of the different Species of Air " ; and in 1785 " On the Nature and Varieties of Fermentation ". In 1793 the Prize Question consisted of four queries regarding animal electricity. The essays were to be written in English, French or Latin ; and Drs. Adair, Black, Duncan, Gregory, Hutton, Monro and Rutherford were appointed a committee to adjudge the prize.[1] One essay was sent in, which, in the opinion of the committee, displayed great ingenuity ; but the committee did not consider the author of it to be entitled to the prize as he only answered the first of the queries proposed. In 1795 the Society renewed the offer of a prize of twenty-five guineas for the best essay on the same four questions. The same committee were to adjudge the prize. In 1797 the Society

[1] *Medical Commentaries* (1794), Decade Second, vol. viii, pp. 465-467.

F

received a Latin dissertation ; and in 1798 the prize was adjudged to the author of it, Professor Creve of Mainz.[1]

Relinquished in 1796, the Prize Question was renewed in 1801, with modified conditions. A medal or set of books, to the value of five guineas, was to be given annually to the author of the best dissertation on an experimental subject, and the competition was to be confined to members of the Society.

In March 1811 the prize committee reported that they had received only one dissertation which they unanimously thought to be deserving of the prize. The author was James D. Maycock, one of the presidents. It was resolved that the dissertation should be transcribed into the Society's *Transactions* ; that an extraordinary public meeting should be held for the purpose of hearing the dissertation read from the Chair ; and that visitors should be admitted as usual. Another committee was appointed to select the Prize Question for 1812. It consisted of three distinguished senior members, Andrew Coventry, first Professor of Agriculture in the University of Edinburgh, Robert Jameson, Professor of Natural History, and Andrew Duncan, junior, Professor of Medical Jurisprudence. It is possible that Professor Jameson found consolation in this renewed contact with the Society, for his subject evidently did not appeal to Edinburgh students, other than those studying medicine. He considered " the too engrossing influence of the law as being the most immediate and effectual of all the dampers under which his favourite study has so long languished. . . . He informed me that three-fourths of the students who attend his lectures are strangers and students of medicine, chiefly English." [2]

In 1839 the Prize Essay scheme did not appear in the laws, and there is no further mention of the scheme in the minutes until 1907, when a decline in the membership appeared to demand special efforts to attract more members. One proposal was to revive the Prize Essay. Three members

---

[1] *Annals of Medicine* (Edinburgh, 1800), vol. v, p. 259.
[2] *Peter's Letters to His Kinsfolk* (3rd ed., 1819), vol. i, pp. 259-260. The Author was J. G. Lockhart, Sir Walter Scott's biographer.

were appointed a committee to enquire into the subject and to report. Early in 1908, they reported that a careful examination of the records of the Society had convinced them that they could not recommend a revival of the scheme.

In April 1779 a copy of the Feu Contract, which had occupied so conspicuous a place in the policy adopted to procure a Royal Charter, was deposited with the Society for the inspection of members, in order that it might be passed, and the principal duly completed. The Surgeons generously fixed the feu duty at £5 *per annum*. Mr. Balderston, W.S., Clerk to the Surgeons, was appointed law agent to the Society.

The Society was now firmly secured in regard to its proper object, the free discussion of dissertations. The discussions were soon to have an added value and influence by the participation in them of intellects of the highest order. Just as the reputations of the first Professors in the Faculty of Medicine brought students to Edinburgh in the middle of the eighteenth century, so in the latter half of the century students were attracted by the celebrity of Cullen, Black, Gregory and Monro, *secundus*, by the unique system of clinical teaching, and by the presence in Edinburgh of many men who were acknowledged leaders in science, philosophy and literature. Other causes of the increase in the number of students of medicine at Edinburgh were the Test Act, which still excluded nonconformists from the English universities, and the French Revolution and Napoleonic wars which closed the Continent to those who wished to study medicine at the schools there. But there was another and more gratifying reason for the increase in numbers and for the high quality of the students of medicine at Edinburgh at this time. Those who had studied under that great man, the first Monro, were in practice all over the world, and they were advising men, who intended to study medicine, to go to Edinburgh. Many of them had been members of the Society, and they urged their protégés to join the Society. In that way, and by the recommendation of the medical professors at Edinburgh, who had themselves experienced its benefits, the Society gained many valuable members.

Mention of the French Revolution revives the memory of two members of the Society, Dr. William Buchan (1761), author of a " best seller " entitled *Domestic Medicine*, and Dr. Hugh James (1771), for it was on their recommendation that Marat, the French revolutionist, obtained the degree of M.D. from the University of St. Andrews. " Marat was bred to medicine, which he studied at the University of Edinburgh with very respectable results." [1]   His name is not on the Matriculation Roll, but it is known that he passed at this stage in his career (1773-74) under various names.   The statement that he taught tambouring in the city under the alias, " John White ", has been applied to his second sojourn in Edinburgh : [2] but it is applicable also to his first stay in the city in 1773-74.   The Matriculation Roll of the University, which then stated the subjects of study, shows that in 1773 a " John White " studied anatomy and surgery, practice of medicine, and botany, and in 1774, anatomy and surgery, and physiology.   Dr. Henry Lonsdale of Carlisle, who was twice a president of the Society, stated that Marat, " the incarnation of the repulsive " yet, almost inconceivably, " so highly regarded ", studied medicine at Edinburgh.[3]   It is likely then that " John White " was Marat.   The St. Andrews degree of M.D. was equivalent to an honorary one, in those days, and was given on the recommendation of two medical men known to the Senate.   The diploma was forwarded on receipt of the graduation fee.

Prior to 1775, when he obtained the degree, Marat had published several works anonymously.   The diploma, applied for and granted in his real name, conferred a prestige on him. In 1775 there appeared " An Essay on Gleets " ; and in 1776, " An Enquiry into the Nature, Cause, and Cure of a singular disease of the eyes " ; and the author's name appeared on the title-page, " By Jean-Paul Marat, M.D. ".[4]

Two distinguished members, who were presidents in this great period of the Society's history, have recorded their

---

[1] *Poetry of the Anti-Jacobin* (1854 ; ed. Charles Edmonds), p. 248.

[2] Sidney L. Phipson, *Jean-Paul Marat* (1924), p. 110.   [3] *Ibid.* pp. 15-16.

[4] *Reprint of Two Tracts*, by Jean-Paul Marat, M.D.   Edited by James B. Bailey, Librarian, Royal College of Surgeons of England, 1891.

estimates of the debates. Thomas Beddoes wrote : " If examinations are regarded as powerful incentives to diligence, none can equal in severity those which are carried on at the voluntary meetings, which it has long been the custom to hold at the great school of medicine in Scotland ".[1] Sir James Mackintosh was equally emphatic : " Such debates were the only public examinations in which favour could have no place, and which never could degenerate into mere formality ; they must always be severe, and always just." [2] This high standard was owing to the quality of the dissertations, and the importance which was attached to the strict observance of every rule of procedure concerning them.

In a manuscript copy of the Code of Laws transcribed under the superintendence of a committee appointed near the close of the 44th session, in 1781, the rules for the providing of subjects and the delivering of papers are very clearly laid down. At the first ordinary meeting in March the president ordered every ordinary member, and such honorary ones as received the books in circulation, to deliver to the secretary at the next ordinary meeting, the History of a Case, a Medical or Philosophical Question, and an Aphorism of Hippocrates, each written on a separate paper, and signed by the member. The papers were delivered to a committee, who selected thirty-six sets as subjects for dissertations. Each set being numbered and sealed in a separate cover was, at the next ordinary meeting, delivered by the committee to the secretary, with a report giving the names of the members whose papers were contained in each of the numbered covers. The president then ordered each member who intended to write during the next session to declare his intention at the next meeting, when each of the thirty-six oldest members who intended to write was required, from numbers on slips of paper, corresponding with those marked on the sets, to draw one. After the lots were drawn, the secretary during the succeeding fortnight transcribed into a book, which was kept in the library for the inspection of members, all the

---

[1] J. Brown, *Elementa Medicinae,* trans. by Author (ed. T. Beddoes), vol. i, p. liii.
[2] *Life of Sir James Mackintosh,* by his son, R. J. Mackintosh, vol. i, p. 26.

sets of papers, marking each one with its proper number and the name of the member who was to write upon it. He then delivered to each member the original set which corresponded with the number allotted to him.

Six months at least elapsed before the delivery of papers ; and before any dissertation was delivered, it was communicated in writing to every member in turn.

On the first Friday in October the president ordered the three senior members, then resident in Edinburgh, to deliver to the president in the Chair, on the last Saturday of the month, each a paper ; the senior, a Comment on the Case ; the second, a Dissertation on the Question ; and the third, a Comment on the Aphorism. On the following Saturday the senior member was required to deliver a Dissertation on the Question ; the second, a Comment on the Aphorism ; and the third, a Comment on the Case. On the following Saturday each was required to deliver his remaining paper. Succeeding members, according to seniority, delivered their papers in sets of three, in the same order.

There could be no excuse for a perfunctory dissertation, as authors were allowed to petition for permission to write on subjects of their own choice. The frequent entry in the minutes, " Mr. —— is allowed for his Question . . . " showed that the request was often made and granted.

For some years it was a rule of the Society to appoint, each week, three impugners whose function was premeditated criticism of the papers to be read in the following week. In 1780 this practice was discontinued. Its revival in a modified form was attempted in 1857, and again in 1912. In the former year the proposal was to appoint a critic to open the debate on each paper. The plan was to be tried on four successive nights, and to be adopted permanently, if it were successful. The treasurer proposed, very properly, that the mover of the motion should undertake the duty at the next meeting. In 1912 it was proposed that, when a dissertation was handed in, the president in the Chair should appoint a critic to study it during the interval before it was read ; and that it should be the duty of the critic to sum up the discussion after the dissertation was read. Neither attempt to revive the practice was successful.

In 1796 the Aphorism was omitted from the sets of papers ; and in 1816 the Case was dropped.

At the outset of the Society, the meetings were held throughout the whole year ; but in 1764 the summer session was abandoned.

The meetings were held weekly on Saturdays, and, according to the Code of Laws of 1781, they commenced at four o'clock for private, and at six o'clock for public business. Ordinary members were obliged to attend throughout the meeting ; and the president could only give permission to a member to leave the hall after ten o'clock. On 16th December 1796, " Mr. Charles Bell was allowed to leave the Society during the Session at ten o'clock, on account of the ill state of health of one of his friends ". The Session opened on the third Saturday of October, and continued every Saturday " until eight sets of members had given in papers " ; until the Aphorism was dropped in 1796, twenty-four meetings were held during the Session. In 1796 the evening of meeting was changed to Friday, and has never been altered. In 1868 a committee was appointed to investigate the probable causes of the decrease in the number of students joining the Society. The system of Saturday class examinations was alleged by some members to be detrimental to the Society, as students would not join a society which met on the evenings immediately preceding the examinations. A petition to modify the system was drawn up, to be laid before the Senatus Academicus ; but it was considered unlikely that it would be successful ; and it does not appear to have been presented. A proposal was made in the committee to change the evening of meeting from Friday to Monday or Saturday. The objection was so great that the committee could not recommend the proposal to the Society. In 1919 a motion was made, that owing to changes in the social life of the University—so many functions being held on Friday evenings—the meetings should be held on another evening. The motion was defeated.

The great increase in the number of students of medicine at Edinburgh towards the close of the eighteenth century led to the establishment of many institutions similar to the Society, which was the oldest debating society in the city,[1] and the original from which the others were derived. There were the Royal Physical, the Chirurgo-Physical, the American Physical, the Hibernian Medical, the Chirurgo-Obstetrical and the Natural History Society. Some of those, after a short period of usefulness, were only saved from dissolution by union with others. The excessive number of student-societies must be ascribed to the Scottish system of education which left to the students great latitude in the conduct of their studies. The societies were beneficial. The danger that they would encourage desultory study and a love of dialectical subtlety was outweighed by the positive benefits, the fostering of a spirit of independent enquiry, the urge to ardour in study, the confidence acquired in public speaking, and the salutary stimulus upon the youthful mind of the respect and applause of equals in age.[2]

No description of the essential value to youth of such societies can surpass that given in the Address delivered, in February 1863, to the Associated Societies of the University of Edinburgh by James Moncrieff, then Lord Advocate and Dean of the Faculty of Advocates, " with whom eloquence was unquestionably a matter of genius ".[3] Moncrieff said :

" I look on our societies not with interest only, but with genuine respect. No one who has buffeted the waves of life, and tasted its real conflicts, can fail to regard with something deeper than sympathy the workshops in which the material of active duty is hammered and tempered for its coming contests. Truth, among you, not only may, but must, be pursued for her own sake, and your way is unentangled by the briars and thorns which beset the efforts of riper years."

[1] *Life of Sir Robert Christison, Bart.*, vol. i, p. 52.
[2] J. E. Stock, M.D., *Life of Thomas Beddoes, M.D.*, p. 379.
[3] James Crabb Watt, Advocate, *Memoir of John Inglis, Lord Justice-General of Scotland* (Edinburgh, 1893), p. 86.

The Royal Charter, and the Hall and library helped to ensure the continued existence of the Society, but its real strength lay in its laws and traditions, and in its fulfilling an essential function in the life of the medical student. The Society underwent the alternation of prosperous and lean periods, which appears to be the lot of all societies : but the lean periods were of short duration, and almost uniformly due to a cause beyond the Society's control—a decline in the number of students of medicine in the University.

In 1779 the Society unanimously adopted a resolution to offer the use of the Medical Hall to the Philosophical Society —later the Royal Society of Edinburgh—for their monthly meetings.

In 1782 the Right Hon. David, Earl of Buchan, M.D., was elected an honorary member of the Society, on the proposal of Dr. John Aitken, an extra-mural lecturer in medicine, and a former senior president of the Society. Lord Buchan had received the degree of Doctor of Medicine of the University of Edinburgh, when, as Lord Cardross, he was heir to the earldom.

Lord Buchan may perhaps be claimed as another link between the Society and the United States of America. " He was wont to speak of George Washington as his friend *and cousin*, which most persons thought absurd ; but after all, it was only a question of American, or Scotch, cousinship— a term of some elasticity. They were both descended from the Fairfax family, as is well known, though what was the exact degree of relationship regarding which George Washington corresponded with the Earl of Buchan it would perhaps be hard for the genealogist to determine. But he ' claimed kindred there, and had the claim allowed ', as fully appears from a letter written by General Washington to Lord Buchan. . . . As the cousin of George Washington, he thought it incumbent upon him to show all attention to the nation over whom his relative presided. Many distinguished Americans were entertained by him at Dryburgh." [1]

In 1785 two brilliant members of the Society, James

[1] Lieut.-Col. A. Fergusson, *The Hon. Henry Erskine* (1882), p. 487.

Mackintosh and John Haslam, played prominent parts in a misunderstanding which occurred between the Managers of the Royal Infirmary and the students. Thomas Beddoes was chosen chairman at a general meeting of all the students of medicine who formed themselves into a body under the title of " The Associated Students ". " In this dispute, the Managers appear to have erred in form rather than in principle. A hasty resolution regulating the hours of admission for the students attending the Infirmary, and implying a general censure upon the whole body for some individual instances of misconduct, produced a strong spirit of resistance on the part of the latter, who conceived their privileges invaded. As chairman, Mr. Beddoes was, of course, the organ of the demands of the students, and those who are acquainted with his character will easily believe that they were enforced with sufficient spirit. The intervention of the Medical Faculty happily terminated the misunderstanding, and harmony was restored."[1] The students published a *Narrative*[2] in connection with the dispute. The introduction to the *Narrative* is a clever epitome of the rise and rapid development of the Medical School of Edinburgh, and in it a tribute is paid to the University. " But of so rapid an advance to eminence, other causes might be assigned, besides the merit of its teachers. Circumstances concurred that gave a stability to the University of Edinburgh which the labours of Gaubius could not preserve to Leyden, nor the genius of Haller procure for Göttingen. Its discipline was more liberal, and its institutions less monastic than those of universities founded at earlier periods. The ready access it afforded to well-furnished libraries obtained for the student of medicine an easy acquaintance with the most valuable writers of his profession. And, to these advantages were added a spirit of investigation, and freedom of enquiry, hardly known in other seminaries."[3] The committee of " The

---

[1] J. E. Stock, M.D., *Life of Thomas Beddoes, M.D.*, pp. 14-15.

[2] " A *Narrative* of some late injurious proceedings of the Managers of the Royal Infirmary against the students of medicine in the University of Edinburgh " (1785).

[3] *Ibid.* p. 2.

Associated Students ", which was appointed to submit a representation to the Managers of the Royal Infirmary, consisted of a chairman, who was a member of the Society, and nine students, eight of whom were members of the Society.

This organisation of students of medicine was evidently maintained for a few years longer to safeguard their rights for all purposes. In the copy of the *Narrative* in the Society's library, there is an addition, in manuscript, relating their proceedings during a misunderstanding with the University authorities, in connection with the ceremony of laying the foundation stone of " the New College of Edinburgh ", as it was called at the time, on the 16th November 1789. The meetings were held in the Society's library. The misunderstanding was about an invitation to the ceremony, and was trivial. It is only of interest because Francis Foulke, a member of the Society who was killed in a duel a month later, took part in it. He was a member of the committee appointed to conduct the proceedings.

The importance of the Society to the fame of the Medical School of Edinburgh during this period, 1780–1810, is shown by the number of old members who filled, with distinction, the Chairs in the Faculty of Medicine.

The students who were active members at this time were no less distinguished in later life. Dr. John Edmonds Stock (1793), the biographer of Thomas Beddoes, wrote : " It is honourable to Edinburgh that mental industry and activity are there fashionable. They are the only passports to fame." [1] It was acknowledged by the senior members of the University that this widespread enthusiasm in study, which was one of the causes of the celebrity of the School of Medicine, was especially stimulated and sustained by the Royal Medical Society.

One of the most brilliant students was James Mackintosh, who arrived in Edinburgh from Aberdeen in 1784. In 1785 he joined the Society, and became a president in the following year. A fellow-president was John Haslam, who was the first to discover and describe general paralysis of the insane

[1] J. E. Stock, M.D., *Life of Thomas Beddoes, M.D.*, p. 379.

(1798).[1]   The subject of the dissertation which Mackintosh read before the Society was intermittent fever.   It was a proof of the attractiveness of the Edinburgh School of Medicine to foreigners that five of his fellow-members in that Society, who were also members of the Royal Medical Society, hailed from such widely distant parts as Russia, Spain, Brazil, Sweden and France.   In 1787 Sir James Mackintosh graduated M.D. at Edinburgh, his Thesis being entitled *De Actione Musculari.*

He early forsook medicine for the English Bar, where he gained considerable success.   His speech in defence of Peltier, a French emigrant-royalist, was regarded as a model of forensic eloquence.   He acquired great influence in the political world, and was the friend of men in both parties. In 1802 he was among the crowds of English who, availing themselves of the Peace of Amiens, visited Paris and were introduced to Bonaparte.[2]   In 1814 he was again in Paris ; on this occasion he was in close contact with his friend the Duke of Wellington.[3]   In 1820 he declined the Chair of Moral Philosophy at Edinburgh, which was offered him on the death of Dr. Thomas Brown.   Two years later he was elected Rector of the University of Glasgow in succession to Lord Jeffrey.   The unsuccessful candidate was Sir Walter Scott.[4]

Sir James was always ready, when requested, to use the influence of his great public position on behalf of the Royal Medical Society, over whose debates he had presided when he was a student.

In the late autumn of 1787 another student destined to a great career, in this instance within the profession, arrived at Edinburgh.   Astley Paston Cooper brought with him letters of introduction to Dr. Joseph Black and Dr. James Gregory.   He hired a lodging in Bristo Street, and for seven

---

[1] *The Discovery of General Paralysis, or from Haslam to Bayle : an Address to the Royal Medical Society, 1922,* by the late G. M. Robertson, Professor of Psychiatry at Edinburgh.

[2] *Life of Sir James Mackintosh,* vol. i, p. 76.

[3] *Ibid.* vol. ii, p. 314.

[4] Lord Cockburn, *Life of Lord Jeffrey,* vol. i, pp. 266-267.

months applied himself to his studies with unremitting diligence. He had already studied for two years at Guy's Hospital, and was a member of the Guy's Hospital Physical Society. Soon after his arrival in Edinburgh he was admitted a member of the Royal Medical Society. He attended the debates regularly, and always received an attentive hearing from the members when he addressed them. In the Medical Hall he found that the accurate knowledge of anatomy, which he had acquired under his master, the celebrated Cline, and from the lectures of John Hunter, was an advantage, as it imparted freshness to his ideas and confidence in expressing and maintaining his opinions before a critical audience. He does not appear to have read any paper before the Society, a rule which was probably waived on account of the circumstance which curtailed his sojourn in the city. He had been articled to Mr. Cline for seven years, with a proviso that he should, if he wished, be permitted to stay for one winter session at Edinburgh. In conformity with the prevailing passion for culture, and on the proposal of Charles Hope, afterwards Lord President of the Court of Session, Astley Cooper entered the Speculative Society. His interest, however, lay almost entirely in his professional studies. When he returned to London he discovered that he had gained a great deal of knowledge at the Medical School of Edinburgh, and most of it from three men, Dr. Gregory, Dr. Edward Ash and Andrew Fyfe, lecturer in anatomy. Ash was a prominent member of the Society when Astley Cooper made his acquaintance in 1787, and was elected a president in 1788. Like so many of his contemporaries in medicine, he combined a wide knowledge of philosophy, metaphysics and the classics with professional learning. Andrew Fyfe was dissector to Alexander Monro, *secundus*, and, in the altered terminology, prosector to Alexander Monro, *tertius*. Sir Astley Cooper described him as " a horrid lecturer, but an industrious, worthy man, and good practical anatomist ".[1] Fyfe was " one

---

[1] Bransby Blake Cooper, *Life of Sir Astley Cooper, Bart.* (1843), vol. i, pp. 158-181 *passim*.

of the last in Edinburgh to wear the pig-tail ".[1] In 1779 he was admitted a member of the Society, and in 1782 he was elected a president. The Committee of Fines is mentioned for the first time in the minutes of the Society in connection with his professional duties. In January 1781 " the Committee of Fines are invested with a power to fine or excuse Mr. Fyfe according as they shall find him actually employed in anatomical business ". Fyfe was a highly respected man, and in 1804 he was unanimously chosen for the office of treasurer, which he held until his death, twenty years later. From Dr. James Gregory, Professor of the Institutes of Medicine at the time, Sir Astley Cooper wrote afterwards that he received much kindness as well as information. He said : " Gregory's lectures on clinical medicine were admirable, yet he thought most highly of his physiology on which he enlarged in his evening lecture on therapeutics. Having on one occasion been confined to my room by illness, I expressed my regret to Dr. Gregory at losing his clinical reports, but he said, ' Sir, that does not signify, but you have lost my therapeutics.' " [2] Many years afterwards, speaking in Edinburgh at a banquet given in his honour by the Royal College of Surgeons, Astley Cooper acknowledged the advantage he had derived from the clinical instruction of Dr. Gregory. In his student days, Edinburgh was the only British school of medicine where clinical instruction was given. Sir Astley used the method with success when he lectured on surgery at St. Thomas's Hospital ; and by 1837 it had been generally adopted.

Sir Astley Cooper was always warmly attached to Edinburgh ; and when the Club of that name (Edinburgh University Club of London) was instituted in London, in 1800, he at once joined it. He was much gratified when the Royal Medical Society elected him an honorary member in 1813 ; and he expressed great pleasure when his nephew, Bransby Blake Cooper, who had joined the Society in 1815, was elected a president in the following year. When the Royal College

[1] *Life of Sir Robert Christison, Bart.*, vol. i, p. 68.
[2] Bransby Blake Cooper, *Life of Sir Astley Cooper, Bart.*, vol. i, pp. 170-171.

of Surgeons of England directed that a copy of the catalogue of their museum and library should be presented to the Royal Medical Society of Edinburgh, the presidents were appointed to return thanks to Sir Astley, and through him to the Royal College.

In 1837 the Royal College of Surgeons of Edinburgh gave a banquet in his honour in the Hopetoun Rooms. Sir George Ballingall, President, was in the Chair. Dr. Maclagan proposed the toast of " The Royal Medical Society ". He said that the Society had long formed a prominent feature in the institutions of the Edinburgh School of Medicine, and had exercised an important influence, not only in drawing out the intellectual talents of the members, but in elevating their moral feelings. He pointed to the illustrious names that adorned its annals, of which that of Sir Astley Cooper was not the least conspicuous.

On the following morning Sir Astley was presented with the Freedom of the City of Edinburgh in recognition of his great professional achievements.

CHAPTER VI

The New Town and its Dispensary—John Allen—John Thomson—
John Gordon—John Yelloly—Henry Brougham's visit—John
Bostock—Sydney Smith—The *Edinburgh Review*—Henry Bicker-
steth—Niebuhr's visit—Francis Foulke

THE City of Edinburgh had now emerged from its mediaeval
state. Suburbs appeared on the south side. George Square
was begun in 1766 and its environs soon followed.[1] The
great enlargement, however, of the City was towards the
north, and took place after the completion of the North
Bridge. The building of the New Town brought crowds
of new residents. It was to meet the needs of the sick poor
there that a dispensary, called the New Town Dispensary,
was established. A chief founder of the institution was Dr.
John Thomson, who was a senior member of the Society.

Many lifelong friendships have commenced in the Society ;
and many students have developed in the debates a bent
which has determined their life's work. John Thomson had
this experience. He joined the Society in 1790 when John
Allen was senior president, and the two students soon
became close friends. Thomson discussed with Allen the
current doctrines of the proximate cause of inflammation,
and he read a dissertation on " Catarrh " before the Society.
This contained the germ of Thomson's *Lectures in Pathology*,
published in 1813.

Thomson and Allen were admitted members of the Speculative Society on 26th November 1791, when Walter Scott
was secretary. They were among Francis Jeffrey's powerful
competitors in debate in the Society.[2]

[1] Hugo Arnot, *History of Edinburgh* (1779), p. 324.
[2] *History of the Speculative Society* (1845), p. 194 ; Lord Cockburn, *Life of Lord
Jeffrey*, vol. i, p. 54.

In 1800 Thomson, with his friends Henry Brougham and Francis Horner, formed a chemical society. Two years later he took part with them and others in the first consultations which led to the founding of the *Edinburgh Review*, and he contributed several papers to the earlier numbers.[1] Allen also contributed articles to the *Review*. Lord Cockburn considered that Allen's historical publications, chiefly in the *Review*, especially those on the constitutional history of England, were of high value.[2]

William Russell, a president, with Thomson, of the Society, was a colleague of Allen and Thomson in 1791, when they were house surgeons in the Royal Infirmary. Russell afterwards joined the Medical Board of Calcutta. He received a baronetcy in 1831, on his return from an investigation of cholera in Russia.[3]

John Allen never settled in practice. He became the foremost extra-mural lecturer in physiology in Edinburgh, and his lectures aroused more interest than any others given in the University in that subject. But he was a Whig, and, with the Town Council a close corporation and Tories to a man, he had no hope of their patronage in election to a chair. In these circumstances he accepted an invitation to attend Lord and Lady Holland on their travels in France and Spain during the peace of Amiens, and in 1805 he returned with them to become the confidential friend of Lord Holland. He did not abandon his scientific pursuits, but his chief interest henceforth lay in politics and the constitutional history of England. " The theatre of his great reputation was Holland House, where he was the admitted chief among the wits and scholars who frequented the hospitable table there."[4] It was said that he would have attained international celebrity if he had continued his study of physiology,[5] but he

---

[1] *Life of Lord Jeffrey*, vol. i, p. 136 and p. 141.

[2] Lord Cockburn, *Memorials of his Time*, p. 178.

[3] John Thomson, *Life of William Cullen, M.D.*, vol. i, Biographical Notice of Dr. Thomson, p. 11.

[4] *Life and Times of Lord Brougham* (1871), written by himself, vol. i, Appendix Note XVIII.

[5] Lord Cockburn, *Memorials of his Time*, p. 178.

chose another walk in life, and his reputation faded with his generation.

John Thomson went to London in 1792 and attended John Hunter's school in Leicester Square, with the intention of qualifying himself for teaching anatomy. He relinquished the idea on his return to Edinburgh when he found that John Bell's class was firmly established. In 1800 he was one of the six surgeons who were appointed to the Royal Infirmary when the Managers ended the system by which all the Surgeons attended in turn. Soon afterwards he began to teach surgery ; and the value of his lecture courses was perceived by those interested in the improvement of surgical teaching in Edinburgh. In 1804 the Surgeons instituted a professorship of Surgery in their College and conferred the appointment upon Thomson. The Surgeons had long felt dissatisfaction with the monopoly of surgical teaching by the Monros. In 1777 they petitioned the Crown to create a Chair of Systematic Surgery in the University, but they were checkmated by Monro, *secundus*, who persuaded the Town Council, as patrons of the University, to grant him a new Commission " expressly bearing him to be Professor of Medicine, and particularly of Anatomy and Surgery ". No objection was raised to the teaching of clinical surgery ; and in 1802 James Russell, a former president of the Society, was successful in a petition to the Town Council to have his clinical lectureship in practical surgery erected into a professorship in the University, on condition that he did not lecture on systematic surgery, and that Monro's rights were not interfered with. Russell's appointment was confirmed in 1803 by a Commission from George III. The Surgeons' appointment of Thomson, in 1804, roused great opposition from the Senatus, who were making vain efforts to have the professorship abolished. However, a Commission was received from the Crown in 1806 creating a Chair of Military Surgery in the University, and appointing Thomson to be the Professor. The Chair had a comparatively short existence. Thomson was succeeded in it, in 1823, by Sir George Ballingall, a retired Army surgeon. After

Ballingall's death in 1856 the Chair was abolished on the recommendation of James Syme, Professor of Clinical Surgery. The creation of the Chair of Systematic Surgery in 1831 had made it superfluous.

In 1821 Thomson resigned his appointment as Professor of Surgery to the Royal College of Surgeons to devote himself to practice, and he became a candidate for the Chair of Practice of Physic rendered vacant by the death of James Gregory. In this candidature he was unsuccessful, and shortly afterwards, in 1831, when a Chair of Pathology was added to the Faculty of Medicine, Thomson was appointed the first occupant.

In 1832 Thomson published the first volume of his *Life of William Cullen*. The book was completed after Thomson's death by David Craigie (1818), a physician to the Royal Infirmary, and a copy was presented to the Society by Drs. Allen Thomson and Craigie in 1859, when the work was published in two volumes.

Thomson's writings on varioloid and smallpox were important contributions to a vexed question which was the subject of many dissertations in the Society: " What is the cause of the mildness of the smallpox following inoculation as compared with the natural disease ? "

His energy was remarkable.[1] When close on sixty years of age he was in the habit of retiring to bed at ten o'clock, rising to resume work at four in the morning, and dictating his lectures to an amanuensis between the hours of six and nine. No less remarkable was his moral courage. This courage, as well as his devotion to his profession, ensured the establishment of the New Town Dispensary [2] in the face of so fierce an opposition that Lord Cockburn described it as a civil war. The opposition, oddly enough, was led by Dr. Andrew Duncan, senior, who was the founder of the Old Town Dispensary. The dispute arose regarding the method of election of officials, and the offer of treatment at home to patients who were unable to attend the Dispensary. This

---

[1] John Thomson, *Life of William Cullen, M.D.*, Biographical Notice of Dr. Thomson, p. 62.   [2] *Ibid.* vol. i, p. 50.

was an innovation, for the Old Town Dispensary made no such offer and insisted that its physic should be swallowed on the premises.[1]   Thus the present dispensary system in Edinburgh, which introduces students to general practice, dates from the days of John Thomson.

In 1814 Dr. Thomson was elected an honorary member of the Society, in whose prosperity he took a constant interest. Two of his sons were members.   William Thomson (1819), became Professor of Medicine in Glasgow ;   and Allen Thomson (1826), whose dissertation " On the Formation of the Egg, and the Evolution of the Chick "[2] heralded his fame as an embryologist, was successively Professor of Anatomy at Aberdeen, of the Institutes of Medicine at Edinburgh, and of Anatomy in Glasgow.

A notable quality of Dr. Thomson was his readiness to find opportunities of advancing students whom he esteemed in their careers.   This encouragement was conspicuously rewarded by the careers of James Young Simpson and John Gordon.

John Gordon was born in Forres in 1786.   He began his career in medicine under the auspices of Dr. Thomson, to whom he was articled as a pupil in 1801 ;   and he combined the University curriculum with extra-mural lectures on anatomy by Barclay, surgery by Thomson, and chemistry by John Murray.   Gordon also attended the class of Moral Philosophy under Dugald Stewart, and that of Natural Philosophy, which was brilliantly taught by Robison.   In 1803 Gordon was admitted a member of the Society, and became a president in 1806.   He read a dissertation on " The Process of Nature in the healing of Wounds ", which was the germ of the Thesis, *De Vulnere Natura sanando*, with which he graduated M.D. in 1805.   Gordon obtained the diploma of the Royal College of Surgeons, with the intention of qualifying for a post with the East India Company, but, on Thomson's advice, he gave up the idea and decided to become a lecturer on anatomy and physiology in Edinburgh.   He

[1] Lord Cockburn, *Memorials of his Time*, pp. 283-284.
[2] *Dissertations of Royal Medical Society* (1892), pp. 158-172.

went to London to study practical anatomy at William Hunter's school in Great Windmill Street, which was being carried on by James Wilson and Benjamin Brodie.

When Gordon returned to Edinburgh he commenced lecturing on anatomy and physiology, but after a few years he realised the impossibility of teaching physiology as an appendage to anatomy, and resolved to follow his own predilection, and John Allen's success, by giving a course of lectures on physiology only. His reading and work on the anatomy of the brain raised him to the first rank of British anatomists, and enabled him to criticise the claims of the phrenologists, Gall and Spurzheim, to original discoveries in cerebral anatomy. Those German physicians pressed their claims in a book, written by Spurzheim, entitled, *The Physiognomical System of Drs. Gall and Spurzheim.* A review of the book, written by Gordon, appeared in the *Edinburgh Review* in 1815 ; and it brought Spurzheim from Dublin, where he was lecturing, to defend his doctrines in Edinburgh.[1]

Gordon had attacked the statement that man was endowed with thirty-three faculties as untrue to experience, and as meaning no more than that he was endowed with intellect and intuition. Though the authors admitted that they could not map out the locality of these functions on the surface of the brain, they claimed to have mapped them out on the surface of the head. The lack of correspondence between brain and cranium, together with the authors' admitted inability to map out the faculties on the surface of the brain, disposed of this claim, and so of the whole basis of phrenology.

George Combe, an enthusiastic phrenologist, witnessed a dissection of a brain by Spurzheim in Edinburgh, " and soon saw that the brain dissected by Dr. Spurzheim exhibited a structure very different from that which had been described in the *Edinburgh Review* ".[2] It seems that a contribution might have been made to neurology if the absurdities of phrenology had not discredited the authors so completely. In 1817 Spurzheim gave two demonstrations in Dr. John

[1] George Combe, *Life and Correspondence of Andrew Combe, M.D.* (1850), p. 44.
[2] *Ibid.* p. 46.

Thomson's theatre in Edinburgh. Gordon was present, and he later criticised the claims of the phrenologists in a work, which was commended by Cuvier, and which was generally regarded as finally dismissing them.

Gordon's career was cut short by his death in 1818 at the age of thirty-two.

Two days after Gordon's death the Society held an extraordinary meeting, and a subscription, confined to members of the Society, was opened to procure a bust of Dr. Gordon, which was to be placed in the Hall. Samuel Joseph, who was later a Foundation Academician of the Royal Scottish Academy, was chosen the sculptor. Although he had never seen Gordon, and only had a miniature to guide him, he completed the work to the entire satisfaction of Dr. Gordon's friends. The bust stands in the Hall, on the right of the president's chair, as a reminder of the Society's spontaneous admiration of greatness of character.

In 1883 Professor Allen Thomson presented several manuscript papers of Dr. Gordon to the Society. These are on " Injuries of the Thorax ", " Muscular Motion ", " What is the process of Nature in the Healing of Wounds ? " and " Diseases of the Testes ", and are remarkable for the neatness and beauty of the writing.

In November of the same year, John Chiene, Professor of Systematic Surgery at Edinburgh, and a former president, delivered the Inaugural Address to the Society, and chose as his subject, " Dr. John Gordon ". In 1884 the Society, with the consent of the relatives, placed an inscription on Dr. Gordon's tombstone. An eager advocate of this additional mark of respect was Henry Alexis Thomson, at that time a secretary, who later filled, with distinction, the Chair of Systematic Surgery in the University.

Prominent among Dr. Gordon's contemporaries in the Society were Henry Herbert Southey (a younger brother of the Poet Laureate) who became a president of the Royal Medical and Speculative Societies in 1804–5, and who settled in practice in London ; Daniel Ellis, who was a fellow-president with Dr. Gordon in 1806–7, and who wrote his biography as well as contributing to the literature of vegetable physiology ; and John Vetch (1802) who wrote a treatise on diseases of the eye.

John William Turner (1807) was, like Dr. Gordon, a pupil and friend of Dr. John Thomson, with whom he was associated in practice for some years, and whom he succeeded as Professor of Surgery to the Royal College of Surgeons.[1] When the Chair of Systematic Surgery was created in 1831, Turner was appointed to be the Professor. One of his students described him as " a timid, shy man, who could not look his class in the face, and seemed fitted by nature for anything rather than the duties and responsibilities of an operating surgeon ".[2] However, the appointment gave Dr. Thomson as much pleasure as his own appointment, at the same time, to the newly created Chair of Pathology.[3] The creation of these two Chairs was principally owing to his influence with the Whig government of Reform Bill fame. It is probable that Dr. Thomson owed much of his success as an innovator in the Medical Faculty to his early association with the Earl of Lauderdale, whom he had instructed in chemistry.[4]

Turner died at the age of forty-five, and was succeeded in the Chair of Surgery by Sir Charles Bell, a former member of the Society, whose great fame rests on his discovery of the sensory nature of the posterior nerve roots and his description of facial palsy.

Two prominent members at this time were Alexander Marcet, and Gaspard Charles de La Rive, who both joined the Society in 1795. Marcet was born in Geneva in 1770. He came to England in 1793, when the revolutionary fever was at its height. Indiscreetly he expressed, in public, political opinions for which he and his friend, de La Rive,

[1] John Thomson, *Life of William Cullen, M.D.*, Biographical Notice of Dr. Thomson, p. 35 and p. 60.

[2] Jessie A. Wilson, *Memoir of George Wilson . . . Professor of Technology in the University of Edinburgh* (1860), p. 42.

[3] John Thomson, *Life of William Cullen, M.D.*, Biographical Notice of Dr. Thomson, p. 67.

[4] *Ibid.* p. 15. Sir A. Grant, *The Story of the University of Edinburgh*, vol. ii, p. 442.

were committed to prison on their return to Switzerland in 1794. The sentence of imprisonment was commuted to five years' banishment, and the two men decided to study medicine at Edinburgh. While there, Marcet received an unusual request from Louis Odier, Professor of Medicine at Geneva, who was physician to de Saussure, the French physicist. De Saussure had been struck down by an illness resembling that which had attacked Professor Adam Ferguson of Edinburgh. Ferguson had recovered under the treatment of his relative, Dr. Black, the celebrated chemist ; and de Saussure asked Odier to ascertain, from Dr. Black, the mode of treatment. On receipt of Dr. Odier's letter, Marcet, accompanied by Professor Dugald Stewart, called on Dr. Black, who willingly gave him a written account of his relative's illness, and of the treatment he had given.[1]

Marcet went to London, and became a lecturer on chemistry at Guy's Hospital. He discovered xanthin in urinary calculi ; and wrote a *Chemical History of Calculous Disorders*. In London, he was closely associated with Dr. Yelloly.

John Yelloly (1795) was assiduous in introducing visitors. Repeatedly, the minutes record, " Dr. Yelloly brings a visitor ". One of his visitors was John Leyden, Sir Walter Scott's friend, the poet and oriental scholar, who included a sufficient knowledge of medicine among his numerous accomplishments to enable him to go out to India as an assistant surgeon. After graduating M.D. at Edinburgh in 1796, Yelloly went to London where he became physician to the Aldersgate Street Dispensary, and, later, to the London Hospital. He rose to great eminence in the profession. He was one of the founders of the Edinburgh Club, instituted in London in 1800. The Club was confined at first to those who had studied in Edinburgh, and among former members of the Royal Medical Society who joined the Club were Sir Astley Cooper, Peter Roget, John Richard Farre, Benjamin Travers and George Birkbeck.[2]

---

[1] John Small, Librarian to the University, *Biographical Sketch of Adam Ferguson, Professor of Moral Philosophy in the University of Edinburgh* (1864), p. 32, footnote.

[2] Bransby Blake Cooper, *Life of Sir Astley Cooper, Bart.*, vol. i, pp. 283-286.

Dr. Yelloly is best remembered as the chief founder of the Medical and Chirurgical Society of London, established in 1805, and incorporated by Royal Charter in 1834. " In conjunction with his friend, Dr. Marcet, he formed a plan for the establishment of a society embracing every branch of the medical profession, and to be conducted by such changes in its governing body as should ensure its continuance on high and independent principles." [1] The concluding words of the quotation refer to the dissatisfaction felt by some members of the Medical Society of London with the monopoly of the presidentship of their Society by one member, and with the feeling of party spirit which had arisen in the Society.[2] Accordingly, at its commencement, the Royal Medical and Chirurgical Society consisted chiefly of members who had seceded from the Medical Society. Among the earliest members were Sir Astley Cooper, Sir Gilbert Blane and Sir Walter Farquhar. The first president was Dr. William Saunders, a senior member of the Royal Medical Society of Edinburgh.

Dr. Yelloly's activity on behalf of the Royal Medical and Chirurgical Society was the subject of a tribute, which was paid to his memory, in an Address, delivered to the Society a few weeks after his death in January 1842. " As the foundation of this Society was mainly due to Dr. Yelloly, so its prosperity was always a subject of the deepest interest to him, and he often in merriment called it his ' eldest son '. The formation of the library, also, is principally owing to his exertions. He used, for the basis of it, the catalogue of the Royal Medical Society of Edinburgh."

In 1907 the Royal Medical and Chirurgical Society was one of eighteen societies which coalesced into one body under Royal Charter, and under the name of the Royal Society of Medicine.[3]

Dr. Yelloly's friend, Dr. George Birkbeck (1794), who

---

[1] *Lancet*, 1841–42, " Dr. Williams' Address to the Royal Medical and Chirurgical Society of London ", vol. ii, p. 194.

[2] Bransby Blake Cooper, *Life of Sir Astley Cooper, Bart.*, vol. ii, p. 35.

[3] *British Medical Societies* (London, 1939 ; ed. Sir D'Arcy Power), p. 267.

was twice a president, is chiefly memorable in the history of the Royal Medical Society by his introduction of his fellow-student, Henry Brougham, as an extraordinary visitor. In his *Life and Times*, written in old age, Lord Brougham described his visit to the Society.

" Long before entering the Speculative Society, and when only somewhat trained in the young Debating Society, after little more than one session at the college, I had an opportunity of trying my voice at a great meeting, that of the Royal Medical Society, a chartered body, to which almost all the medical students, and one or two others, belonged. The meetings were weekly, and between 100 and 150 were often present, including a small number of visitors. The subjects, of course, were almost always medical, or connected with medical science, but occasionally subjects were broached which had little or no connection with it. The subject on which I spoke was the much-vexed question of ' liberty and necessity ', and, I found that, after the first alarm had abated, I had no difficulty in making my way, and my speech was far better received than it deserved ; the impression made being very much owing to my youth, which appeared very clearly from my person, and might have done still more from my topics." [1]

In April 1860 Lord Brougham, over eighty years of age, as first Chancellor of the University of Edinburgh, under the Universities (Scotland) Act, 1858, delivered his impressive Installation Address. In an allusion to some of his fellow-students, he mentioned the name of George Birkbeck.

Birkbeck had graduated M.D. at Edinburgh in 1799. Soon afterwards, he was appointed Professor of Natural Philosophy at Anderson's College, Glasgow. Later, he settled in practice in London. His fame rèsts on his endeavours towards the establishment of mechanics' institutes, of which the London Mechanics, called after him the Birkbeck Institute, was the first.

The names of John Bostock and Peter Roget appear regularly beside the name of Birkbeck in the minutes of the

[1] *Life and Times of Lord Brougham* (1871), written by himself, vol. i, pp. 80-81.

Society during the years 1796–98. Bostock was admitted a member on the same day in 1794 as Birkbeck, and was elected a president along with him in 1797. He followed a family tradition, as his father, John Bostock, a Liverpool practitioner of great promise, who died at an early age, joined the Society in 1765 and was a president in 1768. He graduated M.D. at Edinburgh in 1798 and settled in practice in London, where he later became a physiologist of some eminence and vice-president of the Royal Society. Furthermore, he was a medical historian. In his *History of Medicine*, which he dedicated to Richard Bright, he wrote : " Perhaps no single institution has contributed more to the improvement of our profession than the Edinburgh Medical Society, which, for so long a period, has maintained a reputation that reflects the greatest credit, not merely on its members, but even on the university to which it is attached."

Peter Roget (1796) resembled Birkbeck and Bostock in enthusiasm in the business of the Society. At a meeting in December 1797 he introduced Francis Horner as a visitor. His interest was chiefly in chemistry, as appears from an entry in the minutes, " Mr. Roget is allowed for his Question, ' What are the laws of chemical affinity ? ' " and by the subject of his graduation thesis in 1798, *De Chemicae Affinitatis legibus*. In 1805 Dr. Roget succeeded to the post of Physician to the Infirmary at Manchester, rendered vacant by the death of Dr. Thomas Percival, a distinguished senior member of the Society. Later he went to London. He was, for many years, secretary to the Royal Society, and from 1833–36 Fullerian Professor of Physiology at the Royal Institution. As the author of a Bridgewater Treatise, intended to reconcile science and religion, he participated in the division of the Earl of Bridgewater's bequest along with, among others, Dr. Thomas Chalmers, the great Scottish Free Churchman, and Sir Charles Bell. Dr. Roget was the compiler of an amazingly popular *Thesaurus of English Words and Phrases* which has passed through very numerous editions.

In 1796 Thomas Brown, who became Professor of Moral Philosophy at Edinburgh, was admitted a member. He was

a law student before he entered upon the study of medicine.
Brown's propensity to philosophy and literature appeared
early in his academic career, and, in 1801, an unsuccessful
attempt was made to place him in the Chair of Rhetoric.
He graduated M.D. in 1803 ; and two years later he was
taken into partnership by Dr. James Gregory. In 1810 he
was appointed conjunct Professor of Moral Philosophy with
Dugald Stewart, whose health had failed, but who nevertheless outlived his colleague by eight years.

As a student, Brown was one of the most active members
of " that singular society of the rising young men then in
Edinburgh called ' The Academy of Physicks ' ".[1] The
" Academy of Physicks " was formed in 1797 by a few of the
members of the older " Literary Society ",[2] and its object,
as set forth in the minute of the first meeting, was " the
investigation of nature, the laws by which her phenomena
are regulated, and the history of opinions concerning these
laws." Among the members were Dr. Birkbeck, John
Leyden, Brougham, Francis Jeffrey, Francis Horner and
Sydney Smith. The " Academy of Physicks " is entitled to a
place in the history of English literature because some of the
members founded the *Edinburgh Review*.[3] Dr. Brown was
an early contributor to the *Review*.

Sydney Smith joined the Society in 1799, under favour-
able auspices. When his petition was presented on 1st
February, George Bell, who became an eminent surgeon in
Edinburgh, was president in the Chair ; and Brougham was
a visitor at public business. When the petition was granted,
a week later, Thomas Headlam, intimate with Jeffrey, in the
Speculative Society,[4] was president in the Chair ; and Jeffrey
and Francis Horner were visitors at public business. When
Sydney Smith signed the Obligation, and took his seat in the
Society, Charles Skene was president in the Chair. Skene
became an eminent physician in Aberdeen and Professor of

[1] Lord Cockburn, *Life of Lord Jeffrey*, vol. i, pp. 103-104.
[2] *Memoirs of Francis Horner, M.P.* (ed. Leonard Horner), vol. i, p. 5.
[3] T. Brown, M.D., *Lectures on the Philosophy of the Mind*, with Memoir by David
Welsh, D.D., pp. 11-12.
[4] Lord Cockburn, *Life of Lord Jeffrey*, vol. i, p. 54.

Medicine in Marischal College there.[1]   He was a cousin of James Skene of Rubislaw, Sir Walter Scott's close friend.

A week after Sydney Smith took his seat in the Society, he was appointed a member of a committee to choose subjects for dissertations for the ensuing session.   He does not appear to have read any paper before the Society.   His tutorial and clerical duties entailed long periods of absence, but when he was present he was a firm upholder of the dignity of the Society.   He obtained the degree of M.D. from the University of St. Andrews in the manner recognised at the time.   In a letter, dated April 1805, to his friend Jeffrey, he wrote : " I should be very much obliged to you to transmit the enclosed testimonials to St. Andrews, to pay for the degree, to send me word how much you have paid for it, and I will repay you immediately.   The degree itself may be sent to me also by the mail or post according to its size.   Pray do not neglect this affair as the interests of a poor and respectable man depend upon it." [2]

His daughter, Lady Holland, wife of the eminent physician, Sir Henry Holland, has recorded that her father's object in studying medicine was to equip himself more fully for his future profession, the Church.   Afterwards, Smith found that his medical knowledge, especially that gained from Dr. Gregory's clinical lectures, enabled him " to be of the greatest service to the poor of his parish, who entirely depended on him for assistance ".[3]

After referring to Smith's Edinburgh friends, Jeffrey, Horner, Walter Scott, Brougham, Allen, and Leyden, Lady Holland wrote : " Society at that time in Edinburgh was upon the most easy and agreeable footing : the Scotch were neither rich nor ashamed of being poor, and there was not that struggle for display which so much diminishes the charm of London society, and has, with the increase of wealth, now crept into that of Edinburgh.   Few days passed without a meeting of some of these friends, either in each other's

[1] Ella H. B. Rodger, *Aberdeen Doctors at Home and Abroad* (1893), p. 208.
[2] *Life of the Rev. Sydney Smith* (1855), by his daughter, Lady Holland, vol. ii, p. 15.
[3] *Ibid.* p. 63.

houses, or (in what was then very common) oyster-cellars, where, I am told, the most delightful little suppers used to be given in which every subject was discussed with a freedom impossible in larger societies." [1] Her father " divided his time between his pupils, the *Edinburgh Review*, the enjoyment of the choicest society that was to be found anywhere out of London, and the study of medicine, anatomy, and moral philosophy ".[2]

An intimate friend of Sydney Smith in the Society was Henry Reeve, who was a president in 1801–2. Before studying at Edinburgh, Reeve was articled for four years to Philip Meadows Martineau, a Norwich practitioner, and a senior member of the Society, who, according to his niece, the celebrated Harriet Martineau, was considered the most prominent provincial surgeon of his day.[3] Reeve graduated M.D. at Edinburgh in 1803 with a thesis *De Animalibus Hieme Sopitis*, which he afterwards expanded into an essay, published in 1809, on the Torpidity of Animals. He was one of the early contributors to the *Edinburgh Review*. In the spring of 1805, he set out for Switzerland, along with his fellow-student and friend Dr. de Roches, who was senior president of the Society in 1802–3, and later went on to Vienna. While he was in Vienna, Smith wrote characteristically to him : " As to the improvement you get, my dear doctor, in travelling abroad, *credat Judaeus* ! You have seen a skull of a singular conformation at Dr. Baumgarten's and seen a toe in Suabia which astonished you ; but what, in the name of Dr. Gregory, can you see in Germany of a therapeutic nature which you cannot see better in Scotland ? " On his return to England, Dr. Reeve settled in practice in Norwich, where he married Susanna Taylor, one of the celebrated literary family of the " Taylors of Norwich ". His son, Henry Reeve, C.B., a distinguished man who became editor of the *Edinburgh Review*, is mentioned here because he was the recipient of a memorable letter from Lord

[1] *Life of the Rev. Sydney Smith*, by his daughter, Lady Holland, vol. i, pp. 13–14.
[2] *Ibid.* p. 63.
[3] Harriet Martineau, *Biographical Sketches, with Autobiographical Sketch*, p. xvii.

Brougham, who had been invited to be a candidate for the Chancellorship of the University of Edinburgh. In September 1859, a month before his success in the election, Lord Brougham wrote : " Many thanks for your great kindness about the Edinburgh dinner, which I look forward to with some dismay ; for the requisition, which was signed by the heads of all parties, and in very kind terms, makes it impossible not to attend, and, beside the plagues incidental to all such proceedings, I have the excessive sufferings from the blanks by which I shall be surrounded. . . . Jeffrey, Horner, Smith, Allen, Murray, Playfair, Thomson all gone, and of later years, Cockburn, your father, Eyre. It is really a sad thing. And then, beside our set, there were A. Thomson, Moncreiff, T. Campbell, Cranstoun, Clerk, D. Stewart, W. Scott—all, except Horner, Playfair, and Scott, D. Stewart, A. Thomson, and T. Campbell alive in 1834, when I was last in Edinburgh. I must struggle the best I can, but this feeling nearly overpowers me." [1]

In 1801 there was admitted to membership Henry Bickersteth, who, thirty-five years later, narrowly missed the appointment of Lord Chancellor in the Melbourne Administration, when Lord Brougham was passed over in favour of Sir Charles Pepys, Master of the Rolls. Bickersteth was an apprentice to his father, a surgeon in Kirkby Lonsdale, in Westmorland, when his uncle, Dr. Robert Batty (1782) advised him to study medicine at Edinburgh. In the Society he soon distinguished himself, for " he was a remarkably good speaker, very energetic, yet eloquent ". At this time, Bickersteth was appointed house physician to Dr. Andrew Duncan, senior.

In October 1802 he entered Caius College, Cambridge, to study for a degree in medicine. In 1803 his uncle, Dr. Batty, who was a physician to the Brownlow Street Hospital and somewhat eminent in the profession, was requested by the Earl of Oxford to recommend a physician to travel with his family in Italy ; and he successfully recommended his nephew. When Bickersteth returned to Cambridge in 1805, he received

[1] Sir John Knox Laughton, *Life of Henry Reeve*, *C.B.* (1898), vol. ii, pp 34-35.

and acted upon the wise counsel of Dr. Chapman, who writes : " I was tutor when he returned to Cambridge in 1805. I earnestly advised him to take his degree in Arts, and to read hard for his degree." [1] In 1808 Bickersteth was Senior Wrangler and second Smith's Prizeman.

The English Bar was now his objective. In April 1808 he entered himself as a student in the Inner Temple.

Nearly thirty years afterwards, when Lord Brougham was passed over in favour of Sir Charles Pepys, Master of the Rolls, for the office of Lord Chancellor, " Lord Melbourne greatly desired to commit the Great Seal to the custody of Mr. Bickersteth, but he was unable to pass over the claims of the Master of the Rolls, which he would have gladly done if he had been able, for he did not like the phlegmatic character of the man ".[2] Bickersteth became Master of the Rolls and a peer with the title of Lord Langdale.

A notable event in the history of the Society at the close of the eighteenth century was a visit from Niebuhr, the future great historian of Rome. The minutes of 8th March 1799 state, " Mr. Askham brings a Visitor—Mr. Niebuhr ". Thomas Emerson Headlam was president in the Chair ; and his fellow-presidents, George Birkbeck, George Bell and Charles Skene were present.

Niebuhr arrived in Edinburgh, from London, in October 1798. He left a description of the last part of his journey north : " I never saw a more striking contrast than is presented by the two banks of the Tweed. Northumberland was much more beautiful than I expected, although without wood, like all this part of England . . . immediately beyond the town of Berwick you enter a wild country, almost entirely destitute of cultivation. This district extends to Dunbar, a distance of eight-and-twenty miles. I have made acquaintance on the way with a young medical student, from Sheffield named Moorhouse, and we shall very likely lodge together." [3] He was impressed with the teaching in the University, where he studied the natural sciences, particularly chemistry. " I

[1] *Memoirs of Lord Langdale*, p. 228.   [2] *Ibid.* p. 445.
[3] *Life of Niebuhr* (1852 ; ed. and trans. by Susanna Winkworth), vol. i, pp. 123-124.

have never heard or read a more concise, complete, and clear survey of a science, than that with which Dr. Hope opened the course on chemistry. . . . The celebrated Gregory, with a venerable mien, and an excellent delivery, seemed, as far as I could judge, quite equal to the reputation which he here enjoys."

The mention of the *Edinburgh Review* and of the presence, in the Society's Hall, of law students of literary talent, at a time when many members of the Society were also members of the Speculative Society, shows the close association of that generation of students of medicine at Edinburgh with literature and the Bar. Lord Acton wrote : " A distinguished physician informs us that Gibbon, Grote, and Mill made him what he is ".[1] The physicians' acknowledgment of the debt of medicine to literature gains force from this picture of the literary associations which stimulated many of the future leaders of the profession during their student days in the Society.

Members kept abreast also of the advances in science, and a few titles of dissertations show how they speculated on them. Robert Jameson was allowed to choose for his Question, " Is the Huttonian Theory of the Earth consistent with Fact ? "[2] He followed this line of study and was later Professor of Natural History at Edinburgh for half a century. It is probable that Jameson's fame drew Darwin to study at Edinburgh.[3] Among other Questions, on which members were granted permission to write, were Mr. Fawssett's choice, " What is the *modus operandi* of electricity, its sensible effect, and in what diseases useful ? ", Dr. Foucault's " Can we expect any benefit from music in the treatment of diseases ? ", and Dr. Bostock's " By what process is the adipose matter formed in the System ? "

Two members, at this time, who afterwards attained eminence were Thomas Bateman, a president in 1800, who became a pioneer in dermatology, and author of *A practical Synopsis of Cutaneous Diseases according to the Arrangement*

---

[1] Lord Acton, *History of Freedom and other Essays* (1909), p. 393.
[2] *Dissertations of Royal Medical Society* (1892), pp. 32-39.
[3] Sir A. Grant, *The Story of the University of Edinburgh*, vol. ii, p. 434.

H

of Dr. Willan (1813) ; and John Cheyne (1800) whose observations were quoted by Stokes in his classical paper on Cheyne-Stokes' respiration.

The spirit of economy in the Society was stimulated by the window tax. On 19th April 1799 a committee was appointed to determine what number of windows might be shut up without inconvenience to the Society. Their report stated that three windows in the garret, one on each side of the door, one below the stair, and another above the back door might easily be dispensed with " if the Appeal to the Commissioners were not sustained ". The lighting of the Hall was watched carefully. As late as 1814 the Committee of Domestic Economy, which was first set up in that year, decided that seven pounds of candles, at four to the pound, were sufficient to light the public hall during the meetings ; and that the remains of the candles used in the public hall during the meetings should be applied to light the library during the week.

There are memorials on the walls of the Society's Hall to two presidents who died while holding office during this period.

Jacob Pattisson died from natural causes in 1782. His remains were interred in Dr. Andrew Duncan's burial-ground in the churchyard of St. Cuthbert's Chapel (now Buccleuch Church) in Edinburgh. A tombstone was erected by the members of the Royal Medical, the Speculative, and the Physical Societies. Pattisson was a president of the three Societies at the time of his death.

Francis Foulke, a Dublin man, was senior president in 1789, when he was killed in a duel with Mr. Charles Grant, a lieutenant of the 55th Regiment, then stationed in Edinburgh Castle. " The affair originated in a petty quarrel about a dog." [1] On Friday, 18th December, Grant and two companions, having spent the evening together, were going home, when, meeting with Foulke and his party, a scuffle ensued, and next day Foulke sent Grant a challenge by a friend. Owing to certain reports about Foulke, Grant did not think himself called upon to accept the challenge ; but

[1] Kay's *Portraits* (1842), vol. i, p. 422, footnote.

he consulted some officers, who thought that he should not accept without satisfying himself of the truth of these reports. Meanwhile Foulke's friend interviewed Grant, who still declined to accept ; and thereupon, Foulke posted Grant in the coffee-houses. Grant, having ascertained that Foulke's character was unexceptionable, was willing to give Foulke satisfaction, and was on his way for that purpose, when he met a friend who told him that a placard was posted up in the Exchange coffee-house, couched in these terms : " That Charles Grant of the 55th regiment has behaved unbecoming a man of honour and a gentleman, is thus publicly asserted. P.S. The person who makes this declaration has left his name at the bar." Along with this notice, a slip of paper was left, on which was written " Francis Foulke ". On Tuesday morning, at 9 o'clock, the parties met in the King's Park. Owing to a misunderstanding about the arrangements, the parties left the ground. As they parted, Grant assured Foulke that he would post him in return. It was Grant's intention, at this time, to lay the matter before the officers of his regiment, that they might direct him in what manner it was proper to proceed. But Foulke, anxious to have the matter settled, and desiring to give Grant an opportunity of bringing it to a conclusion, sent him a message at 12 o'clock on the same day, informing him that he was ready to meet him. Two o'clock was the time appointed. " Grant, attended by his second and surgeon, met Foulke and his second on the beach to the eastward of Leith. Twelve paces was the distance measured off by the seconds. It was agreed that the parties should exchange pistols, and both fire at the same time. Three shots were exchanged. The last went through Foulke's heart, and proved fatal in a few minutes. He endeavoured to speak ; but the only expression he made use of was, that ' he hoped he died like a man of honour '." [1]

Mr. Grant was a nephew of Dr. Gregory Grant. After the duel he retired from the army, and became melancholy and unhappy.[2]

[1] *Scots Magazine* (22nd Dec. 1789), vol. ii, p. 622.
[2] Kay's *Portraits* (1842), vol. i, p. 422.

CHAPTER VII

Dispute with Extraordinary Members—The Circulation of Papers
—Benjamin Travers—Henry Holland—Richard Bright—Marshall
Hall—John Davy—Thomas Addison—Seven Guy's Physicians—
Charles Hastings

In March 1808 a dispute arose between a section of the active
members and the extraordinary members. Extraordinary
members at this time were those who, having attended
during two complete sessions, or a period equal to two
sessions, and discharged all their debts to the Society, had
written one set of papers—a dissertation, and a comment
on a case. They were obliged, notwithstanding, to deliver
a second set of papers in their turn. The reduction in the
number of sets of papers was made on account of the increasing
number of students joining the Society. Extraordinary
members enjoyed all the privileges of ordinary members.
They were not required to attend meetings. Some ordinary
members thought that the right of voting in the election of
presidents should be confined to those whose attendance at
meetings kept them in touch with the Society ; and, on 4th
March 1808, they proposed that extraordinary members of
more than two years' standing should be debarred from
voting at such elections. A week later the motion was
passed. The extraordinary members at once protested.

On 18th March their protest was read from the Chair.
They stated that they deemed it their duty to call upon the
Society to rescind the regulation, adopted without due
reflection by the meeting of 11th March, because they re-
garded it as illegal and subversive of the constitution of the
Society. They referred to the regulations which secured to

104

them the privileges of ordinary members, and particularly the privilege of voting at the election of presidents. On the faith of these laws they had become members of the Society, fulfilled every duty, and discharged every pecuniary obligation exacted from them. They were entitled, therefore, to regard as a breach of faith every act of the attending members, by which their privileges were encroached upon. The attending members had no more power to take from them the privilege in question than to deprive them of the use of the library, the right to attend meetings, or their proprietary interest in the Hall : they could no more assume to themselves a right to do that which they had attempted to do, than they could to deprive them of the whole privileges of members, dissolve the Society, dispose of its property, or cancel its Charter.

The extraordinary members intended their remonstrance to be a means of affording to those attending members who, by an unguarded vote, had violated the constitution of the Society, an opportunity of reconsidering and repealing the regulation : at the same time, they affirmed their determination not to acquiesce in an encroachment on their rights. Among those who signed the protest were Dr. Andrew Duncan, junior, Regius Professor of Medical Jurisprudence at Edinburgh ; James Wardrop, F.R.C.S.E., author of *Essays on the Morbid Anatomy of the Human Eye* (1808) ; Dr. John Gordon and his friend, Daniel Ellis ; Dr. Robert Graham, later Professor of Botany at Edinburgh, by whose exertions the Botanic Garden was removed to its present site in Inverleith Row ; Andrew Fyfe, treasurer of the Society ; William Wood, William Newbigging, and George Bell, all Fellows of the Royal College of Surgeons of Edinburgh and eminent practitioners in the city ; Dr. Andrew Coventry, Professor of Agriculture at Edinburgh ; and Robert Jameson, Regius Professor of Natural History there.

On 23rd March an extraordinary meeting was held to consider the remonstrance. John Bishop Estlin, the mover of the offending motion, was again prominent. Impenitent and unyielding, he moved an adjournment *sine die* on the

105

ground that members had not had an opportunity of reading the remonstrance, as it had not been inserted in the minutes in sufficient time. The motion was carried. On 30th March, however, another extraordinary meeting was held to consider the remonstrance, and the presence of extraordinary members secured a decision to rescind the regulation of 11th March. Dr. John Gordon seconded the motion. But the victory was not final : the dissenting members were obdurate. On 8th April, Joseph Arnould, seconded by Renn Hamden, the senior president, moved : " That no member shall be allowed to vote at the election of presidents without having attended four meetings in the preceding session ". The minutes of the meeting on 22nd April show that the extraordinary members, and the attending members who agreed with them, had taken the Opinion of Counsel. They had consulted Matthew Ross, " a very distinguished person . . . and a very great chamber counsel " [1] whose " subtlety and extensive ingenuity with extraordinary learning could not be exceeded ".[2]

The Memorial to Counsel stated that ordinary members, having attended for a certain time and performed certain duties, became extraordinary members. As such, they were exempted from compulsory regulations : they shared with the ordinary members the whole rights competent to members of the Society. It was chiefly to the privileges of extraordinary members that the Society had occasion at present to solicit the attention of Counsel. These were summed up in the regulation : " An extraordinary member shall enjoy all the privileges of ordinary members, and shall be subject to all the penalties to which they are liable, unless in such cases as are otherwise particularly specified. He shall, moreover, not be required to attend meetings or to pay contributions." The laws which defined the mode in which ordinary and extraordinary members exercised their privilege of voting in the election of presidents were : " No ordinary member shall vote at the election if he has not been admitted two months

---

[1] Lord Cockburn, *Memorials of his Time*, p. 405.
[2] *Life and Times of Lord Brougham*, by himself, vol. i, p. 232.

before the election shall take place ", and " No extraordinary member, whose name shall not have been on the circulation for three weeks previous to the election, shall vote at the election of presidents, unless he intimate his intention to the secretary by letter, as prescribed by the last preceding law ".

The offending motion was cited : " As it appears that members who never attend the meetings of the Society cannot be competent to decide on the merits of candidates for the honour of being presidents, it is moved, ' that no member shall vote at the election of presidents without having attended four meetings of the Society in the preceding session ' ". The extraordinary members questioned whether it was legal or competent for the Society to enact a law or regulation in the terms of the motion, which would subject them to a certain restriction in the exercise of their privileges of attending meetings and voting in the election of presidents.

Counsel was asked to consider the objection, and say whether it was founded in law. " (1) Had the Society a power to pass the motion in question into a law or regulation ? (2) If the Society had such a power, could it be legally exercised at an ordinary meeting ? or, Could the privileges of extraordinary members be infringed by any authority, short of that of a general meeting, to which every member, of whatever class or description, had been specially summoned ? "

The answers of Counsel were : " (1) I am of opinion that the Society cannot warrantably make a law or regulation in terms of the motion so as to affect the present extraordinary members, because it would deprive them of a *jus quaesitum*, viz. :—that of voting for Presidents as well as exercising other rights of members without being obliged to attendance, on the faith of obtaining which right they became members and have paid the contributions, and performed the duties required from members ; but, if the Society think fit, I conceive they may make such a law to affect future entrants when they shall become extraordinary members. (2) If such a law were to be made, I think it should be at an Extraordinary Meeting held in terms of the existing Laws."

At the meeting on 22nd April the Opinion of Counsel was read, and " Mr. Arnould withdrew his motion accordingly ".

The practice of electing four annual presidents was introduced in 1764, and it has not been altered. At the outset of the Society the law was : " The first President shall be chosen by a majority, and shall continue in office for one week after a Discourse shall have been delivered ; and then, after constituting the Society, he shall resign to the member who has delivered his Discourse ; who shall in like manner resign to the next discoursing member " ; and that law continued in force until 1764. The new law secured greater efficiency in administration and called for the election of the ablest members. The election, safeguarded by wise laws, became a matter of the highest importance to the well-being of the Society ; and for that reason the extraordinary members refused to accept any restriction on their right to vote.

The weekly circulation of the minutes and dissertations, referred to in the Memorial to Counsel, was systematically regulated as its smooth running was necessary to the proper conduct of business.

A sufficient number of copies of dissertations was procured, at the expense of the Society, so that every member should receive them in circulation. At the commencement of the session the secretary arranged the list of circulation according to the seniority of the members, who then intimated to him their desire to have their names placed on it. The names of members, who afterwards desired to be included in the list, were added to it according to priority of application. The original arrangement was not to be altered in any instance, except by the mutual agreement of members to exchange their places on the list. The secretary began the circulation every Saturday, during the session, at 8 o'clock in the morning, by sending the papers to the senior member on the list ; and the papers then circulated among members according to seniority, six hours being allowed to each member. If a member detained the papers more than six hours beyond the time at which he ought to have sent them away, he was not to send them to the next member on the list, but to him whose right it was to have them at the time of delivery. Every member was to send the papers at the appointed time, whether they had been six hours in his possession or not. If the papers were delivered at the abode of any member later than the hour appointed for him to have sent them away, he was not liable to a fine though they should happen to be detained : but he had to endeavour to set the circulation right as soon as possible. A book circulated with the papers, in which were inserted the names and addresses of the members who were to receive the papers, and the hours allotted to each member for the perusal of them. In another part of the book, each member had to mark, in the proper column, the name of the member from whom he received the papers, the hour at which he received them, the name of the member to whom he sent them, the hour at which he sent them, and his own name. The lists of circulation of the preceding week were examined every Friday night by one of the authors whose dissertations were read at the preceding meeting.

For many years the members appear to have conducted the circulation without assistance. On 8th November 1783 Mr. Richard Lubbock moved, " That David the porter be appointed to carry the papers in circulation to and from each member's lodgings at the proper hours " ; but, a week later, he withdrew his motion. And there is no evidence of detailed rules for the porter's assistance until 1823. The printed Laws of that date declare : " He shall conduct the Circulation of the Dissertations and Minutes ; but shall not be obliged to carry Books or Papers beyond the limits of a Circuit, bounded on the North, by the Custom House,— on the South, by St. Patrick's Square,—on the East, by the Palace of Holyrood-House,—and on the West, by St. George's Church ". The limits of the circuit were later extended, on the north, to Fettes Row, and on the south to Montague Street.

The need for strictness in the control of the circulation became less as the number of papers decreased. In 1816 the qualification for extraordinary membership, apart from attendance, was restricted, by dropping the case, to a dissertation only, and one afterwards if required. The change was doubtless due to the increasing demands of the medical curriculum on the time of the student. Each author supplied two copies of his dissertation ; and an official transcriber supplied a third copy, in addition to the transcription by him into the book kept for the purpose. The decision to employ an official transcriber was made in 1782, when it was enacted, " That a person shall be employed to transcribe the papers into our records in the same manner as the secretary formerly did, without diminishing the secretary's income ". Rules regulating the office do not appear in the printed Laws until 1823. In 1832 the office was abolished.

In 1799 a radical alteration in the law regarding admission to membership was introduced. John Allen, who was imbued with French revolutionary ideas of liberty, moved that a petition for a seat should be admitted by a simple majority of the members voting upon it. The proposal, put forward by this distinguished senior member, became law. This was a striking change, considering that at the outset of the Society a simple negative was sufficient to reject a petition ; and it appears to have been unsatisfactory. Three years later the present qualification of a three-fourth's majority was adopted. In 1806 a law was introduced that the names of the six attesting members to the petition must be inserted in the minutes after the name of the petitioner.

In 1806 Benjamin Travers and Henry Holland entered the Society. Travers began his professional studies in London as an articled pupil under the roof of Sir Astley Cooper, and, like his master, proceeded to Edinburgh to obtain the advantage of clinical teaching in medicine. He was an active member of the Society for one session only, at the end of which he was granted the certificate given to members who had not written papers. It is probable that, as in the case of Sir Astley Cooper, there was a clause in his indenture allowing him to spend a winter session in Edinburgh, which was too short a period in which to prepare a dissertation. Soon after he joined the Society he was entrusted, along with John Gordon, Daniel Ellis and other older members, with the responsible duty of providing subjects for dissertations and cases for the ensuing session.

Appointed a surgeon to St. Thomas's Hospital, Travers collaborated with Sir Astley Cooper, who entertained a high opinion of his literary ability, in a valuable work entitled *Surgical Essays*. In 1823 he was elected an honorary member of the Society along with Magendie, the French physiologist.

Henry Holland, who joined the Society in 1806, was a son of a surgeon at Knutsford, Cheshire, an old fellow-pupil with Sir Astley Cooper in the house of Mr. Cline, the celebrated surgeon to St. Thomas's Hospital. He was an enthusiastic member and was elected a president in 1809. In the following year he read a dissertation before the Society entitled, "An Inquiry into the Nature and Origin of the Passions in their Relation to the Intellect and the Bodily Economy of Man ".[1] In 1811 he graduated M.D. at Edinburgh.

He found the society of Edinburgh very agreeable. "At this time, it was not surpassed by that of any city of similar rank in Europe." [2] He was on terms of intimate friendship with Dr. Thomas Brown, the Professor of Moral Philosophy, whose lectures he attended ; and he was deeply interested in metaphysical discussions with John Playfair, who filled the Chair of Natural Philosophy. Debates on metaphysical questions were the fashion in his student days, not only in the Speculative Society, celebrated as a school of oratory for lawyers and statesmen, but also in the Royal Medical Society.[3] This fashion explains the choice of " Liberty and Necessity " as the subject of the debate in which Henry Brougham spoke when he visited the Society.

At this time also he came into close contact with Sir Walter Scott. An essay on the history and literature of Iceland, which he wrote in his student days after spending a

[1] *Dissertations of Royal Medical Society* (1892), pp. 40-63.
[2] Sir Henry Holland, *Recollections of Past Life*, p. 81.   [3] *Ibid.* pp. 85-86.

holiday there, attracted the notice of Scott, whom he already knew, and brought about a closer intimacy. He attended Scott during his illness in 1831 and 1832 ; and Lockhart has described him as " an esteemed friend ".[1]

He was a learned man and an excellent writer, and a close friend of Lord Macaulay, Sir James Mackintosh and Dean Milman.

Dr. Holland attained great eminence in the profession. In 1852 he was appointed Physician to the Queen. A year later he was created a baronet.

Henry Holland was president in the Chair when, in 1809, Richard Bright took his seat in the Society. Holland and Bright were old school-fellows, having been educated at Dr. Estlin's School near Bristol, and they remained inseparable companions at Edinburgh. In the summer of 1810 they accompanied Sir George Mackenzie, Bart., of Coul, Ross-shire, on his visit to Iceland for the purpose, chiefly, of mineralogical research. Sir George was a keen geologist, and was later president of the Physical Class of the Royal Society of Edinburgh. In the preface to his work, *Travels in Iceland*, published in 1811, he wrote : " My intentions being known, two gentlemen of the University of Edinburgh, Mr. Henry Holland (now Dr. Holland), and Mr. Richard Bright expressed a wish to accompany me ; and I did not hesitate to meet their wishes, knowing them to be young men of very superior talents and acquirements, in a high degree pleasing in their manners, and promising me the hope of numbering them (as I now have the happiness of doing) among my friends."

Bright, like Holland, was an enthusiastic member of the Society, and in 1812 was elected a president. His dissertation was " On Gangrene ".[2] In 1813, he graduated M.D. at Edinburgh. An intimate friend, and fellow-president with him in the Society, was John Davy, brother of Sir Humphry Davy. Writing in 1864, in reply to a request for his photograph for the Society's album, Davy stated,

[1] J. G. Lockhart, *Life of Sir Walter Scott*, vol. vii, p. 316.
[2] *Dissertations of Royal Medical Society* (1892), pp. 66-83.

" I would like it placed side by side with that of Dr. Bright, with whom I was then associated ".

Bright was physician at Guy's Hospital from 1820 to 1843. In 1827 he published his *Reports of Medical Cases* which contained the description of Bright's Disease.

Marshall Hall entered the Society a month after Bright ; and, like him, was welcomed to it by Henry Holland, the president in the Chair. Mention may be made here of John Gairdner, one of the attestors of Hall's petition for a seat. Gairdner (1809) was a member of a notable medical family. As President of the Royal College of Surgeons of Edinburgh he presided at the inauguration, in 1832, of the present Surgeons' Hall. He was the author of a *Historical Sketch of the Royal College of Surgeons of Edinburgh.* His brother, William (1811) attained eminence as a physician in London ; and his son, William (afterwards Sir William) Tennant Gairdner, who delivered the Inaugural Address to the Society in 1893, was for many years Professor of Medicine in the University of Glasgow.

Like Holland, Bright and other able students at the time, Marshall Hall was an enthusiastic member. In 1811, he was elected senior president. He was a doctor of medicine of the University of Edinburgh when, in 1813, he read before the Society a dissertation, " On the Dispersive and Refractive Powers of the Human Eye, and on some Motions of the Iris ".[1] A notable instance of enduring regard for the Society occurred in 1864, when Dr. J. C. Cookworthy, a fellow-president with Hall in 1811–12, enclosed his photograph for the Society's album in a letter, in which he wrote : " It is nearly fifty-three years since my friend Marshall Hall and I were elected presidents ".

Although Hall's favourite subject was chemistry, he applied himself particularly to the study of anatomy. During his last session at the University he acted as clinical clerk to each of two clinical professors in succession, Drs. Rutherford and Andrew Duncan, junior ; and, soon after graduating, he was appointed resident physician to the Royal Infirmary of

[1] *Ibid.* pp. 84-94.

Edinburgh. He settled at Norwich, and later removed, to practise in London. In 1857 he was elected an honorary member of the Society. His great achievement was the discovery of the reflex function of the medulla oblongata and the medulla spinalis. He is also remembered by his method of artificial respiration.

In 1811 Dr. William Bromet, the senior president, proposed that, in the rich and flourishing state of the Society, a sum should be set aside for the purchase of anatomical preparations, and that an annual sum of £10 should be allowed for the support of an anatomical museum. The proposal was rejected. Nevertheless, it contained the germ of an idea which, eight years later, developed into an important enlargement of the Society, the establishment of a museum to facilitate the studies of members. In the same year the Society showed its enthusiasm for experiment and enquiry by authorising the Apparatus Committee to purchase a galvanic battery for chemical investigation.

The Apparatus Committee of 1812 included among its members John Davy, who had joined the Society on commencing the study of medicine at Edinburgh in 1811, after completing three years' association with his brother, Sir Humphry Davy, at the Royal Institution.[1] The brothers had made together some experiments on the union of muriatic gas and ammonia in the laboratory of Dr. Charles Hope, Professor of Chemistry at Edinburgh, in the presence of that gentleman and other scientists.[2] The dissertation which John Davy read before the Society was, " On the Diseases peculiar to different Climates ", a suitable preparation for his future prolonged foreign service on the medical staff of the Army. In 1814 he graduated M.D. at Edinburgh.

Davy married the daughter of Archibald Fletcher, a highly respected member of the Scottish Bar, who resided near Sir Walter Scott's house in North Castle Street, Edinburgh. He was at the head of the medical staff at Malta when Scott, in hopeless ill-health, visited the island during

[1] *Life of Sir Humphry Davy, Bart.*, by his brother, Dr. John Davy, vol. i, p. 431.
[2] *Ibid.* vol. i, p. 457.

his Mediterranean voyage in 1831. Davy and his wife were both welcome company to Scott on account of old family friendship ; Mrs. Davy, as the daughter of Archibald Fletcher, and Davy, as the brother of Scott's friend, Sir Humphry, who had died in 1829. Lockhart in his *Life of Sir Walter Scott* has quoted from Mrs. Davy's *Family Journal* an account of the brief sojourn at Malta.[1] In conversation, Scott expressed his pleasure that Davy was engaged in writing the " Life " of his illustrious brother.

A notable contemporary of Davy in the Society was Robert E. Grant who was a president in 1814–15. He became Professor of Comparative Anatomy at University College, London. Joseph Lister was one of his students ; and Lister's early friend, John Beddoe, was another. Dr. Beddoe wrote : " I attended the prelections of Professor Robert Grant, one of the most learned zoologists of his day. He was a dry, melancholic, disappointed, humorous man, devoted to his subject with a burning zeal, a *perfervidum ingenium* much commoner north than south of the Tweed." [2]

Another notable member of the Society at this time was Thomas Addison. He joined the Society in 1813.

Dr. Addison graduated M.D. at Edinburgh in 1815, and proceeded to London where he became house surgeon to the Lock Hospital ; and later he joined the Public Dispensary to gain a knowledge of skin diseases under Dr. Bateman, a former president of the Society. In 1824 he was appointed assistant physician to Guy's Hospital, and in 1837 full physician, and joint lecturer on medicine with Dr. Bright. Both men owed their appointments to Mr. Harrison, the Treasurer, who had a talent for finding men who could make the most of opportunities of clinical research. Harrison deserves some of the credit for the recognition of Bright's Disease as well as Addison's Disease, and Addisonian, or Pernicious Anaemia. Addison made contributions to the knowledge of pneumonia and phthisis, fatty liver and

---

[1] J. G. Lockhart, *Life of Sir Walter Scott*, vol. vii, pp. 329-339.
[2] John Beddoe, *Memories of Eighty Years*, pp. 32-33.

xanthoma, and appendicitis, but his work secured little recognition in Britain during his lifetime.

Prior to Bright and Addison, seven members of the Society were physicians to Guy's Hospital. William Macghie was appointed in 1754. He entered the Society in 1743, and graduated M.D. at Edinburgh in 1746. William Saunders was appointed in 1770. He joined the Society in 1762, and graduated M.D. at Edinburgh in 1765. He was an innovator at Guy's, as he obtained permission to deliver lectures on the theory and practice of medicine, which were open to the medical pupils of Guy's and St. Thomas's. He was an early advocate of the superiority of red Peruvian bark to the pale form in fevers, and he was the first president of the Royal Medical and Chirurgical Society of London.

Thomas Skeete, a native of Barbados, was elected physician to Guy's in 1788. He entered the Society in 1783, and became a president in 1784. He was a member of the Speculative Society, before which he read an essay entitled, " Justice and Propriety of the present State of Slavery in the West Indies ". In 1786 he published his work, *Experiments on Quilled and Red Peruvian Bark*. He entertained a high opinion of Dr. Saunders as a teacher. James Curry was appointed in 1802. He joined the Society in 1783, and graduated M.D. at Edinburgh in 1784. He maintained that disorders of the liver were the universal cause of disease, and calomel the universal treatment, so that he became known as " Calomel " Curry. The three other members of the Society who were elected physicians to Guy's were Alexander Marcet ; James Laird, who entered the Society in 1799, became a president in 1803, and graduated M.D. at Edinburgh in the same year ; and William Back, who was admitted a member in 1804, and graduated M.D. at Edinburgh in 1808.

In an episode in the history of Guy's, a former president of the Society in the person of Mr. Bransby Cooper, surgeon to the hospital, was a leading figure. This was the libel action which Mr. Cooper brought against Mr. Thomas Wakley, editor of the *Lancet*. The facts are well known and need not be repeated here.

Charles Hastings, afterwards Sir Charles Hastings and founder of the British Medical Association, was admitted a member in 1815. In 1817 he was elected a president ; and being *ex officio* chairman of the standing committee when he chose to be present, his signature appears in the minutes of the Apparatus Committee and the Domestic Economy Committee. The dissertation which he read before the Society is remarkable for a student of the period, as showing that he used the microscope in his investigations. His exercise was entitled, " What is the State of the Blood Vessels in Inflammation ? " He describes the results of twenty experiments on cats, dogs and rabbits ; and such passages occur as, " but lastly by the help of the microscope the writer has found " and, " the following experiments were principally made on the web of the frog's foot, because the animal suffers little from having its foot fastened in the microscope and exposed to view ". He had faith in the earnest spirit of enquiry prevailing in the Society, as his conclusion shows : " I have the proud and lasting conviction that within the walls of the Medical Society, the experiments brought forward will be duly appreciated, and deductions drawn from them most consistent with science and with truth ".

Sir Charles Hastings was for many years the leading physician in Worcester ; and it was in the board room of the Infirmary there, at a meeting convened by him, that the establishment of the Provincial Medical and Surgical Association was decided upon, from which the British Medical Association developed.

CHAPTER VIII

Andrew Fyfe, Treasurer—The Museum—New Hall mooted—
Alienation—Haycraft's lampoon—Robert Liston—James Syme—
Dr. John Brown—William Sharpey—Robert Christison—Thomas
Hodgkin—Andrew Combe and phrenology—Dr. Andrew Duncan
senior's portrait—Kay Shuttleworth—Charles Darwin—Use of the
Medical Hall by the Royal College of Surgeons

IMMEDIATELY behind the Society's Hall in Surgeons' Square
was the High School, erected in 1777 to replace the old
building of 1578 which stood to the east of the High School
Wynd ; and the Minutes contain many references to com-
plaints made to the Town Council, as Patrons of the School,
demanding payment of the cost of repairing windows broken
by the boys. The Town Council declined to take dis-
ciplinary action, evidently regarding the boisterous behaviour
of the boys as incorrigible. The Society in 1816 appealed
to the rector, the celebrated James Pillans, and the masters
of the school, and suggested that each pupil should be
obliged to contribute threepence to defray the cost of the
repairs. The levy was intended as a deterrent as well as
a reimbursement. Pillans refused to impose it, but expressed
his willingness to act through the janitor, who appears to
have been a master of the art of persuasion, as there was no
recurrence of the trouble.

More trouble confronted the Society in 1819. The
treasurer, Andrew Fyfe, the well-known teacher of anatomy,
who was unanimously elected to the office on account of his
fine character rather than any business qualities, had neglected
to pay the fire insurance premium despite repeated notices
from the Sun Fire Office ; and all benefit had been forfeited
since the beginning of the year. An insurance committee,

which was fortunately sitting at the time, prevailed on the agent of the company to grant a receipt, and guaranteed prompt payment by the Society. The original policy could not be found. The committee was authorised to take out a new policy with the same office to the extent of £3500. £1200 was to cover the building, £300 the furniture, and £2000 the library. The Sun Fire Office, instituted in London about 1706, was the first company in Britain to insure houses and goods out of London. The company established a branch at Edinburgh in 1733.[1]

Soon after this time (1819), the Society proceeded to establish a museum for anatomical preparations and objects of natural history to which members might have access at any time. The aim was to remedy the defect of opportunities of reference, in regard to morbid and comparative anatomy, and natural history, which had long been seriously felt in Edinburgh. There was every prospect of success. Many members might be expected to present any objects, worthy of attention, falling under their observation. There was reason to think that the Professor of Anatomy in the University would present any pathological specimens from the Infirmary which he did not require for his own use. The Professor of Natural History, who was a member, had promised to give specimens and advise the Society regarding the arrangement and conduct of the museum.

A modest sum was expended on fitting up the attic storey as a museum ; an annual amount was allowed for its support ; and a committee was set up to superintend the collection, under the control of the Society. Early in 1820 the fitting up of the museum was satisfactorily completed.

During this session, 1818–19, the number of admissions to membership reached the record figure of eighty-four. The need of more accommodation, apparent for some time past in the library and the rooms set apart for scientific investigation, was now felt in the hall where the discussions took place. At an extraordinary meeting, held on 28th April 1819, it was resolved that a subscription should be

[1] Hugo Arnot, *History of Edinburgh* (1779), p. 536.

opened for the purpose of altering the premises or building a new Hall. The latter proposal, already mooted, had roused the ire of the veteran Dr. Andrew Duncan, senior, now seventy-five years of age. In a letter to the Society, he wrote that the proposal involved the alienation of the Hall; that it would be a breach of faith with those who had subscribed to build a hall on a particular site and according to a plan suggested by the illustrious Cullen. He considered that the number of members on the attendance roll should never exceed one hundred.

The use of the word " alienation " was a warning to members to be circumspect. Each of them, joining the Society, had signed the Obligation which, at the time and until after the sale of the Medical Hall in 1851, was as follows :

" By subscribing my name to the Laws of the Medical Society of Edinburgh, I publicly declare that I will obey all its Laws and Regulations ; and, especially, that I will be particularly careful of all the Books belonging to its Library; that I will never consent to any alienation of the said Library, or any other property of the Society, unless the same shall have been agreed to at a full and lawful Ordinary Meeting of the Society."

In addition, the statement that subscriptions had been paid for the purpose of building a particular hall on a particular site was one which members had to accept from Dr. Andrew Duncan, the chief promoter of the building of the Medical Hall in 1775; because the Society possessed no written evidence of the terms of the subscription.

In 1819, therefore, a committee was appointed to take such steps as they thought fit to accomplish the purpose of the Society, and ensure the success of the subscription. Dr. Andrew Duncan was a member of the committee, and with him were : the President of the Royal College of Physicians and Dr. James Gregory; the President of the Royal College of Surgeons and Dr. John Thomson; Mr. James Russell, Professor of Clinical Surgery, and Professor Jameson;

THE SOCIETY'S FIRST HALL

From a drawing by Shepherd in 1829

South-west corner of Surgeons' Square : on the left is Surgeons' Hall, on the right, the Hall of the Royal
Medical Society, and in the centre, the building with the pillars, which contained the Lecture Room of
the anatomists Barclay and Knox : in the building between it and Surgeons' Hall, in the background, is
the lecture room of John Thomson

and five ordinary members, among whom was William Cullen, a grand-nephew of the great Dr. Cullen. At their first meeting the committee decided, as necessary preliminary measures, to obtain the opinion of Counsel regarding the competence of the Society to dispose of the Hall, and to consult an architect regarding the practicability of adding to the Hall, and also the probable cost of building a new hall. The solicitors, in preparing the case for the Opinion of Counsel, concluded that the terms of the subscription for the Hall had been lost. Counsel were of opinion that the Society was competent to alienate the Hall in the absence of any written evidence of the terms of subscription ; and that, to avoid all difficulty, the decision should be approved at a meeting satisfying the conditions laid down in the Obligation.

The committee approached Dr. John Barclay, the well-known extra-mural teacher of anatomy, whose rooms adjoined the south side of the Medical Hall, to ascertain whether by a suitable arrangement the Society might enter into possession of his property. There was no immediate prospect, however, of such an arrangement. Dr. Andrew Duncan senior's suggestion to purchase a house on the opposite side of Surgeons' Square, and offer it as alternative accommodation to Dr. Barclay was not entertained.

The matter was not raised again until 1831, when a committee reported early in the following year that they were unable to obtain a sufficient extent of ground from the neighbouring proprietors for the enlargement of the premises ; and that owing to the state of the funds it would not be prudent to attempt any new building or change of situation. Four years later Dr. Barclay's anatomy rooms were for sale. The crime of Burke and Hare, with its disclosures, had adversely affected the popularity of Dr. Robert Knox, Dr. Barclay's colleague and successor. His brilliant lectures and researches in comparative anatomy had attracted as many as 300 students to his class, but a few years after the trial of Burke the numbers dwindled. The anatomy rooms were, however, unsuitable for the Society's purpose, and the price wanted was too high. In 1837 an additional storey to the Hall was proposed. No decision was taken, and it was not until 1850 that the extension of the Royal Infirmary compelled the Society to find other accommodation.

In 1820 a singular incident had occurred in the Society, which Sir Robert Christison, who was a medical professor in the University of Edinburgh for over fifty years, has described in his Autobiography.

" In the session of 1819–20 several able papers were read in the Medical Society, and ably discussed. But on the whole the members shone chiefly in the Society's private business. In that year a great occasion arose for oratorical display. A clever poetical lampoon appeared on the library table, describing at considerable length, in ludicrous colours and rather libellous terms, one of the Society's most exciting debates. The members were thereby thrown into a great ferment, and much curiosity was felt as to the authorship. All acknowledged the cleverness of the production, and this induced the author in an unlucky hour to print and publish it. The Society applied to the Court of Session for an interdict against the publisher, on the double ground that one of the Society's fundamental laws prohibited the publication of its transactions without its consent, granted by a resolution ; and that a lampoon, abounding in falsehood and in matter amounting nearly to libel against individuals, was injurious to the interests of a body established for such purposes as the Royal Medical Society of Edinburgh. The Court granted the interdict, and all unsold copies were delivered up and destroyed.

" At the same time traces of the authorship, ably followed up, all centred on Thomas Haycraft, a silent member, and not otherwise remarkable. He was thereupon brought to trial before the Society for breaking the law against publication. . . . The Society found Haycraft guilty by a large majority. The Senior President, Dr. Stroud, offered to abandon all further proceedings if Haycraft would confess and apologise ; a kindly suggestion, since Stroud was himself the chief object of the lampoon. The offer was now accepted, and Haycraft escaped expulsion — a nice question, however, arising, whether, by the vote of guilty, he was not, in terms of the Society's by-law, *ipso facto* expelled." [1]

The original manuscript of the lampoon is in the Society's library. It is entitled, " Digestion, a Poem. Being a Sketch of a Public Debate which took place in the Hall of the Royal Medical Society of Edinburgh on 7th January 1820. By Walsh Pindar."

A few months later, Stroud and Haycraft appeared as arbiters in a quarrel between two members, Scholefield and Duignan. Scholefield addressed a letter to the president in the Chair accusing Duignan of having provoked him to issue a challenge. The parties were persuaded to submit to arbitration, and the dispute was amicably settled. The settlement was the more creditable to the arbiters, as the challenger was a Yorkshireman and the provoker an Irishman.

Stroud's enthusiasm inspired him to activity in every part of the Society's business. In 1822, as joint-superintendent of the work, he presented, in a single volume, the 1820 edition of the laws, library catalogue, and list of members, preceded by an account of the Society's origin, constitution, and progress. He explained that, in preparing for the press the first three parts of the volume, he had occasion to collect many interesting particulars relative to the Society, which, for want of being embodied in a regular narrative, were little known and seemed likely to be lost. He had ventured to offer his services to supply the deficiency ; and the plan, which he had pursued, was to exhibit the Society in its relation to the Medical School of Edinburgh. An extraordinary meeting was held on 2nd April 1822, at which the History of the Society was read, and unanimously approved.

The arrival of George IV in Edinburgh in 1822 was the signal for the reappearance of Dr. Andrew Duncan, senior, first physician to His Majesty the King in Scotland. He moved that a Loyal Address should be presented to His

[1] *Life of Sir Robert Christison, Bart.*, vol. i, pp. 163-165.

Majesty; and, as a member of the committee appointed to prepare it, his handiwork is evident. The Right Hon. Robert Peel, then Home Secretary, acknowledged the Address in a letter to the senior president.

In 1817 Robert Liston entered the Society, followed soon afterwards by James Syme, Robert Christison, and William Sharpey. Liston was then acting as demonstrator of anatomy to Dr. Barclay. Owing to a misunderstanding with Dr. Barclay, he left him and commenced to teach anatomy; and he was in that position, with a class of his own, when, in 1820, he read before the Society his dissertation " On Fracture of the Neck of the Femur ".[1] In 1823 Liston devoted himself entirely to the teaching of surgery, which he was practising successfully. Ten years later, as senior surgeon to the Royal Infirmary of Edinburgh, he was at the height of his fame as an operator. He was a man of powerful physique. " He used to perform amputation at the thigh single-handed, compress the artery with the left hand (no tourniquet), and do all the cutting and sawing with the right, with only the assistance of his house-surgeon to hold the limb and tie the ligatures on the arteries." [2] In 1833 Mr. James Russell, Professor of Clinical Surgery, decided to resign the Chair on condition that his successor paid him the sum of £300 per annum. There were no retiring pensions in those days. Liston was marked out as Russell's successor, but, when the terms were announced to him, he refused point-blank to negotiate. Two years afterwards he accepted an invitation to fill the Chair of Clinical Surgery at University College, London.

At University College Hospital, in December 1846, Liston performed the first major operation in which ether was used as a general anaesthetic in this country. It is said that, as a young student, Joseph Lister was present at the operation.

A meticulous person might insist on the inclusion here of Sir James Young Simpson's statement in his lectures on

---

[1] *Dissertations of Royal Medical Society* (1892), pp. 95-103.
[2] Robert Paterson, M.D., *Memorials of Professor Syme*, p. 67.

midwifery, that ether was first used for anaesthetic purposes in Britain, at Dumfries, by the surgeon of the ship who brought the news over from America.[1] But that fact, if fact it is, can scarcely be held to detract from the statement that anaesthesia was introduced in this country at University College Hospital by one of the greatest of modern surgeons.

James Syme's dissertation " On Caries of the Bones "[2] fell like a bombshell on the Society. It was a fitting prelude to a professional career which abounded in controversies. The author referred to the carious affection as a disease of the utmost obstinacy uniformly requiring the assistance of Art ; and he wished, therefore, to characterise it so clearly that the merest surgical tradesmen might never mistake it for a healthy action. He also spoke of surgeons " arguing from cases entirely unconnected with caries and resembling it only in their confused and perplexed imaginations ". By a majority of 57 votes the Society decided that a declaration should be inserted at the head of the paper in the dissertation book that however meritorious the essay might be, it was objectionable on account of the asperity of censure and personality of allusion in which it indulged ; qualities which the Society, with every disposition to encourage rational liberty of discussion, was determined to discountenance as injurious to its interests.

Syme was a useful and active member. He served on the Museum Committee of 1821, which took a special interest in forming a materia medica section, a valuable addition in those days. As a student he was an enthusiastic botanist ; and, throughout his life, horticulture was his chief diversion in hours of leisure. In the early morning and in the evening he was among his flowers at his suburban residence, Millbank, which is now the site of one of the pavilions of the Astley-Ainslie Hospital to which convalescent patients from the Royal Infirmary may be sent. There, in 1868, he entertained Thomas Carlyle. " In the autumn of 1868, Carlyle, then

[1] MS. notes of Simpson's lectures by Edwin Thompson, a member of the Royal Medical Society.

[2] *Dissertations of Royal Medical Society* (1892), pp. 104-117.

Lord Rector of our University . . . was persuaded, on account of some little ailment of his, to come to Edinburgh and put himself under the care of Professor Syme. . . . Syme, proud of such a patient, and resolved that he should have his best skill, would hear of no other arrangement than that Carlyle should be his guest for the necessary time. . . . It was very pleasant, at the dinner table, to observe the attention paid by the manly, energetic, and generally peremptory and pugnacious, little surgeon to his important guest, his satisfaction in having him there, and his half-amused, half-wondering glances at him as a being of another *genus* than his own, but whom he had found as lovable in private as he was publicly tremendous." [1]

Before deciding on the choice of a profession Syme was an ardent student of chemistry, and a member of a chemical society consisting of a dozen young enthusiasts. Sir Robert Christison, who was a member, wrote of it, long afterwards : " It very nearly made a chemist, instead of a surgeon, of Syme. Before it came to an end by the dispersion of its members, he had begun to work at the subject of the solvents of india-rubber; and his inquiries ended in his discovering its solubility in the cheap menstruum, coal-tar naphtha, and the waterproofing of cloth by means of this solution. He published his discovery, at a very early age. . . . Nevertheless he has never got the credit of this discovery. Macintosh, the manufacturing chemist, reaped all the honour as well as the profit." The Chemical Society, and Syme in particular, had a startling experience owing to an overheated retort, when Syme and Christison together were demonstrating the preparation of sulphuric ether. " It was found that the retort had been blown to the farthest corner of the cellar, twenty feet off, where Syme had fled for protection—bending down with his head well in the corner, and the least vulnerable end of his body presented towards the enemy. The retort had been shivered to pieces against the wall close to his ear." [2]

[1] Professor Masson, *Edinburgh Sketches and Memories*, pp. 404-405.
[2] *Life of Sir Robert Christison, Bart.*, vol. i, pp. 61-62.

Syme's choice of medicine as a profession may have been due to Liston's influence. The friendship of these early years was subsequently marred by unseemly quarrels, but happily a reconciliation took place before Liston's sudden death in 1847. Syme studied anatomy, first under Barclay, and then under Liston. In 1820 he was appointed medical superintendent of the Edinburgh Fever Hospital where he had an attack of fever which nearly proved fatal. Soon afterwards he obtained a resident clerkship in the Royal Infirmary where his close friend, Christison, was house surgeon. Later he went to Paris where the study of anatomy was not hampered, as in Edinburgh, by the difficulty of procuring bodies for dissection. There he formed an acquaintance with William Sharpey which ripened into a lifelong friendship. His intention was to equip himself to become an independent extra-mural teacher of anatomy as Liston, with whom he was associated, was more and more identifying his career with pure surgery. On his return from Paris he was admitted a Fellow of the Royal College of Surgeons of Edinburgh, having previously become a member of the Royal College of Surgeons in order that his course of practical anatomy should be recognised as a qualifying one by the London examining boards. The anatomy lectures had a brief spell : a quarrel put an end to the association with Liston. Syme could not afford to carry on the rooms alone, so he decided to join what came to be known, from the situation of the rooms, as the Brown Square School of Medicine. There he lectured on surgery and anatomy. This connection also was brief. A visit to Dublin in 1826 impressed him with the skill of the Irish surgeons, and he returned with the determination to emulate their example. A vacancy in the surgical department of the Royal Infirmary seemed to offer an opening, but the Managers were unwilling to run the risk of a feud between Liston, already a surgeon to the institution, and Syme. Stung by the refusal, Syme resolved to establish a surgical hospital of his own.[1] This he did at Minto House, which stood near the middle of the north side of the area now called Chambers

[1] Robert Paterson, M.D., *Memorials of Professor Syme*, chapters ii-iii *passim*.

Street, and on the ridge overlooking the Cowgate. For four years he conducted the hospital successfully, along with three assistants, one of whom was Dr. John Brown ; and there the incidents happened which inspired Dr. Brown, " The Scottish Charles Lamb " as he was sometimes called, to write *Rab and his Friends*.

Brown had graduated M.D. before he joined the Society in 1837. His signature appears in the minutes of the library committee of that year. In 1839 he read before the Society his dissertation " On the Adaptation of the Eye to Distances ".[1] In 1861 he was elected an honorary member ; and, in his letter of thanks, he referred to the Society as " That noble, old and yet young institution, one of the chief glories of the Edinburgh School of Medicine ". In the same year he presented to the Society a copy of his *Horae Subsecivae* inscribed " To the Royal Medical Society, with the filial regards of the author ".

In 1833 Syme accepted the offer of Professor Russell, which Liston had contemptuously rejected, and succeeded to the Chair of Clinical Surgery which he filled with pre-eminent distinction for thirty-six years, with only one break of a few months, in 1848, when he filled the Chair in University College, London, left vacant by Liston's death. Finding London uncongenial, he resumed his original Chair which, during his absence, had not been filled.

Throughout his great career Syme was a staunch supporter of the Society. In 1843 he was elected an honorary member.

In the Society's Rooms there is a photograph of Professor Syme which was presented in 1909 by his daughter, Miss Lucy Syme.

William Sharpey joined the Society a year before Syme. His name appears with commendable regularity in the minutes of the Domestic Economy Committee, 1820–21. In 1823 he read his dissertation " On Cancer of the Stomach ".[2]

While in Paris in 1822 he witnessed Syme's delight when Dupuytren, chief surgeon to the Hôtel-Dieu, used a pair of

[1] *Dissertations of Royal Medical Society* (1892), pp. 254-267.   [2] *Ibid.* pp. 140-157.

Liston's forceps to divide the bones in a case of diseased nose. Syme was the donor of the forceps.[1]

Sharpey settled in Edinburgh, where he taught anatomy. In 1836 he left to take up his duties as first Professor of Physiology at University College, London. There he came in contact with Joseph Lister, then a young student. Among his pupils were John Burdon Sanderson, Michael Foster and Edward Albert Schäfer. Sharpey spent part of every summer with Syme; and these two, along with Allen Thomson, were, according to Sir Rickman Godlee, " the presiding geniuses over Lister's early career ".[2]

Robert Christison graduated M.D. at Edinburgh in the summer of 1819, and entered the Society a few months later. In his Autobiography he has related an unexpected result of the voting at the election of presidents in that year. " The four annual presidents of the Royal Medical Society have always been the *élite* of the advanced students and young graduates; and, with few exceptions, they have distinguished themselves afterwards in professional or scientific life. In 1819 the members, about 150 in number, were much divided in opinion at the election, on account of the number of able candidates. Many, therefore, in order to secure the success of three of their favourites, threw away their fourth vote on someone who, they thought, had no chance of being chosen. Such a man was Sheil—a clever debater in the Society, but rude and unscrupulous, and therefore much disliked. To any one surveying the company for the purpose, nobody would appear so suitable for a sacrificed vote. But so many agreed in this conclusion that Sheil was returned fourth president." [3]

The election of presidents is now conducted differently. Seniority among the presidents was determined by the number of votes obtained by each, until 1934, when the law was altered so that the senior president should be elected first, and three other presidents immediately afterwards.

[1] Robert Paterson, M.D., *Memorials of Professor Syme*, p. 16.
[2] Sir Rickman J. Godlee, *Lord Lister*, p. 18.
[3] *Life of Sir Robert Christison, Bart.*, vol. i, pp. 162-163.

This change was to lessen the chance of some member being elected on " sacrificial " votes cast for him as an outsider in an attempt to ensure the election of someone else, and to allow members to vote for the election, as junior president, of one whom they were unwilling to elect as senior president. At the same time it was enacted that members must have had at least twenty attendances at meetings recorded by the secretaries in order to vote or stand in the election of presidents. This restriction sought to prevent the election of a president solely on account of his reputation outside the Society, as might happen if many voted who seldom attended the meetings. It was found that, after the abolition of fines for non-attendance at meetings, a considerable number of such members did vote in the election.

Of Christison's teachers, James Gregory, who adorned the Chair of Practice of Physic, impressed him most. As a lecturer, Gregory's " measures for the cure of disease were sharp and incisive. In acute diseases there was no *médecine expectante* for Gregory. He somehow left us with the impression that we were to be masters over nature in all such diseases. . . . The consequence was that Gregorian Physic—free blood-letting, the cold affusion, brisk purging, frequent blisters, the nauseating action of tartar-emetic—came to rule medical practice for many years, in all quarters throughout the British Islands and the Colonies. For Edinburgh had long been the only medical school of fame and resort in the British empire, whither students flocked from its most distant regions." [1]

Dr. Gregory showed his regard for the Society by honouring it with a presentation copy of his *Conspectus Medicinae Theoreticae* in 1783, five years before he published the work. There is a bust of this celebrated physician and distinguished member in the Hall. It was executed as a memorial for the Society soon after his death in 1821.

Dr. Gregory's death occasioned changes in the Medical Faculty. Home succeeded to the Chair of Practice of Physic ; Andrew Duncan, junior, succeeded Home in the

[1] *Life of Sir Robert Christison, Bart.*, vol. i, p. 79.

Chair of Materia Medica ; and Alison succeeded Duncan in the Chair of the Institutes of Medicine, leaving vacant the professorship of Medical Jurisprudence, to which Christison was appointed in 1822.

When Christison commenced to prepare his lectures, his framework was the medico-legal science of France. He made use, also, of " a few systematic treatises, meagre enough, yet creditable to the infancy of English medical jurisprudence ".[1] He does not mention that the first English work on the subject was *Elements of Medical Jurisprudence*, published in 1788 by Samuel Farr who studied medicine at Edinburgh and joined the Society in 1763.

An outstanding historical event during his tenure of the Chair was the discovery in 1828 of the Burke and Hare murders. For a period of twenty-four hours Christison was an auditor or actor in the proceedings connected with the trial. The undoing of the ruffians was the murder of Margery Campbell, whose dead body was observed by a lodger beneath Burke's bed. In the early morning the body was conveyed to Dr. Knox's anatomy rooms, adjoining the Medical Hall. But the lodger, who had seen the victim in life, informed the police, who traced the body, which was at once claimed by the authorities. Christison and a surgeon, William Newbigging, were appointed to conduct a post-mortem. There was no positive proof of the cause of death. But the evidence, though not strong enough to support a capital charge was such as to excite the gravest suspicion, which was justified when Hare turned " King's evidence ". Before Hare's confession was communicated to him, Christison had an interview with Knox to whom he pointed out that the body must have been warm and flexible when it was delivered at his rooms. Knox made light of the suggestion, stating that he had received several bodies in as recent a state, purchased from the keepers of lodging-houses in the low parts of the city. Christison's opinion was that Knox must have been aware that a death in one of those dens was the signal for an orgy until burial. Syme had found that the stream of

[1] *Ibid.* p. 288.

visitors to " view the body " made it impossible to obtain bodies from these lodging-houses. Christison judged Knox to be lacking in principle and heart, but as guilty only of " blamable carelessness ". Nevertheless, Knox never recovered from the stigma attaching to him. He was nearly destitute when he died.[1]

In 1832 Christison was transferred to the Chair of Materia Medica, and became a teacher of clinical medicine in the University. He was Dean of the Faculty of Medicine when Syme wrote his historic letter in 1840 to the Town Council recommending the recognition of extra-mural teaching as serving to qualify for the medical degree of the University. The Medical School of Edinburgh consisted then of two bodies, the Medical Faculty of the University and the extra-mural school of the city, composed of lecturers who were Fellows of the Royal Colleges. The Senatus supported the majority of the Medical Faculty in opposing the proposal. Fifteen years of legal strife elapsed before recognition was obtained.

In the social life of Edinburgh, Christison was widely known as one of " the singing doctors " in great demand at dinners, the others being Drs. Hughes Bennett, Peddie and Douglas Maclagan. Douglas (afterwards Sir Douglas) Maclagan succeeded to the Chair of Medical Jurisprudence on the death in 1862 of Professor Traill, who had enjoyed the unusual experience of dandling his predecessor, Christison, as an infant on his knee.[2]

In 1871 Christison was made a baronet. He hesitated before accepting the honour, and consulted his " dear friend ", Dr. John Brown, who urged acceptance, as it was not only personal but intended for the profession in Scotland, and the University of Edinburgh.

In 1927 the Society had the pleasure of hearing an Address in their Hall on " Poisons in History and Romance ", which was given by Dr. A. J. Clark, Professor of Materia Medica and Pharmacology in the University of Edinburgh, and a great-grandson of Sir Robert Christison.

[1] *Life of Sir Robert Christison, Bart.*, vol. i, pp. 306-311.   [2] *Ibid.* vol. ii, p. 303.

Thomas Hodgkin joined the Society in 1820. He is remembered for his description of lymphadenoma, which he published in 1832, when he was Pathologist to Guy's Hospital and was engaged in collecting and cataloguing its Pathological Museum. His paper was forgotten, and his name is associated with the disease only because Sir Samuel Wilks, when he described the disease more accurately some thirty years later, insisted on giving Hodgkin the credit. Hodgkin also published an account of the clinical and pathological features of aortic valvular disease,[1] which anticipated Corrigan's account,[2] and, in a paper read to the Physical Society on his return from study under Laennec in 1822 he introduced to Guy's the use of the stethoscope.

In Edinburgh at this time the stethoscope was in use, for in 1823 J. C. Williams read a dissertation to the Society entitled " On the Stethoscope "; and the dedication of William Stokes's " Introduction to the Use of the Stethoscope " is to William Cullen (grand-nephew of the great Cullen), in recognition of " his unremitting attention to the light which mediate auscultation is now throwing on the obscurity of disease ".

Several dissertations of great interest were read before the Society during this period. Benjamin Bell (1819) read one in 1822 on " The Classification of Ulcers "; and there were several on puerperal fever—notably one by Thomas Annandale in 1825—and on contagion in fevers, which showed that thoughtful minds were exercised at the time of Pasteur's birth about the subjects on which he shed so much light. Other dissertations on heart disease, chemistry and toxicology showed which subjects were attracting the attention of members.

In 1823 Andrew Combe, an old school-fellow of Sir Robert Christison, provided the material for one of the most sensational debates in the history of the Society. He, and his elder brother, George, who was long the leader of the phrenologists in this country, were among the first to embrace

[1] T. Hodgkin, *Medical Gazette*, 7, 3 (1829).
[2] D. J. Corrigan, *Edinburgh Medical and Surgical Journal* (1823), vol. xxxvii, p. 225.

the doctrines of Spurzheim. He did not graduate M.D. until 1825 ; but he had gained the diploma of the Royal College of Surgeons of Edinburgh in 1817, had studied in Paris under Esquirol on Spurzheim's advice, and had commenced practice, when he read before the Society his dissertation, " Does Phrenology afford a satisfactory explanation of the Moral and Intellectual Faculties of Man ? " The essay " attracted an unusual attendance of members, and as the society admits visitors, the number of strangers was still greater. The society's hall was found inadequate to contain one half of the persons assembled for admission ; but Dr. Duncan junior having handsomely permitted the use of his class-room in the College, an adjournment to it was proposed and adopted. . . . It was calculated that at least four hundred persons were present." [1] The debate lasted till 2 A.M. An adjournment was unanimously agreed to ; and, four days later, the discussion was resumed at 7 P.M. and continued until 3.45 A.M.

A few days after the reading of the paper, a letter was received by the Society from the editor of the *Phrenological Journal*, asking members to furnish him with notes of their speeches, as he intended to write an account of the debate, and desired to be as accurate as possible, in order that the public might judge the merits of the question. The request was unanimously refused, and a committee was appointed to take the necessary steps to prevent publication. Meantime a rumour spread that the editor would publish, in the next number of the *Journal*, a detailed account of the debate. The committee instructed the Society's law agent to warn the editor, and ascertain from him if they had been misinformed. As no explicit answer was forthcoming, the agent was instructed to consult Counsel regarding the Society's right of property in its debates, and the propriety of applying to the Court of Session for an Interdict against the editor.

Counsel stated that, though the issue of a lawsuit would be doubtful, the Society possessed substantial grounds for

[1] George Combe, *Life and Correspondence of Andrew Combe, M.D.* (1850), pp. 130-131.

affirming and defending the right in question ; and that their doubts of the Society's right of property applied only to its proper debates, and not to the essays read before it, which belonged exclusively to it and could not be published without an obvious infringement of undoubted right. The committee decided to apply for Interdict, but shortly afterwards the editor and publishers of the *Phrenological Journal* intimated their willingness to compromise the dispute ; and the Society agreed not to sue for expenses, provided an obligation was undertaken not to publish any account of the debate. The offers were mutually accepted, and the dispute terminated.

As in the libel action of 1784, the Society had found that the right of property in its debates, as the law stood, was much more doubtful than was generally imagined ; but they were satisfied that visitors would be effectually and legally bound not to publish the transactions if their submission to the laws against publication were declared in express terms on the tickets of admission. It was enacted, therefore, that " Each Visitor shall be required to sign the following declaration on his card of admission : ' I consider myself bound to observe the Laws of this Society, particularly those affecting Publication ' ".

Combe's petition to the Society to be allowed to publish his dissertation was granted. Apart from phrenology he had sound professional knowledge, and he was highly respected for his kindly disposition.

On 10th November 1826, James Phillips Kay, the senior president, in name of the subscribers, presented to the Society a full-length portrait of Dr. Andrew Duncan, senior, to be placed in the Hall. At the time of the presentation Dr. Duncan was over eighty years of age.

The portrait represents the venerable physician and professor with right arm outstretched, as though repeating to the Society the noble words he addressed to it in 1771 : " The name of the Medical Society stamps a certain degree of reputation upon all its members : this reputation you obtain even before you have done anything to deserve it.

You owe it to your predecessors, and it is your duty to pay it to posterity."

In 1830 Dr. Alexander Monro, *tertius*, wrote to the Society, " I beg leave to inform you that it is the wish of the members of the Senatus Academicus to adorn their Hall in the College with a good likeness of the late Dr. Duncan. You will, therefore, confer upon me a particular favour by allowing Mr. Watson Gordon to have the use of the one he painted for the Royal Medical Society, during the summer recess, that a copy might be taken of it." The request was granted.

John Watson Gordon was distantly related through his father, Captain Watson, R.N., to Sir Walter Scott's mother. His half-length portrait of Sir Walter resting his hands on his staff, with his stag-hound Bran on his left, is considered a masterpiece. In 1850 he was knighted, and elected President of the Royal Scottish Academy. The Chair of Fine Art in the University of Edinburgh, called the Watson Gordon Chair, was founded in his memory by his brother and sister.

Kay, who made the presentation of Dr. Andrew Duncan's portrait, assumed the name of Kay-Shuttleworth on his marriage. He read before the Society a dissertation on " Asphyxia ", which he studied under Professor Alison to whom he later became clinical clerk at the Royal Infirmary. He went into practice near Manchester, and continued his researches on asphyxia, which gained for him the Fothergillian Medal of the Royal Humane Society. He became interested in the conditions of life of the poorer classes. In 1835 he was appointed an Assistant Commissioner to the recently formed Poor Law Board, and there developed the system of pupil teachers which greatly improved the teaching in Poor Law Schools. From 1839 to 1849 he was the Secretary to the Committee of Council on Education—a " precarious and obnoxious position ". In 1870 he was presented for a D.C.L. at Oxford as " the man to whom, probably more than any other, we owe national education in England ". His pamphlets and speeches showed a power of marshalling facts, and the development of an eloquence which distinguished him in the debates in the Royal Medical Society's Hall.

In his autobiography, Charles Darwin, who joined the Society in 1826, mentions Kay-Shuttleworth as the best speaker in the debates in the Medical Hall.[1] He describes a visit to the Royal Society of Edinburgh where he saw Sir Walter Scott in the Chair as president ; and he adds, " I think it was owing to this visit during my youth, and to my having attended the Royal Medical Society, that I felt the honour of being elected a few years ago an honorary member of both these Societies, more than any other similar honour ".[2]

In 1884 an etching of Darwin was presented to the Society by Dr. R. S. Marsden, a former president, in the name of the subscribers. On the occasion of the Darwinian Celebration at the University of Cambridge in 1909 the Society presented an Illuminated Address.

Shortly before the commencement of the session 1828–29, the Society received a letter from Mr. William Wood, P.R.C.S.E., stating that the Surgeons had been for some time in search of building accommodation for their meetings, and for the preservation and proper display of their valuable collection of anatomical and pathological preparations, but it was only lately that they had been successful in obtaining ground upon which a suitable building was to be erected without delay. The College had been informed by professional men, appointed to inspect the state of their Hall, that it was in such a state of disrepair and decay that it was not safe for meetings to be held under its roof and that there were no means of remedying the evil, even for a time. They had obtained temporary accommodation for the museum, and committee meetings, but had not succeeded in procuring a room for general meetings. Would the Society favour them with the use of the Medical Hall ?

The presidents were out of town, as the session had not commenced. The Chairman of the Finance Committee, convinced that the Society would endorse his action, assumed

[1] *Life of Charles Darwin*, with autobiographical chapter, vol. i, p. 40.
[2] *Ibid.*

the responsibility of meeting the request of the College at once, lest they desired to hold an immediate meeting. The good feeling which prevailed between the College and the Society is shown in Mr. Wood's acknowledgment. " I have been favoured with your letter intimating that the application of the Council of the Royal College of Surgeons has been laid before Mr. J. F. Macfarlan, Chairman of the Finance Committee of the Royal Medical Society, and that he conceives that the Society will approve of his proposal that the College should avail themselves of the use of the Medical Hall, till they have an opportunity of considering the application. I feel assured that the College of Surgeons will be much gratified with Mr. Macfarlan's kind attention to their request, but as it is unlikely that there will be any general meeting of the College till early in November, it will not be necessary for them, I trust, to intrude upon the premises of the Society before they have had full opportunity of considering the matter. Should circumstances, however, render an earlier meeting necessary, I shall, without hesitation, avail myself of Mr. Macfarlan's offer by calling the College together in the Medical Hall."

A year afterwards, the Society received the thanks of the College for the use of the Medical Hall, and a request for the continuance of the favour during the erection of their new building in Nicolson Street. The College accompanied the request with a handsome donation to the Society's library, which was acknowledged " with a high sense of the conduct of the Royal College of Surgeons ".

Again, two years later, the College presented a donation to the Society's library. On this occasion the gift was in money, thirty guineas ; and the selection of books was left to the Society. It was resolved that the books should be stamped with the Arms of the College.

CHAPTER IX

The Treasurership—J. F. Macfarlan—The President's Medal—
The Accumulating Fund—Petitions to Parliament—Order from
the Select Committee of the House of Commons on Medical
Education, 1834

AT the outset of the Society, one member performed the duties of secretary, treasurer and librarian. After 1771, however, when the subscription for building the Medical Hall was opened, the treasurership, in the hands of Dr. Andrew Duncan, senior, became a separate office.

Dr. Duncan remained treasurer until 1786, when he was satisfied that the Hall and its appurtenances were in working order. He was succeeded by William Hutchison, a junior member. A notable event during Hutchison's treasurership was the appearance of Astley Cooper as a member of the committee appointed to examine his first yearly statement of accounts ; and Cooper's signature appears on the certificate of approval which is preserved among the Society's records. Hutchison's appointment was not a success : at the time of his death in 1803 he was in debt to the Society. It was resolved that henceforth the treasurer, on assuming office, should give such security to the extent of £200 as the Society should deem to be satisfactory. Early in 1804, after a brief reappearance of Dr. Duncan as treasurer, Andrew Fyfe, the anatomist, was elected to the office, which he held until his death in 1824, when his son Dr. Andrew Fyfe, later Professor of Chemistry at King's College, Aberdeen, succeeded him. In 1828 Dr. Fyfe resigned office. His successor was John Fletcher Macfarlan, the former chairman of the finance committee, who continued in office until his death in 1861.

Macfarlan held the diploma of the Royal College of

Surgeons of Edinburgh, and was in practice in the city for a short period before he joined the Society in 1818. A case which he attended in 1815 led to his name appearing in the Edinburgh controversy in 1857 regarding blood-letting. In a letter to Dr. W. P. Alison, the protagonist of the supposed change of type of inflammatory diseases, he wrote : " I recollect well the commencement of the typhus epidemic of 1815, when I was called to attend a young woman, of a strong plethoric habit, who was labouring under fever of a violent inflammatory type. I bled her freely ; but recollecting Dr. Gregory's injunctions as to typhus, I got alarmed, but persevered, and she was relieved. In the course of the forenoon you were kind enough to visit her with me, and recommended her to hospital. There they poured in wine, and she died in a day or two. Then, nothing but bleeding answered well. Now it has changed again, and bleeding is nearly discarded, certainly not as Dr. Bennett maintains, but entirely as you have so distinctly pointed out." [1] In an article in the *Edinburgh Medical Journal*, Dr. Alison referred to written opinions in support of his views, which he had received, and, " particularly to that of our friend Mr. Macfarlan ". Dr. Hughes Bennett, Dr. Alison's chief opponent, replied in characteristic fashion : " If mere opinion were to determine the question, that of Dr. Alison alone would be quite sufficient ".

In 1821 Macfarlan read his dissertation, " Are there any grounds for maintaining the distinction of mental faculties as established by Gall and Spurzheim ? " He questioned the accuracy of the criticism of Dr. John Gordon and others, but stated that he could not join with them in their condemnation of the anatomy of Gall and Spurzheim. " When I consider the candour and love of truth which appear to pervade the works of Gall and Spurzheim, and the immense number of opportunities they have enjoyed of examining the brain, I feel inclined to pause ere I admit any observations made in this country as sufficient authority for setting aside the views of Gall and Spurzheim."

[1] *Edinburgh Medical Journal* (September 1857).

In 1822 Macfarlan was elected a president ; and two years later he was nominated for the treasurership, along with Dr. Andrew Fyfe and Dr. William Cullen, who was then a physician to the Royal Infirmary. Fyfe was elected.

A few years previously, about 1817, he had succeeded to an old and influential pharmacy owned by John Moncrieff, a surgeon-apothecary, described as " Herbalist or Apothecary to the Queen in Edinburgh ", to whom he had served his apprenticeship. John Moncrieff was a younger brother of the Rev. Sir Henry Moncrieff, minister of St. Cuthbert's, whom Lord Cockburn described as " one of the most remarkable and admirable men of his age ".[1] He was an honorary member of the Royal Physical Society of Edinburgh and author of " An Inquiry into the Medicinal Qualities and Effects of the Aerated Alkaline Water, illustrated by experiments and cases ".[2] His son, Dr. William Moncrieff, deserves mention as having presented in 1831 a cane to the President and Fellows of the Royal College of Physicians of Edinburgh for the use of the President.

Macfarlan was, therefore, a man of considerable experience when he entered on his thirty-three years' treasurership of the Society in 1828. In 1850 he was elected an honorary member.

Among distinguished men of science who were elected to honorary membership along with Macfarlan was Sir William Hamilton, Bart., Professor of Logic and Metaphysics at Edinburgh. It may appear anomalous that a Professor in the Faculty of Arts should be elected. Yet Hamilton, whose grandfather and father were Professors of Anatomy at Glasgow, was a student of medicine at Edinburgh during the winter session 1806–7 ; and for some time he regarded medicine as his future profession. In November 1806 he wrote to his mother : " I am hesitating whether to enter a member of the Royal Medical Society this year or not. I won't, I believe. They have a most elegant building belonging to it." [3]   A

---

[1] Lord Cockburn, *Life of Lord Jeffrey*, vol. i, p. 184.
[2] *Medical Commentaries* (1795), Decade Second, vol. ix, p. 105.
[3] Professor Veitch, *Life of Sir William Hamilton, Bart.*, p. 25.

regard, however, for the study of philosophy which was acquired at Glasgow, and later greatly increased at Oxford, prevailed over his early inclination for medicine. Nevertheless in 1832 he wrote a brilliant article " On the Revolutions of Medicine ; in reference to Cullen ", taking as his starting-point, the first volume of Dr. John Thomson's *Life of William Cullen*, which had appeared in that year.[1]

At a meeting of the Society in February 1860, James Crichton-Browne, then a secretary, seconded by Thomas R. Fraser, moved " That a committee be appointed for the purpose of collecting subscriptions to procure a fitting and lasting memorial of our respected Treasurer, Mr. J. F. Macfarlan ". The gold medal which is worn by the president in the chair is the Macfarlan Memorial.

The form of the memorial might have remained a mystery ; and there might have remained a doubt as to any materialisation of the proposal. In January 1912, however, a letter was received from Sir Robert Simpson of Messrs. R. R. Simpson & Lawson, W.S., legal advisers to the Society, offering a gold medal which had been presented many years ago to J. F. Macfarlan by the Society in token of his long and faithful service as honorary treasurer. The offer was accepted ; and in the following October, Sir Robert Simpson, on behalf of Miss Margaret Macfarlan, a daughter of J. F. Macfarlan, presented the medal to the Society. The inscription on the medal is :

Viro Ornatissimo
Socio ac Præsidi Suo Emerito
Spectatissimo
JOHANNI F. MACFARLAN
Societas Reg : Med : Edinb.
quippe qui de ea optimo
meritus est
hoc gratitudinis et amicitiae
testimonium
gratum esse
voluit.

On 23rd February 1923 Mr. W. R. Terry requested the president in the chair to relate the history of the Macfarlan

[1] Sir W. Hamilton, Bart., *Discussion on Philosophy, etc.* (1853), pp. 242-262.

Gold Medal. A week later, Mr. Terry, seconded by Dr. W. McKie, proposed that the medal should be worn by the president in the chair, and by the senior president at the annual dinner of the Society. The motion was carried. After the election of presidents at the commencement of the ensuing session, the retiring senior president called on his successor to take the chair, and handed over to him the Macfarlan Gold Medal to be worn by him as his badge of office.

Not the least of Macfarlan's services to the Society was his vigilant care of the accumulating fund. This fund was first instituted in 1818, two months after the erection of the finance committee in December 1817. At the legislative meeting on 21st February 1818 Dr. William Beilby, seconded by Charles Hastings, proposed that the finance committee should have charge of a fund, to be laid aside from the annual income of the Society, and vested in its name in public securities, for the purpose of keeping the house and premises in repair, and for making any necessary additions or alterations thereto ; and that the sum to be laid aside should be at the rate of 10 per cent when the annual income amounted to or exceeded £300, and of 5 per cent when it was under that sum. The motion was unanimously agreed to, and was incorporated into the laws.

The story of the accumulating fund might furnish material to the moralist and the economist ; to the former, as showing by impressive results how much may be achieved in the development and discipline of the mind on a margin of material resources ; and to the latter as a shining example of reasonable thrift. The foundation of the fund was laid on 30th March 1819, when an account was opened with the Bank of Scotland and the sum of £120 : 6s. was deposited. Deposits continued to be made, and the account to be operated upon until 31st May 1831, when the Society resolved that the whole amount should be invested in 3 per cent Consols. The amount, £779 : 9 : 11, was increased, by the addition of £20 : 10 : 1 from the ordinary funds, to £800 which enabled the Society to purchase £935 3 per cent

Consols. The dividends were lodged regularly with the Bank of Scotland. In 1844 the stock had nearly reached par ; and it was realised with a net profit of £144. The proceeds were invested in 58 shares of the National Bank of Scotland. In May 1847 the dividends, along with sundry sums, lodged with the Bank of Scotland amounted to £473 : 17 : 7. As the Bank of Scotland only allowed interest at the rate of 2 per cent, the total sum was withdrawn. £400 was deposited with the Exchange Bank at 5 per cent and the balance was added to the ordinary income.

At this time the income of the Society, owing to a great reduction in the number of students of medicine attending the University, had decreased, and the dividends from the Bank shares, along with the deposit interest from the Exchange Bank, were used to defray the ordinary expenditure to the extent of nearly £300. The wisdom of the originators of the fund was thus made manifest, and the Society was saved from what would otherwise have been a serious embarrassment of its pecuniary affairs. Notwithstanding this reverse, the fund continued to increase. When the Exchange Bank gave up business, the deposit of £400 was repaid. Thirty additional shares of the National Bank of Scotland were purchased.

The stock of the Society amounted now to 88 shares of the National Bank of Scotland, which yielded an annual dividend of £55 : 10 : 8. In addition, the Society possessed the fund in the Bank of Scotland which increased when sums could be spared from ordinary expenditure, as happened in periods of prosperity. Thus there was a prospect of such further increase in the funds as would have enabled the Society to defray the ordinary expenditure from this source and set free the ordinary income, arising from the admission of members, for making additions to the library and museum. In 1851, however, the sale of the Medical Hall to the Royal Infirmary took place, and other accommodation had to be found. Some members urged the realisation of the accumulating fund for the purchase of a hall : others opposed the appropriation of any part of the fund for that purpose. The Society resolved to open a subscription. The response was liberal. It fell far short, however, of the sum required for the purchase price—£2000—and the furnishing of the premises in Melbourne Place ; and, with the unanimous approval of the Society, the deficiency was supplied by the realisation of 53 shares of the National Bank of Scotland and the withdrawal of the sum deposited with the Bank of Scotland. The total contribution of the fund towards the purchase and furnishing of the new premises was £1018 : 12 : 6 ; and there remained £525 at the credit of the Society, being the value of 35 National Bank of Scotland shares. The Society had, therefore, the satisfaction of owning a hall, admirably suited for all its requirements and free of debt, with a residuary amount which, it was hoped, would again accumulate to a large sum.

In 1863 the National Bank shares were converted into £350 stock ; and in 1872 the Society applied £150 to the purchase of an additional £50 stock of the same Bank. Thus, when the City of Glasgow Bank stopped payment in October 1878, the Society, as owners of bank stock, were alarmed, for there was no such thing as limited liability for bank shareholders in those days. A committee, called the Investment Committee, consisting of a senior member, Dr. P. Heron Watson, and four junior members, Drs. C. W. Cathcart, D. Berry Hart and Blair Cunynghame, and Mr. R. Mackenzie Johnstone, convener, was appointed forthwith, with power to sell the stock at once and reinvest the proceeds in a first-class security. In February 1879 the committee reported that the sale of the stock had realised £1052, an increase of £377 on the purchase price, £675 ; and that they had purchased a feu duty in the City of Edinburgh. The Report was approved by the Society. To facilitate further reference, the committee wisely entered full minutes of their meetings in the Minute Book for Occasional Committees.

Those minutes, along with the story of the accumulating fund written by J. F. Macfarlan in the New Hall Committee Book, are a fascinating part of the history of the Society. The sums of money mentioned appear to be paltry in connection with a Royal Society ; but they are not so, when it is remembered that the Society is chiefly an association of students with a fluctuating membership. And the names of many of the members who took part in those transactions are written large in the history of medicine and the sciences connected with medicine. It is well to remember that the originators of the proposal to institute the accumulating fund were William Beilby, who, as P.R.C.P.E., delivered the Address before the Royal College of Physicians of Edinburgh at the opening of their New Hall in Queen Street in November 1846, and Charles Hastings, the future founder of the British Medical Association.

The Society still derives an income from the feu duty. After the removal from Surgeons' Square, the practice of setting aside part of the ordinary income in the accumulating fund was not continued with the regularity of previous years ; although the extraordinary income, from investment and bank deposits, was allowed to accumulate annually, when it was not required to meet an excess of ordinary revenue over expenditure. But during the last years of the Great War, 1914–18, a maintenance fund was created by the generosity of old members and certain corporate bodies to enable the Society to carry on under the exceptional circumstances. A gratifying contribution, largely due to the representations of Dr. R. Mackenzie Johnstone, a former senior president, was one from the Edinburgh University Court. Part of the total sum was employed to keep the Society going. After the war was ended the first surplus income of the Society was utilised to restore the maintenance fund to the original amount, as part of the Society's capital ; and it was resolved that the fund should be regarded as a reserve, only to be used if another national emergency, such as war, were to arise. More recently, in 1928, a fund, called the Bicentenary Endowment Fund, was instituted in connection with the forthcoming Bicentenary of the Society in 1937. One of the principal objects of this fund was the improvement and efficient upkeep of the library.

In 1828 the Society framed their first petition to Parliament. The grievance was the unsatisfactory condition of the Edinburgh Anatomical School owing to the difficulty, then at its height, of obtaining subjects for dissection ; and the petition was one of repeated appeals from anatomical schools in the United Kingdom to remove the necessity of employing men of the worst description of character in the desecration of churchyards. The Marquis of Lansdowne, a former student at the University of Edinburgh, was requested to present the petition in the House of Lords, and Sir James Mackintosh, a former president of the Society, in the House of Commons.

A petition to Parliament from a society almost entirely conducted by " clear-eyed, ingenuous youth " was an uncommon event. The petition to the House of Lords appears in the minutes of the Society *in extenso*. It ran :

" Unto the Right Honourable the Lords Spiritual and Temporal of the United Kingdom of Great Britain and Ireland in Parliament assembled

" The Humble Petition of the Medical Society of Edinburgh Incorporated by Royal Charter

" Sheweth,

" That your Petitioners respectfully approach your Honourable House to lay before your Lordships a statement of the difficulties under which they, as members of the Medical Profession, labour in the acquisition of a most important branch of their professional knowledge.

" They humbly yet earnestly submit to your Lordships that without a thorough knowledge of the structure of the human body no one can become a good physician or an expert surgeon, and that such knowledge can be acquired only by frequent and repeated Dissections. And so universal is this conviction amongst all the eminent teachers of Medical Science that, by the Universities and Schools of Physic, Certificates of Dissection are required previous to the admission of candidates for examination, and also by the public medical boards as a preliminary to employment in the public service.

" Your Petitioners would, therefore, implore your Lord-

147

ships' attention to the grievance under which they labour, that all important to your Petitioners as is the knowledge of anatomy, and positively required though it be by the constituted authorities, no legislative provision is made for the complete attainment of it ; that moreover, whilst on the one hand, as medical practitioners, they are exposed to actions for damages on account of real or supposed ignorance, on the other hand, in their endeavours to attain the requisite information, they are visited with prosecutions and actually subjected to fines and imprisonment—that, in short, the law at the same time punishes for ignorance and denies the means of removing it.

" Your Petitioners would further humbly represent to your Lordships that students are thus induced to resort to foreign countries to obtain information, for the acquirement of which, facilities are there afforded which are here denied ; and that, as only the more wealthy class can avail themselves of such facilities, the great body of medical students are precluded from the attainment of a competent anatomical knowledge.

" Lastly, your Petitioners feel quite satisfied that it requires no laboured argument or lengthened statement to convince your Lordships that in proportion as the members of the Medical Profession extend their knowledge of the Human Frame both in health and disease, so are their skill and ability increased to remove or alleviate the sufferings incident to Humanity, and consequently their usefulness to the Country at large.

" May it, therefore, please your Lordships, taking the preceding Petition into your serious consideration, to adopt such measures as in your Lordships' great wisdom may seem best fitted for affording your Petitioners the requisite facilities for the attainment of anatomical knowledge. And your Petitioners shall ever pray. Signed in name and by appointment of the Society.

" (Sgd.) F. RAWDON, M.D. ⎫
" Medical Hall,   „   W. LENNARD   ⎬ Presidents."
  3rd April 1828.   „   ROBT. ARROWSMITH ⎭

In 1822 a member had proposed a petition to Parliament for the same purpose. But practical students of anatomy were few at the time and subjects were more easily obtained; and the enlightened proposal of Charles Adair (1820) was rejected.

Mention of Adair's name may justify a brief digression, for he is the last member of the Society who is known to have fought a duel ; and his second was William Cullen, a grand-nephew of Professor Cullen, and a former president (1818–19). The story is told by Sir Robert Christison, who was then studying in Paris. Adair " had passed as Writer to the Signet, but changing his mind, began the study of medicine, and in its pursuit went to Paris. . . . He was . . . decidedly harum-scarum. It was in character for him, therefore, to go to the masked ball of the Opera in the part of a drunken Englishman. But some of his practical jokes were taken *au sérieux*, and next morning he found several cards of exchange in his waistcoat pocket. One only brought forth fruit. An envoy arrived with a cartel of defiance to the Bois de Boulogne with pistols. Cullen, chosen by Adair for his second, proved in his novel position, as he did in every other, quite in his element. . . . The Frenchman's bullet was nowhere. Adair's hit the ground immediately in front of his antagonist, and threw the gravel upon him. ' Load again ', exclaimed Cullen. But the French second interposed, ' Non, monsieur ! C'est assez ! . . . L'honneur de mon ami est satisfaite.' . . . Adair was again disposed to demur . . . but Cullen was master of ceremonies. The combatants bowed to one another, and the party separated." [1]

The revolting disclosures during the exposure of Burke and Hare in 1828 showed the urgent need of placing some measure on the statute-book to remove the temptation to ruffians to commit murder for the purpose of selling subjects to anatomists. In 1830 the Society resolved to present a second petition to Parliament ; and Mr. Holroyd, a former president, was requested to take the petition to London, and use his influence with the members of either House, to whom

[1] *Life of Sir Robert Christison, Bart.*, vol. i, pp. 255-257.

he had access, in favour of the measure. Lord Melville agreed to present it in the House of Lords. In a letter to the Society, he wrote that he would take an early opportunity to present the petition. In 1831 Warburton introduced, in a modified form, his Anatomy Bill of 1829, which he had withdrawn ; and in 1832 the Bill became law. Perhaps Sir Astley Cooper's evidence before a committee of the House of Commons did much to facilitate the passage of the Bill. In reply to a question, he stated : " The law does not prevent our obtaining the body of an individual if we think proper ; for there is no person, let his situation in life be what it may, whom, if I were disposed to dissect, I could not obtain." [1]

In 1831 a claim to parliamentary representation on behalf of the Scottish Universities received the support of the Society. A petition to Parliament was drawn up " in support of that part of the motion of the Earl of Haddington in the House of Lords, which proposes the election of a Member of Parliament to represent the University of Edinburgh ". The Society entertained no doubts about the superiority of the Medical Schools of the Scottish Universities over those of the Universities south of the Tweed : " The interests of the Scottish Universities are in many respects equal, and, as regards the science of medicine, superior to those of the other Universities in the United Kingdon." Lord Brougham was requested to present the petition in the House of Lords, and Sir James Mackintosh in the House of Commons. The claim of the Scottish Universities was negatived in the House of Lords.[2]

Contact with Parliament was made once more, when the Society received an order in 1834, from the Select Committee of the House of Commons on Medical Education, under the chairmanship of Henry Warburton, to present a summary of the Society's origin, constitution, and purposes. The order ran :

[1] Bransby Blake Cooper, *Life of Sir Astley Cooper, Bart.*, vol. i, p. 407.
[2] *Political History of England* (ed. William Hunt and Reginald Lane Poole), vol. xi, p. 306.

" House of Commons
Select Committee
21 April 1834

" Henry Warburton in the Chair.

" Ordered

" That there be laid before this Committee by the Royal Medical Society of Edinburgh, answers to the following questions.

" 1. State the origin or early history of the Royal Medical Society.

" 2. Of whom was it composed at its commencement? and the object of its foundation.

" 3. Is there a Medical Library—What is its extent?

" 4. Are the members freely permitted the use of the books? and, are the books much consulted?

" 5. Give a list of all the Office-bearers, and the emoluments or salaries attached to each appointment.

" 6. Give a list of the Presidents from the year 1790 up to the present time, and the mode of their election.

" 7. Give an account of the income of the Society, and the sources from which it is derived in each year from 1820 to 1st January 1834, and the amount of the expenditure for the same period; and specify the amount expended on books during the same period.

" 8. Are the questions discussed purely medical, akin to medicine, or general subjects?

" 9. Is there any museum or collection of chemical or philosophical apparatus for the use of the members?

" 10. Transmit a copy of any resolutions passed by the Society in reference to the recent regulations of the University of St. Andrews for conferring degrees in medicine.

" 11. Transmit a copy of the Incorporation of the Society.

(Sgd.) HENRY WARBURTON
Chairman."

151

The answers of the Society were :

" 1. The Society was instituted in 1734 : but the first
authentic documents in its possession are dated
1737.
" 2. The Society was composed, at first, of a few medical
students who met for the purpose of reading
original dissertations on medical subjects, and
deriving mutual instruction and benefit from the
discussions which ensued.
" 3. Yes ; nearly 11,000 volumes.
" 4. Yes, according to regulations : the books are very
much consulted.
" 5. Four Presidents annually elected, whose office is
purely honorary. A Treasurer whose services are
also gratuitous.
A Secretary, who acts also as Librarian and receives
a salary of £60 *per annum.*
An Assistant-Librarian who resides on the premises,
and is obliged to be in attendance seven hours
daily for the purpose of giving out books, with a
salary of £60 *per annum.*
" 6. The Presidents are elected annually by ballot.
" 7. The Society's income is derived from
" (a) Contributions of members—1st year, £4:10s.:
2nd £3 : 5s. : 3rd £2 : 4s.
" (b) Fines for non-attendance at meetings of the
Society and Committees.
" (c) Sums paid for diplomas. A certain portion
of the annual income is set apart for an
accumulating fund.
" 8. The questions discussed are purely medical or akin
to medicine.
" 9. There are a museum and chemical apparatus.
" 10. In January 1834 the Society received from the Royal
College of Surgeons of Edinburgh a copy of their
printed series of resolutions regarding the new
regulations of the University of St. Andrews. As

a result of this communication, an Extraordinary Meeting of the Society was convened, at which it was resolved unanimously ' That the Society thank the Royal College of Surgeons for sending them notice of their proceedings regarding the St. Andrews degrees. The Medical Society concur completely in the sentiments so ably expressed by the Royal College, and are glad that the College is ever ready to advance the real interests of the students, and enhance the dignity of the Profession by endeavouring to secure, as far as possible, an extensive and liberal course of education.'

" 11. A copy of the Charter of Incorporation is to be found in Dr. Stroud's History of the Society."

The answers were signed by the presidents, transcribed by the secretary, and transmitted to the chairman of the Select Committee.

In the summer of 1834, the British Association held its annual meeting at Edinburgh ; and the Society offered to the members of the Association the use of the Medical Hall.

CHAPTER X

Douglas Maclagan—Hutton Balfour—William Gregory—J. Y. Simpson—John Reid—William Henderson—John Goodsir— Martin Barry—John Hughes Bennett—William Carpenter—The *Catalogue raisonné*—The Centenary Celebrations, 1837

On 29th March 1833 James Young Simpson petitioned for a seat in the Society. Douglas Maclagan was in the chair; and during the evening Dr. William Gregory, son of the celebrated Dr. James Gregory, gave in his dissertation.

Sir Douglas Maclagan was a lifelong supporter of the Society. In 1829 he was admitted to membership. In the same year the Society acted in accordance with its traditions as a scientific body by electing to extraordinary membership, " to save him expense ", Joseph Bassas de Roger, a Spanish refugee officer who was studying medicine. Like many young members who rose to eminence, Maclagan served on the Apparatus Committee. In 1832 Maclagan was elected a president; and, during his term of office, the death of Robert Newbigging, a fellow-president, occurred. There is a memorial to Newbigging, erected by his fellow-members, in the Society's Hall. A few years later, Dr. Maclagan proposed the toast of the Royal Medical Society at the complimentary dinner given to Sir Astley Cooper by the Royal College of Surgeons of Edinburgh. He referred to the important influence of the Society in drawing out the intellectual talents of its members as shown by the discoveries and improvements that had emanated from within its walls. On the death of Professor Traill in 1862 he succeeded to the Chair of Medical Jurisprudence. In 1883 he was elected an honorary member.

154

In 1831 William Gregory and John Hutton Balfour were fellow-presidents. Balfour was twice elected a president; and he also was an enthusiastic supporter of the Society throughout his life. In 1845 he succeeded to the Chair of Botany which he held for thirty-four years. His son, Sir Isaac Bayley Balfour (1875) occupied the same Chair from 1888–1922. In 1868, when the abolition of Saturday class examinations was proposed by some members, his duty as Dean of the Faculty of Medicine conflicted with his regard for the Society. His attitude, amusing in a way, reflected the integrity and sincerity of the man. In his Address to the Medical Graduates in 1869, he emphasised the value of a knowledge of the classics—" As men of science you must know Latin and Greek if you wish to understand terminology and classification ".

William Gregory, " a favourite pupil and friend of Baron Liebig ", was a graduate in medicine when he entered the Society in 1830. In 1834 he described to the Society some new compounds of nitrogen discovered by Liebig. He was as zealous in private as in public business. He is said to have steadily kept before him, from early youth, the idea of succeeding Thomas Charles Hope in the Chair of Chemistry.[1] In 1844 he realised his ambition. The election caused the Society's treasurer some moments of perturbation. The Town Council were the patrons of the Chair. As the time of the election drew near, Macfarlan, who was a bailie, was in London on civic business, along with Adam Black, Lord Provost of Edinburgh. He wrote : " I am in a sad fix here. Our Bill does not go into Committee till Monday next, and I have intimated that I must be away. But they tell me they will take out a Speaker's Warrant to detain me ; and they went to-day to procure one. Whether they have procured one or not, I do not yet know. If not, I will be off, to a certainty. But they intend to stop the Provost also, and as he has intimated as much as that he is likely to vote for Dr. Gregory, this will be a sad misfortune, unless they either agree to elect the Doctor or delay till we return. I hope they

[1] Sir A. Grant, *The Story of the University of Edinburgh*, vol. ii, p. 399.

will delay and thus save us from being in a very unpleasant position." He was really under an obligation to support Dr. Gregory's candidature. In 1831 Dr. Gregory had contributed an article to the *Edinburgh Medical and Surgical Journal* on " A process for preparing economically the Muriate of Morphia ". Macfarlan communicated the paper to his assistant, later his partner, David Rennie Brown, whose skill as a technical chemist and chemical engineer enabled his master to become the first producer of morphine on a commercial scale.

In November 1835 J. Y. Simpson, who had graduated M.D. at Edinburgh in 1832, after obtaining the Surgeons' Diploma two years previously, delivered his dissertation " On the Diseases of the Placenta " before the Society.[1] His immense capacity for work is thus early revealed : " Of the dissertation . . . he says : ' It is 5 A.M. I have been up all night, correcting the last sheets of my paper. I was up all Monday night, and have done with three or four hours' sleep for several others.' "[2] The dissertation was printed in the *Edinburgh Medical and Surgical Journal* in January 1836 and in the *London Medical and Surgical Journal* in the summer of the same year. Shortly afterwards translations of it appeared in German, Italian and French journals.

Simpson was elected senior president a week after he delivered his dissertation. His fellow-presidents were Martin Barry, J. H. Pollexfen, and his close friend, John Reid. Simpson and Reid had served together on the library committee. As senior president, Simpson constituted the Society at the commencement of the centenary session ; and three years afterwards he was Professor of Midwifery at Edinburgh.

He had resolved to devote himself to obstetric medicine while he was acting as assistant to John Thomson, Professor of Pathology, by whom his graduation thesis, " Death from Inflammation ", had been examined. " In taking my degree

---

[1] *Dissertations of Royal Medical Society* (1892), pp. 173-196.
[2] Eve Blantyre Simpson, *Sir James Y. Simpson* (Famous Scots Series), pp. 34, 35.

here last summer, I had the good fortune to attract the notice of Dr. John Thomson, a physician of the greatest eminence, who was then looking out for a person to assist him. . . . It was at an early part of that period . . . that, at Dr. Thomson's urgent suggestion and advice, I first turned my attention more especially to the study of Midwifery, with the view of becoming a teacher of this department of medical science." [1] In 1837 Professor Thomson, in a letter to the patrons (the Town Council), recommended the appointment of Dr. Simpson as interim lecturer in pathology.

When Professor James Hamilton died in 1839, Simpson announced himself a candidate for the Midwifery Chair. It was necessary to canvass the thirty-three members of the Town Council who were the Patrons of the Chair, as there were other candidates in the field. Eventually, the choice lay between Simpson and Dr. Evory Kennedy of Dublin. On 4th February 1840 Simpson secured the Chair by a majority of one—17 voted for him, and 16 for Dr. Kennedy.

In 1922 Sir Byrom Bramwell delivered the Inaugural Address to the Society, and took as his subject, " The Edinburgh Medical School and its Professors in my Student Days, 1865–1869 ".[2] Speaking of Simpson, Sir Byrom said : " Simpson was, in my opinion, the greatest, by far the greatest of my teachers. . . . Simpson was a man of extraordinary mental ability and power—a genius, a very versatile genius ; he had a prodigious and most accurate memory, a far-sighted imagination, an optimistic temperament which made him believe all good things possible. Further, he was a man of great personal charm, of imperturbable temper, though a very keen controversialist and fighter. Simpson ' adopted obstetrics when it was the lowest and most ignoble of our medical arts ; he left it a science numbering among its professors many of the most distinguished of our modern physicians '."

The connection between the family of this great man and the Society is still unbroken. In 1904 his nephew, Sir Robert Simpson, who was legal adviser to the Society, wrote, " I

[1] J. Duns, D.D., *Memoir of Sir James Y. Simpson, Bart.*, pp. 37-38.
[2] *Edinburgh Medical Journal* (1923), vol. xxx, pp. 133-156.

have acted for the Society for more than thirty years, and have always taken a deep interest in its prosperity. This interest has been increased by the fact that six near relatives of mine have had the honour of being Presidents of the Society." In March 1937 Sir Robert Simpson's son, Mr. S. Raleigh Simpson, W.S., of Messrs. R. R. Simpson & Lawson, W.S., legal advisers to the Society, presented certain papers relating to his grand-uncle, Sir James ; and in November 1938, Sir James's grand-nephew, Dr. G. F. Barbour Simpson, who was a president in 1898–99, presented to the Society his grand-uncle's diploma of honorary membership, with its seal. The diploma bears the signatures, among others, of W. P. Alison, Robert Christison, James Syme, Robert Jameson, John Goodsir, William Gregory, Douglas Maclagan, John Hutton Balfour, Thomas Anderson, who was afterwards Lister's colleague in Glasgow, R. J. Mackenzie, who died in the Crimea, W. R. Sanders, Sir George Ballingall and John (afterwards Sir John) Scott Burdon-Sanderson.

In 1927 Colonel Richardson, father of Major F. M. Richardson, R.A.M.C., who was a president in 1926–27, presented a bust of Sir James Y. Simpson to the Society.

Less than three years after the discovery of general anaesthesia, Simpson's old school-fellow and fellow-student, John Reid, lay dying from a painful disease ; and Dr. George Wilson wrote,[1] " Before the final close, the suffering but for chloroform would have been extreme ".

John Reid had graduated in medicine and was a partner with Dr. Knox and Mr. William Fergusson (afterwards Professor of Surgery at King's College, London) in the School of Anatomy in Surgeons' Hall when he entered the Society. Sir J. Y. Simpson said that both Reid and he would have joined the Society much sooner had the fees been smaller. In the debates, at public business, Reid was very prominent. " The Society was the chief scene of those feats of intellectual gymnastics and gladiatorship by which he acquired that acquaintance with his own skill and prowess, that confidence in his own capacity and resources, and that command of

[1] George Wilson, M.D., *Life of Dr. John Reid*, p. 298.

language, which secured him so high a place in the estimation of others, both as a teacher and a discoverer." [1] His biographer has described the contemporary state of the Society. " The great majority of the regular attendants at the meetings are bona fide students. . . . The active students willingly submitted to restrictions which they knew to be for the advantage of the Society, and they took care that their less attentive brethren should attest their membership by their presence, (unless when illness rendered this impossible) or by the proxy of one of her Majesty's coins. There was occupation for every one. The most ignorant or idle of students, however slow to open his mouth on questions involving a knowledge of anatomy, chemistry, or physiology, could give an opinion on a question of finance ; and as an hour was devoted to private business, and silence was irksome, opinions were freely enough given. . . . I question whether any dignity can compare in the eyes of a medical student with that which attaches to the office of senior president." [2]

In 1836 Reid read his dissertation before the Society. The subject was, " Can acquired Habits and Physical Configuration of Body descend to the Offspring ? " [3] In the same year he became F.R.C.P.E. and commenced as an extra-mural lecturer in physiology. He was reluctant to incur even the appearance of competition with the revered Professor of Physiology, Dr. Alison ; and only Dr. Alison's advice, and a requisition to lecture signed by his medical friends, overcame his reluctance. Among the signatories was Dr. William Henderson (1829), afterwards Professor of Pathology at Edinburgh. " Henderson's early professional life and work gave great promise of success and distinction. In 1835–37 he published a series of clinical studies on ' Diseases of the Heart and Great Blood Vessels ' which are of value and importance. He was the first to point out that typhus and relapsing fever were two distinct diseases, and not, as had been supposed, merely different types (sthenic and asthenic) of the same disease. . . . Unfortunately he

[1] *Ibid.* p. 38.   [2] *Ibid.* pp. 48-51.
[3] *Dissertations of Royal Medical Society* (1892), pp. 197-214.

became entangled in the sophistries of homeopathy . . . and a career, whose early brilliance was so full of hopeful promise was lost to science." [1]

In 1838 Reid was appointed pathologist to the Royal Infirmary of Edinburgh. His successor in the office, Professor Hughes Bennett, wrote : " During the period he was pathologist, there was introduced under his superintendence that regular method of inscribing the leading facts connected with each case in a register which has since prevailed ; and he it was who compiled the first series of statistical tables published by the Managers ". [2] In 1841 he was elected Professor of Anatomy at St. Andrews. He died at the early age of forty, of a carcinoma of the tongue. When the Society again resolved in 1864 to have an album for presidents' photographs, Reid's photograph was obtained.

Reid's friends, John Goodsir and John Hughes Bennett were fellow-members with him in the Society. Although Goodsir became a member in 1833, he did not commence to take an active part until 1840, when he was appointed curator of the library. He was elected senior president in 1841, and again in 1842. The autograph manuscript of his dissertation, delivered in 1842, " On Continued Fever " is in the Society's archives.

Goodsir commenced his career as an apprentice to Mr. Nasmyth, F.R.C.S.E., dentist, whose example raised dentistry " from the back-slums of surgery, where it dwelt before his time ".[3] After two years' experience he yearned to devote himself to the studies of medicine and surgery ; and Nasmyth generously released him from his indenture before the expiry of the legal term. Goodsir studied anatomy in Knox's rooms, where William Fergusson and his friend and counsellor, John Reid, were demonstrators. His surgical teacher was Syme, to whom he acted as dresser and frequently as assistant, and who was afterwards his firm friend. His remarkable friendship with Edward Forbes, the distinguished naturalist

---

[1] Inaugural Address to the Society by Sir Byrom Bramwell, 1922.
[2] George Wilson, M.D., *Life of Dr. John Reid*, p. 88.
[3] *Life of Sir Robert Christison, Bart.*, vol. ii, p. 317.

of later days, commenced in Knox's rooms. He and his brothers and Forbes lodged together in No. 21 Lothian Street, close to the University, and their domicile " was approached by a public flight of stairs, to which six different families had access, and consisted of the half of a top flat or storey, with attics—rented at £17 a year ".[1] In 1835 he became L.R.C.S.E. After a few years in practice in Anstruther, Fife, his native place, along with his father, Goodsir succeeded in gaining the appointment of conservator of the museum of the Royal College of Surgeons of Edinburgh. In 1843 he resigned his appointment and accepted Syme's offer of a part-curatorship of the University museum ; and in the following year he was appointed demonstrator to Alexander Monro, *tertius*, Professor of Anatomy.

In 1846, on Monro's retirement, Goodsir was elected to the Chair of Anatomy. The only other candidate for the Chair was Dr. P. D. Handyside (1825), an extra-mural lecturer in anatomy.

" The Goodsirs of Anstruther had formed family ties with —1st, the historical Forbes of Culloden . . . 2nd, with John Monro of Milton, the father of Dr. Monro, *Primus*, and founder of the Anatomical School of Edinburgh ; 3rd, with Dr. John Gregory of Aberdeen, and his son Dr. James. . . . These direct and collateral blood-affinities of John Goodsir might constitute a pretty family chapter, in which the medical and the historic would find large space and mention ; and his being linked with the Monros the most curious of all—the Monros who established the fame of the Anatomical Chair of the Edinburgh University, and continued to hold it for three generations, and then resigned their place and trust to him (John Goodsir), to uphold, extend, and dignify." [2]

Goodsir showed, early in life, a passion for anatomical pursuits. In his twenty-fourth year he communicated to the British Association the results of his inquiry " On the Origin and Development of the Pulps and Sacs of the Human

---

[1] Biographical Memoir prefixed to *Anatomical Memoirs of Goodsir* (ed. William Turner, M.B., Professor of Anatomy at Edinburgh), vol. i, p. 97.
[2] *Ibid.* p. 10.

Teeth ". Professor Hutton Balfour, in an obituary notice, wrote : " Goodsir's views regarding the origin of various morbid products, amplified by Professor Virchow, constitute the basis of modern pathology ".[1]

Goodsir bore the physical characteristic which, according to Professor Syme, is the indispensable mark of greatness— a large mouth.

Sir Byrom Bramwell gave his memory of Goodsir as a teacher : " When I knew Goodsir he was a very sick man. I shall never forget his appearance as he came into the lecture-room on the first day of my first session—a tall, gaunt, emaciated man in a black skull-cap, staggering in on the arm of his stalwart assistant, the curator of his museum, Mr. Stirling. Goodsir had suffered for many years from tabes ; and it was remarkable how, though frequently racked with severe lightning pains and heavily handicapped by the other disabilities which advanced tabes entails, he for many years went on fulfilling the duties of his professorship and prosecuting those researches which made his name famous." [2]

A biographical memoir of Goodsir was written by Dr. Henry Lonsdale, an intimate friend, and a fellow-president during both his terms of office as senior president. It is prefixed to the anatomical memoirs, which were edited by Sir William Turner, Goodsir's successor in the Chair, and afterwards Principal of the University of Edinburgh.

Two of his brothers were members of the Society. All three were Conservators of the College of Surgeons Museum. Harry Goodsir perished in the Franklin expedition to the Arctic in 1845 ; and Robert sailed twice to the Arctic Regions with Captain Penny (in Lady Franklin's ship) in search of his brother. After his first voyage, Robert published an account of it, entitled, " An Arctic Voyage to Baffin's Bay and Lancaster Sound, in search of Friends with Sir John Franklin. By Robert Anstruther Goodsir. Late President of the Royal Medical Society of Edinburgh." He presented a copy of the work to the Society.

[1] *Transactions of the Botanical Society of Edinburgh* (1866–67), vol. ix.
[2] Inaugural Address to the Society, 1922.

Goodsir's reply to a request for his photograph, in 1864, illustrates what his biographer called " his severe modesty ".

" The College
Feby. 26/64

" MY DEAR SIR,

" As I never had a *carte de visite* taken, I regret exceedingly my inability to contribute to the Society's album.

I am,
Yours truly,
JOHN GOODSIR.

" A. D. N. Munro, Esq.,
    Secretary,
        Royal Medical Society."

When he was elected to honorary membership in 1850, he wrote : " I beg leave to express the high sense which I entertain of the distinguished honour which the Royal Medical Society has conferred on me in electing me an Honorary Member ".

Martin Barry was an Edinburgh graduate in medicine when he joined the Society on the same day as his close friend, John Goodsir. " Their names are to be found associated in the field of histology and embryology ; the latter was Barry's *forte*, sometimes called his earthly idol. No man in Britain helped more to extend the horizon of cell-discovery during the first years of its history than Dr. Martin Barry. . . . His experienced use of the microscope, his indefatigable enquiries—sacrificing 150 rabbits to ascertain one fact in physiology, being almost equal to Haller's 190 experiments to determine the single point of muscular irritability and thorough knowledge of developmental anatomy were of the greatest service to Goodsir." [1]

In 1835 Barry read a paper before the Society on his ascent of Mont Blanc : he was the twelfth Englishman to make the ascent. In 1836 he read his dissertation, " On the Unity of Structure in the Animal Kingdom ".[2] He was

---

[1] Biographical Memoir, pp. 67-68.
[2] *Dissertations of Royal Medical Society* (1892), pp. 215-236.

at one time a candidate for the Chair of the Institutes of Medicine at Edinburgh ; but he withdrew his candidature because, as a Quaker, he was unable to declare his acceptation of the Confession of Faith and avowal of obedience to the Church of Scotland—the test then rigorously demanded from all professors. John Hughes Bennett was the successful candidate in the election when Barry withdrew from the field.

Hughes Bennett, who was a president during the Centenary Session, was a most enthusiastic member of the Society. In his inaugural address, as president, he said : " Cullen's name descends to posterity, not only in connection with the University, whose celebrity he caused to be extended over the world, but as the individual who, in the year 1775, laid the foundation-stone of the Medical Hall, and contributed by his advice and exertions so much to the Society's reputation."

Hughes Bennett was elected to the Chair of the Institutes of Medicine in 1848. " He was the first man to institute practical classes in the University, and the first man in this country systematically to teach the use of the microscope in physiology, pathology, and clinical medicine. He introduced cod-liver oil to the notice of the profession in this country, and was the first to use it in the treatment of phthisis ".[1] Principal Sir Alexander Grant, in his *Story of the University of Edinburgh*, wrote that Professor Hughes Bennett was an honour to the University on account of his scientific reputation in Europe and America.

William Benjamin Carpenter was senior president during the Centenary Session. In 1839 he read his dissertation, " On the Physiological Inferences to be deduced from the Structure of the Nervous System in Invertebrata ".[2] Nearly fifty years afterwards, when he presented to the Society a framed photograph of himself, he drew their attention to the fact that he was senior president during the Centenary Session ; and he concluded his letter with these words,

[1] Inaugural Address to the Society by Sir Byrom Bramwell, 1922.
[2] *Dissertations of Royal Medical Society* (1892), pp. 237-253.

" rejoicing at the continually increasing prosperity of the Society to which I owed, while a student in the University, what I may regard as some of the greatest benefits I derived from my residence in Edinburgh ". After his death, in 1885, his son, acknowledging a letter of condolence from the Society, wrote : " The tie which bound my father to Edinburgh was no ordinary one, and for some years of his life, as I well remember, the Chair of Natural History in its University was his great ambition ". Professor Carpenter filled the Chair of Medical Jurisprudence at University College, London, where he had two old Royal Medical Society men as colleagues—Sharpey in the Chair of Physiology, and R. E. Grant in the Chair of Comparative Anatomy. Lister was one of his students.

David Skae, another member of this group of friends, joined the Society soon after Carpenter and he was a president in 1837–38. His work as resident physician of the Royal Edinburgh Asylum for the Insane brought him distinction.

The friendship of those eminent men is the more memorable on account of the devotion shown by them to John Reid throughout his long suffering under a mortal disease.

In 1837 the Society published a *Catalogue raisonné*. Various attempts had been made since 1800 to form such a catalogue, but without success. In the winter of 1835 a few members renewed the attempt, and the Society, anxious to render their library as useful as possible to students, strenuously encouraged the design, and resolved to print the catalogue at the Society's expense. The committee which superintended the progress of the work through the press showed a laudable eagerness to present the catalogue at the commencement of the hundredth session of the Society. This labour was cheerfully performed for the good of the Society. A library which includes folios published at Venice and Amsterdam in the sixteenth and seventeenth centuries was worthy of such selfless labour.

In December 1836 Professors T. C. Hope, Syme, Christison, John Thomson, Graham and Traill, Drs. Craigie,

Douglas Maclagan, Abercrombie,[1] Hutton Balfour and Andrew Wood, the four presidents, the treasurer, and four ordinary members were appointed a committee to make arrangements for celebrating the hundredth session of the Society. On their recommendation the Society resolved that a Dinner should take place on the 17th of February ; that admission should be restricted to members, with the exception of the Principal of the University of Edinburgh, and the Presidents of the Royal Colleges of Physicians and Surgeons of Edinburgh, who should be invited as guests ; that Professor Thomas Charles Hope, on account of his long standing in the Society, should be requested to take the Chair ; that the four presidents should act as croupiers ; and that the senior president should deliver an oration immediately before the dinner.

The dinner took place in the Hopetoun Rooms. For various reasons many members were unable to travel to Edinburgh for the occasion. Among those who sent apologies for absence were : Sir James M'Grigor, Director-General of the Army Medical Department ; Dr. Bostock, medical historian ; Mr. Travers ; Dr. Stroud historian of the Society ; and Dr. John Conolly, later of Hanwell ; and local absentees were the venerable Principal Baird, Professor John Thomson, and Dr. Abercrombie. Professor Alison was present as P.R.C.P.E., and Sir George Ballingall as P.R.C.S.E. The oration delivered before the dinner by Mr. W. B. Carpenter, the senior president, " was received with unanimous approbation, " and Professor Christison proposed that it should be printed at the expense of the Society, together with a list of members present at the celebration. After the dinner more than twenty toasts were given ; and among the speakers was Sir Charles Bell.

[1] Dr. John Abercrombie was never an ordinary member. He was elected an honorary member in 1830. Goodsir referred to him as " a perfect clock, as rich as a Jew, and a great physician besides ".

CHAPTER XI

WHEN the combined office of treasurer, secretary and librarian
was divided, the various duties were assigned to different
individuals.

Moreover, the offices of secretary and librarian were
given to non-members, for the earliest extant minutes, April
1778, show that a Mr. Frearson and a Mr. Fitzgerald, whose
names are not in the list of members, were elected secretary
and librarian, respectively, after they had petitioned the
Society. According to the manuscript code of laws of 1781,
the offices of secretary and librarian had been reunited, and
endowed with an annual salary : " The offices of Secretary
and Librarian shall be both performed by the same person ;
and, as long as he discharges them faithfully, he shall receive
annually the sum of £10 Sterling ". This law was the outcome
of Stephen Pellet's proposal, in 1779, " That a proper person
be appointed by the Society to execute the office of secretary
and librarian, during pleasure, with a proper annual salary ".
It remained in force until 1840, but the modest salary was
gradually increased to £100, " on consideration of his paying
the Annual Wages of Forty pounds Sterling to the Porter ".
In time, the title of porter was changed to the more dignified one of assistant librarian, although the duties remained
the same. Robert Salmond was secretary when Pellet's

proposal became law. In 1780 he resigned office and entered the Society. Thereafter, the secretary was clearly a paid official who was a non-member, for the manuscript code of laws of 1781 states, " The same form shall be observed in his expulsion as in that of a member ". Robert Wemyss, who succeeded Salmond, died two years after his appointment. John Miller, his successor, resigned in 1783. He was followed by Alexander Cumming, who retired in 1811 after twenty-seven years of " unwearied attention to the interests of the Society ". His successor, Nicolson Bain, who died while holding office, was secretary for twenty-nine years. He was also assistant librarian of the University of Edinburgh during his whole period of service with the Society. Between 1747 and 1854 the University librarian was always a Professor ; but the office was often almost honorary, and the principal assistant librarian did the work. Bain's portrait is in the library of the University.

When Bain died suddenly in 1840 the laws relating to the offices of secretary and librarian, and of assistant librarian, were revised. It was enacted that two honorary secretaries, who were members of the Society, should perform the duties of secretary. They were relieved of all duties connected with the library. These duties were transferred partly to the library committee, and partly to the assistant librarian, whose title was altered to that of sub-librarian. The library was placed under the charge of a curator who was appointed to act as chairman of the library committee and as superintendent of the sub-librarian. With some modifications, the laws enacted in 1840 are still in force. Thomas Anderson and Hugh Cleghorn were the first members to be elected honorary secretaries ; and George Edward Day was the first member to be elected curator of the library. The first honorary secretaries created a precedent by their election as annual presidents in the following session. The first curator of the library, who became senior president in the same session, was Thomas Anderson, later Professor of Chemistry in the University of Glasgow. He deserves special mention for having drawn the attention of Lister, then

Professor of Surgery at Glasgow, to the work of Pasteur. His original investigations of the products of the destructive distillation of animal matters have left a permanent record of his name in the history of chemical discovery.[1]

It is noteworthy that the names of two presidents during the session 1840–41 should be associated with events which influenced the career of Lord Lister ; Thomas Anderson, as a colleague on the Medical Faculty of the University of Glasgow ; and Richard James Mackenzie, by his death. Mackenzie was an extra-mural lecturer in surgery and an assistant surgeon to the Royal Infirmary of Edinburgh when he volunteered, in 1854, for service with the forces in the Crimea. His description of his impressions of the field of battle after the passage of the Alma affords a significant glimpse of the conflict of emotion and will, with will triumphant, in the mind of a brilliant operator working amid war conditions. " What a sight ! Reading of it gives no idea of the field of a murderous battle such as our passage of the Alma yesterday. There was the excitement of victory, however, to counteract the effects of the dismal scene ; but this morning it floored me when I went over the field, the ground strewed with the ghastly dead and wounded. I cannot tell what number of limbs I have removed to-day. I have operated from morning till night." [2] Four days after the battle Mackenzie fell a victim to cholera. He had been with the 79th Cameron Highlanders when they advanced ; and Sir Colin Campbell, the Commander of the Highland Brigade, would not allow the fire, near which Mackenzie lay ill, to be put out although orders had been given to extinguish all the camp fires. Mackenzie's death left vacant the extra-mural lectureship in surgery and the assistant-surgeoncy to the Royal Infirmary. Lister succeeded to both vacancies, and in them he commenced his career.

In 1840 the Bombay Medical and Physical Society gave a donation to the Society's library. This was a reminder to

[1] Testimonials in favour of Thomas Anderson, M.D., a candidate for the Chair of Chemistry in the University of Edinburgh, p. 18.
[2] *Edinburgh Medical and Surgical Journal* (1855), vol. lxxxii, pp. 290-291.

the Society of the work being carried on by senior members in India for the promotion of medical education in that country. It was also a second indication to the Society of the prominent part which many old members were taking in the improvement of medical practice in India, for in 1826 the Medical and Physical Society of Calcutta, whose first president was James Hare (1795), presented a copy of the first volume of their transactions. The inscription, " To the Royal Medical Society of Edinburgh from the Medical and Physical Society of Calcutta " was dated 30th May 1825 ; and the volume was received in the middle of the following October. No wonder Lord Macaulay wrote of his voyage to India in 1834 : "During the whole voyage I read with keen and increasing enjoyment. I devoured, Greek, Latin, Spanish, Italian, French and English ; folios, quartos, octavos and duodecimos." [1]

The Bombay Medical and Physical Society was founded in 1835. The chief founder and first secretary was Charles Morehead (1824). In 1829 Morehead entered the Bombay Medical Service, and, in 1831, he was appointed to the personal staff of Sir Robert Grant, Governor of the Presidency, and brother of Lord Glenelg, President of the Board of Control (1830–34). Sir Robert Grant aimed at establishing an Indian medical profession among the natives of India because he deplored the needless suffering caused by grossly ignorant native practitioners, and because he believed that a system of medical education was the only means of raising general education in Western India. In March 1838 he drew up an elaborate minute, based on a Report of the Bombay Medical Society, drafted by Morehead, in which he urged the establishment of a seminary for " the education of natives, to fit them for the useful and safe practice of surgery and medicine, and not the training of the hospital servants of the State ".[2] Sir Robert Grant died in the following July. It was resolved that a building for the seminary which he had advocated should be erected as a memorial. Grant Medical

[1] Sir George Trevelyan, *Life of Lord Macaulay*, vol. i, p. 361.
[2] H. A. Haines, *Life of Charles Morehead, M.D.*, p. 18.

College, Bombay, was opened in 1845. Dr. Charles Morehead became the first Principal, and continued in office for
fifteen years. His Edinburgh training was soon in evidence.
" The chief feature of the Grant College education, in virtue
of which it was, from the outset, far in advance of any other
medical school of the time, was the careful imparting to the
students of practical instruction at the bedside of the sick." [1]

In 1861 Dr. Morehead was appointed an honorary surgeon
to the Queen ; and in 1881 he received the C.I.E. On his
death, in 1882, Sir Joseph Fayrer, President of the Medical
Board at the India Office, who, as an assistant-surgeon, had
distinguished himself in the defence of Lucknow, wrote :
" Morehead was a great physician in the best and highest
sense of the term, a great benefactor to medicine and of the
people of India ".[2]

It may be mentioned that Sir Joseph Fayrer was elected
an honorary member of the Society in 1885.

In 1882 a subscription was opened to perpetuate Dr.
Morehead's memory in connection with Grant Medical
College. The amount raised was accepted by the University
of Bombay to endow " The Charles Morehead Scholarship in
Chemical Medicine " to be awarded annually to the graduate
in medicine of Grant Medical College who showed the highest
proficiency in chemical medicine.[3]

Another member of the Society who rendered eminent
service to Grant Medical College was George Birdwood, who
was a president in 1854, the year in which he graduated M.D.
at Edinburgh. In 1857 he became Professor of Anatomy
and Physiology in Grant College, and later filled the Chair of
Botany and Materia Medica there. " He had a solid knowledge of the natural products of India, of the art and history
of its peoples, and a fund of curious information which made
it a maxim of the India Office, when a puzzling question of
fact or custom arose to ' ask Birdwood '. . . . He came of a
family which has been for four generations connected with
India, and has in this generation produced General Sir W. R.

[1] *Ibid.* p. 22.

[2] *Ibid.* p. 100.   [3] *Ibid.* p. 101.

Birdwood, who commanded the Australian and New Zealand troops at the Dardanelles. . . . With the help of Hindu and Parsee merchants he reconstituted the Bombay Central Museum at the Victoria and Albert Museum at a cost of over £200,000 and produced a *Catalogue of the Economic Products of the Presidency of Bombay*, which has served as a model for other similar publications. . . . Birdwood arranged the exhibition of the presents received by King Edward VII when, as Prince of Wales, he visited India, and in 1878 he organised the Indian section of the Paris Exhibition of that year. . . . He contributed many articles to learned societies, but his real work as a writer was to explain India to the rest of the British empire, and perhaps a little to itself. He received the C.S.I. when Queen Victoria was proclaimed Empress of India (January 1st, 1877), and the K.C.I.E. in 1881." [1]

In 1841 there were elected to honorary membership: Dr. Alison, Professor of the Institutes of Medicine at Edinburgh, a man " greatly loved and venerated by all " ; Professor Dumas of Paris who, with Péligot, first ascertained the chemical composition of chloroform in 1835 ; and Dr. James Cowles Prichard, ethnologist, who had joined the Society in 1805. Dr. Prichard's intimate friends in the Society were John Bishop Estlin and Joseph Arnould, both distinguished students, who figured so prominently in the dispute in 1808 with the extraordinary members ; and the friendship continued for the remainder of their lives.

Dr. Prichard's fame rests on his enquiries in ethnology. His *Researches into the Physical History of Man* placed him in the first rank among the savants of France and Germany, as well as his own country. This work was followed by *The Eastern Origin of the Celtic Nations, proved by a comparison of their dialects with the Sanskrit, Greek, Latin and Teutonic Languages* which proved that the Celtic nations spring from a common stock with the Indo-European group. As a medical author, Dr. Prichard had also considerable repute. In 1845 he was appointed a Commissioner in Lunacy.

In 1841 the birth of the Prince of Wales, and in 1842

---

[1] *British Medical Journal* (1917), vol. ii, pp. 30-31.

the visit to Scotland of the Queen and Prince Albert were the occasions of loyal Addresses from the Society.

In 1841 the Address was : " To the Queen's Most Excellent Majesty, May it please Your Majesty, We, the Presidents and Members of the Royal Medical Society of Edinburgh desire to offer our sincere and heartfelt congratulations on the auspicious event of Your Majesty's giving birth to an heir to the British throne. . . . We fondly hope that the happiness of domestic life, so characteristic of our national habits, may sweeten the cares which surround your high station and that Your Majesty may long be spared to fill the throne of your illustrious ancestors. In name and by authority of the Royal Medical Society." It was signed by John Goodsir, Edwin Wait, and Wm. Scott Carmichael. The Address was sent to Sir James M'Grigor, Director-General of the Army Medical Department, to be presented by him to the Queen.

Sir James M'Grigor had close associations with members of the Society throughout his life. In his student days he spent one session at the University of Edinburgh after he had completed his medical curriculum at Aberdeen. A visit to the Society suggested to him the idea of founding a similar one in Aberdeen. The outcome was the Medico-Chirurgical Society of that city.[1]

In his autobiography Sir James wrote : " On my return from Edinburgh, where I had been elected a member of the Medical and Chirurgical Society, in concert with Dr. Robertson we laid before a meeting of the students at Aberdeen the plan of a medical society for that city." [2] There was no Medico-Chirurgical Society of Edinburgh at that time. The present one was not founded until 1821. The old one, formed in 1767, was followed by the Physico-Chirurgical in 1771 ; and in 1782 the two combined and became the Physical, afterwards the Royal Physical Society.[3] Sir James was never an ordinary member of the Royal Medical Society :

[1] Address to the Society, by Professor Davidson, University of Aberdeen, January 1935.

[2] *Autobiography and Services of Sir James M'Grigor, Bart.*, p. 6.

[3] W. Stroud, *History of the Medical Society of Edinburgh* (1820), p. xlv.

he was elected an honorary member in 1826. A reasonable assumption is that his autobiography was written in his old age.

When Sir James went to London at the outset of his career he was received with kindness which he never forgot by three senior members of the Society, Dr. Saunders, Sir Walter Farquhar and Sir Gilbert Blane.[1] His hospitality to members is illustrated by an entry in J. Y. Simpson's diary, dated April 25th, 1835. Simpson and Douglas Maclagan, later Professor of Medical Jurisprudence at Edinburgh, had arrived in London at the commencement of a tour on the Continent. " Dr. M. and I set off in an omnibus for Camden Hill, to dine with Sir James M'Grigor and family. Sir James has still a considerable dash of the ' Scot ' about him, is exceedingly plain and homely in his manners, and at the same time exceedingly kind and agreeable."

The loyal Addresses in 1842 were presented to the Queen by the Earl of Aberdeen, and to Prince Albert by Dr. Robert Graham, Professor of Botany at Edinburgh. In the Address to the Queen, emphasis was laid on the age of the Society. " As the oldest Medical Society in this City we have the greatest reason to rejoice that an opportunity has arrived of laying at the foot of the throne this testimonial of our deepest gratitude for the advantages which the cause of Science continues to enjoy under a reign particularly distinguished by the gracious protection and encouragement afforded to every branch of useful knowledge." These Addresses bore only one signature, " John Goodsir ", President.

In 1856 H.R.H. Prince Albert presented to the Society a volume entitled *The Natural History of Deeside and Braemar*, by W. MacGillivray.

In March 1845 the Society received a gratifying and valuable addition to their library. The Speculative Society of Edinburgh presented a copy of their *History of the Speculative Society of Edinburgh, from its Institution in M.DCC.L.XIV.* The inscription is : " Presented to the Royal Medical Society of Edinburgh by the Speculative Society in testimony

[1] *Autobiography and Services of Sir James M'Grigor, Bart.*, pp. 5 and 9.

of their respect for a valuable and kindred Institution ".
From the institution of the Speculative Society until the
early years of the nineteenth century many members of the
Royal Medical Society were members of both Societies ;
and members of the Speculative Society sometimes appeared
as visitors at the meetings in the Medical Hall. The first
notice in the minutes of a visit by a member of the Speculative Society is in November 1782. On the 23rd of that
month " Mr. Paterson proposed Lord Ancrum as a visitor
next night ". Lord Ancrum was afterwards sixth Marquis
of Lothian ; and James Paterson is described in the *History
of the Speculative Society* as : " Afterwards of Pyannot and
Gavin, Ayrshire, Doctor of Medicine. He practised as the
principal Physician at Ayr, until 1820, after which he resided
in London." In the section of their *History* entitled, " Historical Review of other Debating Societies ", there is a
description of the Royal Medical Society : " This admirable
institution, which has contributed materially to the education of a greater number of eminent medical men than any
other private institution in the empire, still exists in a state
of the highest efficiency ".

In 1844–45 James Warburton Begbie, George W. Balfour
and D. R. Haldane joined the Society ; and all three
afterwards became physicians to the Royal Infirmary of
Edinburgh.

Begbie was soon prominent in all matters of private
business ranging from finance to the amenity of the Medical
Hall. Dr. Joseph Bell described him as a quiet industrious
student who, in many ways, impressed his fellow-students
with his ability and earnestness. His dissertation was on
" Digestion," and was largely concerned with the principles
established by Beaumont in his experiments on Alexis St.
Martin. He was elected twice to the Chair of the Society,
first, as senior president in 1847, and, secondly, as a junior
president in 1848. When he was at the height of his career
as the leading consulting physician in Scotland, he accepted
an invitation to deliver the Inaugural Address before the
Society at the commencement of the session 1872–73. His

subject was " Hippocrates : his Life and Writings ". In concluding his Address, he said : " I trust that I have succeeded in pointing out to you how worthy and enlightened a model we have for imitation in the ' Father of our Profession '. To you, gentlemen, the members of the Royal Medical Society, who are associated together by an ' obligation ', which, if it be not so strict in its details as the Hippocratic oath, is equally binding, I return my warmest thanks."

Warburton Begbie was a son of Dr. James Begbie, a pupil and later the successor of the celebrated Dr. Abercrombie. In 1852 he was admitted F.R.C.P.E., and " as most young physicians who mean to work do ", he became a medical officer of the New Town Dispensary. Three years later he found his true sphere of activity in his appointment as physician to the Royal Infirmary. At the same time he joined the extra-mural school and gave a summer course of lectures on the History of Medicine, for which he was well qualified on account of his remarkable knowledge of languages, ancient and modern. In addition to the clinical lectures in the Royal Infirmary which he shared with his colleagues, W. T. Gairdner, D. R. Haldane and W. R. Sanders, he lectured on the practice of physic to large classes. On the expiry of his ten years' appointment to the Royal Infirmary, he did not apply for reappointment ; and he ceased to lecture. When his father died in 1869 he gave up general practice and took none but consulting work ; and at the same time he was appointed physician to the Scottish Widows' Fund Life Assurance Society in succession to his father. His report on the causes of death among the assured of this Society from 1867–1873, which was published in the *Edinburgh Medical Journal* for 1874, is a valuable contribution to the statistics of life assurance. Until his death in 1876, he had the largest consulting physician's practice in Scotland ; indeed, in the profession his name was a household word.

In a biographical notice in the *Edinburgh Medical Journal* for April 1876, Dr. Joseph Bell, who was then the editor, wrote : " As a teacher, it must in fairness be owned he was no orator. He had not the marvellous power of swaying the minds of his hearers like Bennett, of clothing fresh thoughts and generalisations in a woven chain of subtle yet lofty argument like Goodsir, or even of nailing a fact to the memory for ever by an epigrammatic aphorism like Syme. . . . Begbie as a teacher was greatest at the bedside. His clinical visits were masterpieces both in precept and example. He taught, not only how to win the patient's confidence, to get his whole history, to examine him carefully yet rapidly, with consideration for his feelings, but he was great both in diagnosis and prognosis ; and, with a rarer power still, had the faith and patience to use and profit by the use of remedies—not drugs merely, but diet, regimen. With him the student learned manners as well as physic, nursing along with diagnosis."

Sir Dyce Duckworth, who was a president of the Society in 1861, and who edited selections from Dr. Begbie's works for the New Sydenham Society in 1882, wrote :[1] " My recollections are still vivid, and the veneration in which I held Begbie upwards of twenty years ago grows not less, but more, as time rolls on. All who knew him in any degree loved him. He was one of those guileless men who could never have an enemy. . . . Personally, he was of commanding stature, with large frame and well-cut features. . . . I think I never saw him frown, or roused to exhibit a trace of ill-temper or vexation. Equable and uniformly bland and courteous, never, apparently, worried or pressed, he had a simple, friendly, modest manner, and a marvellous power of attraction for everybody. Anyone could readily approach him, and secure his aid or counsel. None who worked under him can ever forget his manner either as a physician or a teacher."

In 1921 Sir Dyce Duckworth delivered the Inaugural Address to the Society. In the Address, which was on " Art in relation to Modern Medicine ", he revealed the lasting influence of Begbie's example and teaching on his professional career. The address was an exposition of the art of the accomplished physician ; and it included a warning on the danger of producing physicians wholly reliant on the laboratory for their diagnosis.

[1] *Selections from the Works of the late J. W. Begbie* (London, 1882), p. xv.

By a fortunate dispensation, the vote of thanks to Sir Dyce Duckworth was moved by Sir Byrom Bramwell, one of the greatest teachers of medicine that Edinburgh has produced. This association of the names of three brilliant clinicians, Warburton Begbie, Dyce Duckworth and Byrom Bramwell is a striking occurrence, and justifies the oft-repeated opinion that the Society is a valuable adjunct to the Edinburgh School of Medicine.

Dr. D. R. Haldane was senior president of the Society in 1846–47. He became an extra-mural lecturer in pathology, and was pathologist as well as a physician to the Royal Infirmary. The dissertation which he read before the Society in 1846 on " The Present Fever of Edinburgh " was an able discussion of the differentiation between typhoid and enteric fevers. He noted the absence of typhoid when employment was good and the poorer classes more prosperous ; its regular incubation period of fourteen days ; and the frequent occurrence of case to case infection. In contrast the " gastric " or " enteric " fever was usually sporadic, though epidemics occurred among labourers engaged in making the railway : it had apparently an incubation period of three weeks, and it was often impossible to prove its contagious nature. The findings of morbid anatomists were conflicting. For the modern reader the interest lies in the clinical and epidemiological differentiation of the diseases before the development of bacteriology.

George W. Balfour was eminent among his contemporaries as an authority on diseases of the heart. In 1858 he wrote a pamphlet entitled, *Hematophobia : an Historical Sketch, with special reference to the Treatment of Pneumonia*, which shows him to have been a " master of ripe wisdom and opulent language ". The pamphlet throws a great deal of light upon the controversy which raged around blood-letting at that time in Edinburgh. The protagonists, for and against, were Dr. Alison and Dr. Hughes Bennett, respectively.

W. R. Sanders was a president along with Warburton Begbie in 1847–48. He was a son of Dr. George Sanders, an Edinburgh physician, who was a president in 1810–11.

In 1852, the year following von Helmholtz's invention of the ophthalmoscope, W. R. Sanders contributed an article to the *Monthly Journal of Medical Science* (after 1855, the *Edinburgh Medical Journal*), " On Helmholtz's Speculum for Examining the Retina in the Living Eye ". His opening sentence was : " Having repeated successfully Professor Helmholtz's experiments, and been enabled by his apparatus to view distinctly the retina in the living eye, I venture to lay a short account of his discoveries before the profession in this country ". In 1893 von Helmholtz, then Professor of Physics at Berlin, was elected an honorary member.

In 1853 W. R. Sanders was appointed conservator of the museum of the Royal College of Surgeons of Edinburgh. Later, he joined the extra-mural school as a lecturer in physiology. In 1861 he was appointed physician to the Royal Infirmary in room of Dr. Keiller, who had retired by rotation ; and in 1869 he succeeded William Henderson, the homeopathist, in the Chair of Pathology. His chief merit as occupant of the Chair was his introduction of practical teaching.

John Scott Sanderson, afterwards Sir John Scott Burdon-Sanderson, Bart., was a president in 1850–51. In his Inaugural Address as president, he referred to " the nameless and apparently insignificant band of our ancestors ", and, among them, William Cullen, whom he eulogised. " Thus the career of this great man, which originated with the origin of our Society, only terminated in his giving medicine a name for the first time among the sciences, and in his placing our University in a position, which for a long series of years it occupied—that of the first medical school in Europe." His dissertation was " On Vegetable Irritability "—another of the many instances in the Society of early predilection for a particular branch of science in connection with medicine.

Sanderson was a pupil of William Sharpey, and of Carl Ludwig of Leipzig, for whom he expressed his admiration in glowing terms : " A man who was utterly free from selfish aims and vain ambitions, who was scrupulously conscientious in all that he said and did, who was what he seemed to be and

179

seemed what he was, and who had no other aim than the advancement of his science ".[1]   In 1883 Ludwig was elected an honorary member of the Society.   Sanderson moved to London, and as M.O.H. of Paddington was active in devising measures to combat cholera and tuberculosis, and to improve food supply and housing conditions.   He collaborated with E. Klein, Sir Michael Foster and Sir Lauder Brunton in the production of a *Handbook for the Physiological Laboratory*, which was published in 1873.   In the following year he succeeded Sharpey as Professor of Physiology at University College, London.   In 1896 he was appointed Regius Professor of Medicine at Oxford.   He was brother-in-law of one Lord Chancellor, Farrer Herschell, and uncle of another, R. B. Haldane.   His great contemporary, Sir Michael Foster, was elected an honorary member of the Society in 1882.

Charles Murchison was a fellow-president with Burdon-Sanderson.   In his Inaugural Address as president he reminded his hearers of the origin of the Society.   " For this purpose alone, the discussions on dissertations written by its members, the Society was first instituted."   His dissertation was, " On the Red Corpuscles of the Blood ".[2] His concluding sentence was :   " If the reading of this paper, or the discussion which I trust will ensue, affords to any of you the slightest degree of the benefit which the writing of it has conferred upon myself, I am more than satisfied ".

After a short period of service with the East India Company, Murchison returned to London.   In 1861 he became physician to the London Fever Hospital, and ten years later, physician to St. Thomas's Hospital, where he established his fame as a clinical teacher.   In 1862 he published his *Treatise on the Continued Fevers of Great Britain* which brought him a European reputation ;   and his writings in connection with diseases of the liver established his name as an authority on the subject.   In 1868 he published the *Palæontological Memoirs and Notes of the late Hugh Falconer, A.M., M.D., Vice-President of the Royal Society . . . With a Biographical*

[1] Garrison, *History of Medicine* (3rd ed.), p. 601.
[2] *Dissertations of Royal Medical Society* (1892), pp. 280-299.

Sketch of the Author, which he had compiled and edited. Falconer, who joined the Society in 1826 and graduated in medicine at Edinburgh in 1829, attained a world-wide reputation in science as a palaeontologist in India. He was also a botanist of repute. " His Indian career was spent as Superintendent of the Botanic Gardens of Suharunpoor and Calcutta, and in Calcutta he was also Professor of Botany in the Medical College." [1] He is perhaps best remembered in connection with the discovery of the gigantic fossil tortoise from the Sewalik Hills in the Himalayas, whose remains are preserved in the British Museum, " where there is also a restoration of the shell ".[2] On his death in 1865 it was resolved at a meeting of distinguished scientific men, held in London, to preserve his memory by a marble bust to be placed in the rooms of a scientific society or elsewhere in London ; and it was also resolved to open a subscription in order to found, in the University of Edinburgh, a Fellowship in Natural Science to be called " The Falconer Memorial Fellowship ". Falconer had been deeply interested " up to the latest hour of his life " in " the foundation of Fellowships or Scholarships in the University of Edinburgh, to enable deserving students to prolong their studies beyond the usual academical period ".[3] In the *Edinburgh University Calendar* the Fellowship is described as being " Awarded on the basis of an examination in Natural History as applied to Palaeontology and Geology to a graduate in Science or Medicine of the University of not more than three years' standing ".

Lifelong friendships, originating in the Society, have been mentioned as an impressive feature in its history ; and the friendship of Burdon-Sanderson and Charles Murchison belongs to that category. When the members of the Edinburgh University Club in London resolved to institute a memorial of Murchison, soon after his death, an informal meeting was held in Lord Lister's house to discuss the proposal. Sir Robert Christison occupied the chair, and seven medical professors attended—Douglas Maclagan, William

[1] *Memoirs*, Preface, p. x.   [2] *Ibid.* vol. i, p. 359.
[3] *Ibid.* Biographical Sketch, pp. xlix-l.

Turner, W. R. Sanders, Grainger Stewart, William Rutherford, T. R. Fraser and Professor Emeritus Hutton Balfour. The outcome of those deliberations was the Murchison Memorial Scholarship, awarded in alternate years in London and Edinburgh.

In 1888 Dr. W. S. Greenfield, Professor of Pathology in the University of Edinburgh, who delivered the Inaugural Address before the Society in that year, presented a portrait of Dr. Murchison to the Society.

Thomas Spencer Cobbold had graduated M.D. at Edinburgh when he was elected senior president in 1851. The titles of his dissertations, " Fracture of the Femoral Neck " and " Paraplegia " do not suggest the line of his future career, but it is probable that he simply wrote on the subjects allotted to him ; and the precision with which he details the observations, which he had made in the wards, suggests that he had already the natural historian's instinct for careful observation of everything presented to him. After a period of service as curator of the anatomical muscum in the University of Edinburgh, he removed to London, where he rapidly established for himself a scientific reputation by his investigation of the nature and habits of parasitic worms. His *Entozoa : an introduction to the Study of Helminthology* (1864) was a valuable contribution to the subject.

Thomas Keith had graduated M.D. at Edinburgh before he joined the Society in 1848. In 1851 he tendered his resignation, as he had little prospect of being resident in Edinburgh in the ensuing session. He withdrew it, however, when the Society agreed unanimously " That Dr. Keith be requested to reconsider his resignation ". At the outset of his career he was associated, as a medical apprentice—the last in Edinburgh—with J. Y. Simpson as his master, and also, as a house-surgeon in the Royal Infirmary of Edinburgh, with James Syme. He retained a lifelong regard for the great surgeon, more especially for teaching him three sound principles in surgical treatment, " simplicity, painstaking, and absolute cleanliness ".[1] In 1862 he performed the first

[1] *British Medical Journal*, October, 1895.

successful operation for ovariotomy in Scotland since Lizars' single and partial success in 1823. In the following year he read a paper before the Medico-Chirurgical Society of Edinburgh, " On Ovarian Dropsy, with Cases of Ovariotomy ", in which he acknowledged his indebtedness to Spencer Wells : " No one has done more than Mr. Wells to improve the operation and to simplify its after-treatment ; and it gives me pleasure to acknowledge that when I commenced these operations I took him for my guide ". In 1870 the Managers of the Royal Infirmary of Edinburgh recognised his value as a pioneer by appointing him an extra-surgeon for ovarian disease. There Keith extended the fame of the Edinburgh School of Medicine. In 1888 he removed to London, where he continued to practise abdominal sections with the assistance of his son, Skene Keith (1877).

In 1880 Thomas Keith and Sir Spencer Wells were elected honorary members of the Society, along with Theodor Billroth " the pioneer of visceral surgery ".[1]

Sir Patrick Heron Watson has been mentioned already as a member of the investment committee appointed in 1878, when the City of Glasgow Bank failure occurred. In reply to a letter of thanks at the time, he wrote : " Will you be so kind as convey to the Society my thanks for this great kindness, and assure the members of the sense of gratitude which I shall ever associate with the inestimable advantages I derived in former days from my connection with the Royal Medical Society ". Heron Watson was senior president in 1853–54, and in his Inaugural Address he stated that " in no profession is courtesy of manner and a knowledge of human nature more necessary than in our own, and our Society affords means for the cultivation of both ". He and A. W. P. Pinkerton, a fellow-president, served with the forces in the Crimea. In 1858 Pinkerton commenced to lecture in tropical diseases in the extra-academical school of Edinburgh. It was not until 1898 that the University instituted a lectureship in the subject.[2] So, to repeat Bower's words, " This

[1] Garrison, *History of Medicine* (3rd ed.), p. 636.
[2] John D. Comrie, *History of Scottish Medicine*, (2nd ed.), vol. ii, p. 711.

institution like every other connected with the history of
medicine in Edinburgh, originated with the colleges of
physicians and surgeons ; and at first was most probably
suggested by, but certainly for a time was conducted by, a
private individual ".[1] In 1858 Heron Watson delivered an
address at a conversazione held in the Hall of the Royal
College of Surgeons of Edinburgh in which he described his
experiences in the hospitals in the East during the Crimean
War. " Dr. Watson described the hospitals of Smyrna,
Scutari, Kululi Therapea, the sanatorium above Balaclava,
and at Karani. He maintained that the medical part of the
army had been subjected to most unjust censure, through
unprofessional criticism. He warmly eulogised the conduct
of the lady nurses who, in the discharge of their duties, had
exerted themselves beyond all praise." [2] Heron Watson, like
R. J. Mackenzie who died in the Crimea, was regarded as an
aspirant to the Chair of Military Surgery at Edinburgh,
which was filled by Sir George Ballingall.

His professional attainments were summed up in an
editorial in the *Edinburgh Medical Journal* at the time of
his death in 1907, which occurred on the day following that
of another distinguished former president of the Society,
Thomas Annandale, Regius Professor of Clinical Surgery in
the University of Edinburgh : " In his profession Sir
Patrick was at one time, what we suppose we shall never see
again, *facile princeps* in the practice of both Surgery and
Medicine in Scotland. Without doubt a bold, brilliant
operator, whom nothing appalled and who commanded to an
unusual degree the confidence of his patients, he was no less
a Physician whose advice was sought for by persons from all
parts of the country."

Sir John Sibbald (1850) devoted himself to the treatment
of mental diseases, and became H.M. Commissioner in
Lunacy for Scotland. At the commencement of his career
he found this branch of medical science in a backward state.
In 1870 he read a paper on " Clinical Instruction in Insanity "

---

[1] Bower, *History of the University of Edinburgh*, vol. ii, p. 257.
[2] *Edinburgh Medical Journal* (May 1858).

before the Medico-Psychological Association at a meeting held in Glasgow, in which he said : " It is no exaggerated statement to say, that in the whole domain of disease, there is no important section which receives so little attention from the instructors of our youth as is the case with mental disorder. In 1851 Dr. Skae opened a class for clinical instruction in connection with the Edinburgh Asylum, and this, along with the course of lectures more recently inaugurated by Professor Laycock, has to some extent supplied the Edinburgh School with important advantages." [1]

Sibbald deserves special mention because a communication by him to the Society on " Chloroform prepared from Methylated Alcohol " aroused among the members an enthusiasm for scientific enquiry only paralleled by that shown in the physiological experiments towards the close of the eighteenth century. The communication was read before the Society on 15th February 1856, eight years and three months exactly after the introduction of chloroform into surgical practice by J. Y. Simpson in the Royal Infirmary of Edinburgh. During the interval, technical chemists had discovered that chloroform, however prepared, if properly purified, was all that could be desired. The difficulty was to remove the prejudice prevailing among medical practitioners in favour of chloroform prepared from rectified spirit. In the month preceding the delivery of Sibbald's communication the treasurer, J. F. Macfarlan, had read a paper before the Pharmaceutical Society on " Methylated Spirit and some of its Preparations ", in which he said : " Chloroform from methylated spirit has been used in the Royal Infirmary under the eye of Professor Syme. To-day I saw the excision of the shoulder-joint under this anaesthetic. It is just as safe as that from spirit of wine alone : indeed, the learned Professor stated that he would give it the preference as it seemed to produce the effects more readily than the other." [2]

In the discussion which followed the reading of Sibbald's

[1] " Clinical Instruction in Insanity ", *Journal of Mental Science* (1871), vol. xvi, pp. 528-529.

[2] *Pharmaceutical Journal* (January 1856).

paper, the Society agreed unanimously, " That a committee of five members be appointed to investigate the properties of chloroform prepared from methylated spirit, with a view to ascertain its anaesthetic value as compared with that from pure alcohol, and report to the Society the result of their experiments ". The chairman of the committee was Alexander R. Simpson, a president at the time, nephew of J. Y. Simpson.

A month later the committee reported :

" The objects, which the committee proposed to themselves to ascertain, were :

" 1. The quantity of each variety required for the induction of anaesthesia.

" 2. The time required for the induction of anaesthesia.

" 3. The duration and character of the anaesthesia.

" 4. The subsequent effects.

" In order to ascertain the facts relative to these objects, four gentlemen inhaled the chloroform prepared from pure spirit, on one day ; and a week subsequently, the same gentlemen, as much as possible in similar circumstances, inhaled the chloroform prepared from methylated spirit.

" From the results of the experiments the committee conclude :

" 1. The quantity of chloroform prepared from methylated spirit, which is required for the induction of anaesthesia, is the same as that prepared from pure spirit.

" 2. The time required for the induction of anaesthesia is the same.

" 3. The duration and character of the anaesthesia are similar.

" 4. The subsequent effects are the same ; and this point is of most importance.

" On the whole, the committee consider the action of chloroform prepared from methylated spirit to be the same, in every respect, as of that prepared from pure spirit. In fact, looking at the effects, it would be said that the two articles appear to be precisely the same—and probably they are so—but this point the committee had not to investigate."

The difference in the cost of the articles was a matter of great importance. The treasurer, J. F. Macfarlan, wrote to the chairman of the committee : " I am indeed quite satisfied that the chloroform prepared from methylated spirit is quite as good as the other, but the prejudices existing in London and elsewhere are strong and very difficult of removal. This Report, if the Society were kind enough to permit its publication in one of the journals, might tend much to remove them, and thus confer a benefit of some importance on the country." The Society agreed unanimously " That the Report be given over to the Committee, which drew it up, for revision and subsequent publication ". Nevertheless, the Report does not appear to have been published. The treasurer, however, acted upon it.

Macfarlan's interest in the committee's investigations has been explained by Mr. J. Rutherford Hill, lately resident secretary at Edinburgh, of the North British Branch of the Pharmaceutical Society. " J. F. Macfarlan took a very prominent part in a general agitation, that went on for several years, for permission to use duty free alcohol for industrial purposes. It was largely due to his energetic pressure that this agitation was ultimately successful in obtaining parliamentary sanction for the use of what was called methylated spirit. I think this was about 1857. The spirit consisted of 95% of pure rectified spirit (ethyl alcohol) and 5% of wood spirit (methyl alcohol) ; and this mixture was allowed to be used duty free. That meant a very great reduction in cost, where such duty free spirit could be used in manufacturing processes or making preparations such as spirit varnish for industrial use. Until then, chloroform and ether could be made only from pure, duty paid alcohol. Macfarlan's partner in the firm, J. F. Macfarlan & Co., David Rennie Brown, and later, his son, David Brown, devoted much time and research to the matter, and proved that absolutely pure chloroform could be made by using the duty free methylated spirit, and in this way could be made at much less cost. This claim was challenged, but the Browns completely proved their case. This was why J. F. Macfarlan was so much interested in the work of the Royal Medical Society's chloroform committee. . . . There was a prejudice on the part of many medical practitioners that only chloroform made from pure, duty paid ethyl alcohol could be used safely as an anaesthetic. The Society's chloroform committee ascertained that chloroform made from duty free, methylated spirit was pure and could be used as an anaesthetic. Through action by Lord Macaulay, J. F. Macfarlan succeeded in getting parliamentary sanction for the making of chloroform from industrial spirit."

In the interval between Sibbald's entry into the Society (1850) and the delivery of his communication leading to the appointment of the chloroform committee (1856), the Society had removed from the Medical Hall in Surgeons' Square to their present premises, 7 Melbourne Place (1852). A noble prelude to the removal was the election to honorary membership in 1850 of: J. Y. Simpson; John Goodsir; Robert Jameson, Professor of Natural History at Edinburgh; Sir William Hamilton, Bart., and James D. Forbes, Professors of Logic and Metaphysics, and of Natural Philosophy, respectively, at Edinburgh; Professor Richard Owen of London; and J. F. Macfarlan, treasurer of the Society.

CHAPTER XII

Negotiations with the Managers of the Royal Infirmary for the
sale of the Hall—The New Hall Committee—The Building Fund—
The move to the premises in Melbourne Place

EVER since the Town Council declined in 1819 to grant the
Society the ground for an addition to the Medical Hall, it
was plain that sooner or later the Royal Infirmary, in the
process of expansion, would require the ground on which the
Hall was built.

At a meeting of the Society on 1st February 1850 the
treasurer announced that the Managers of the Royal Infirmary had intimated to him their desire to purchase the
Medical Hall.

A committee was appointed, consisting of Professor
Christison, Drs. W. R. Sanders, Thomas Anderson and
Warden, and three ordinary members, with the treasurer as
convener, to ascertain the amount and kind of accommodation which the Society would require, and to examine the
sites which might be proposed for the New Hall.

They resolved to request an interview with Mr. Hope,
and Mr. Bryce, architect to the Royal Infirmary, before they
reported to the New Hall Committee on the matter of accommodation.   They appointed Dr. Thomas Anderson and Mr.
Nelson to draw up a statement of the accommodation
required by the Society, showing the dimensions of the
principal rooms and of the space that would be needed to
house the Society's library and other property.   This statement was to be considered at the next meeting of the sub-
committee ; and it was to be submitted to Mr. Hope acting
on behalf of the Managers of the Royal Infirmary, and to

189

Mr. Bryce. On 4th April the New Hall Committee met. The treasurer stated that he had met Mr. Hope, who informed him that the sub-committee's statement of accommodation was still in the hands of Mr. Bryce, from whom he expected a report very soon ; and that Mr. Hope would then communicate with the Committee. When the Committee reported to the Society on the following evening that they had received no definite proposal from the Managers of the Royal Infirmary, their request for reappointment to continue negotiations during the recess was granted.

At a meeting on 13th November, the Committee agreed unanimously to add Professor Syme to their number. Professor Syme, seconded by Dr. Handyside, moved that a small committee should be appointed to communicate with the Managers of the Royal Infirmary in order to ascertain their views as to the proposal formerly submitted to them by the Committee, and to receive any proposal they might be disposed to make to the Society. The motion was adopted unanimously.

The senior president during the negotiations was Mr. John Wolley, and the junior presidents were Dr. Alexander Christison, a son of Professor Christison, Mr. John Scott Sanderson and Mr. Charles Murchison.

On 14th December the sub-committee appointed to communicate with the Managers of the Royal Infirmary, which consisted of Professor Syme, Dr. Thomas Anderson, Dr. A. Christison, Mr. Wolley, and the treasurer, met Mr. Hope at the Royal Infirmary, by his request. Mr. Hope said that the building committee of the Royal Infirmary had agreed to propose to the Managers to offer to the Society " that site by Rutherford's Corner ", and £1200. " Rutherford's Corner " was the tavern, 3 Drummond Street, whose owner was called Rutherford ; and it was situated at the southwest angle of the Infirmary ground. Mr. Hope suggested that any further proposal should be made by the Society, and he expressed his opinion that the Royal Infirmary had no other piece of ground to offer. Mr. Syme remarked on the alternative open to the Society to establish itself in its present situation ; and the meeting separated. Two days later, Dr. A. Christison and Mr. Wolley surveyed the site at " Rutherford's Corner ". The plans which they made were afterwards found to correspond almost exactly to those in the possession of Mr. Bryce, of which they subsequently obtained a copy. To this copy they added a plan of part of the new Infirmary buildings that were at some future period to be substituted for the existing buildings. A week later they called upon Mr. Bryce to submit to him plans of the Medical Hall as it stood, but with an additional storey for an additional library which the Society was prepared to build, if necessary, on their present Hall. They showed these plans to Mr. Bryce as the minimum of accommodation which could possibly satisfy the Society. Mr. Bryce, having that morning had an interview with Mr. Hope, undertook to furnish the sub-committee, within a fortnight, on behalf of the Royal Infirmary, with his opinion on these three points :

1. What sum of money would be required to build, on the offered site, such a Hall as that represented in the plans, which are taken from the present Hall, with the addition of another storey ?
2. How commodious a building could Mr. Bryce contrive on the present site ?
3. What did Mr. Bryce consider to be the money value of the site offered ?

Early in January 1851 Dr. A. Christison and Mr. Wolley, accompanied by Mr. Alexander Gifford, S.S.C., the Society's legal adviser, called upon Mr. Bryce, who stated, regarding the first question, that £1800 would be required to build the shell of such a building as that represented in the plans ; and allowing 10 per cent extra, he said, the cost would be £2000, the estimate of £1800 having been made at the rate of the prices fixed for the present Infirmary works. In reply to the third question, Mr. Bryce considered the site to be worth £360, allowing 10s. per foot of frontage. With regard to the second question, Mr. Bryce had no plans completed, but he said that he could, if necessary, build actually joining the Infirmary wing and give the Society an extended front, but not beyond the commencement of the front of the Infirmary wing. He moved an adjournment to Mr. Hope's office. It was pointed out to Mr. Hope that even if the Society allowed that £1200 was a fair offer, the question was whether they could afford to incur the risk of moving on those terms. As individuals Dr. Christison and Mr. Wolley thought that the Society could not. Mr. Hope said that he would call a meeting of the Managers to ascertain whether they were inclined to make any further offer.

A few days later Dr. Christison and Mr. Wolley called on Mr. Bryce to enquire whether he had prepared any answer to their second question regarding the amount of room available in " Rutherford's Corner ". Mr. Bryce had mislaid the former statement of the Society's requirements, and a new and amended one was promised to him. He said that Mr. Tweedie's Church, the Tolbooth Free Church in Infirmary Street, would probably be less expense to pull down than to adapt. He also suggested the corner of the Infirmary grounds near Mr. Tweedie's Church as a site for the Society although he foresaw several objections on the part of the Infirmary. This corner had not previously occurred to him. On the following day, Mr. Wolley sent the promised statement to Mr. Bryce. The requirements included " a room combining the uses of a pantry and cook-room, to accommodate a person who will occasionally attend with refreshments ", and " a sitting-room for members, also to serve as an eating-room. No bookshelves to be placed in this room."

On 10th January the members of the sub-committee breakfasted with Professor J. Y. Simpson, and afterwards they showed him the two corners of the Infirmary ground and Mr. Tweedie's Church. They had also had interviews with Professors Christison and Goodsir. They decided that the two main considerations were : Is the Society willing to accept the site of " Rutherford's Corner " ? What sum of money must the Society have in addition from the Royal Infirmary ? The latter question involved several considertions. What was the least sum the Society could prudently accept ? That would depend on the probable expenses that would be incurred ; to what extent the expenses would likely be met by subscription ; and the possible necessity of a withdrawal from the accumulating fund. Further, at what point would the Royal Infirmary determine it should decide to do without the Society ? The Society had to consider how far their property was a hindrance to the Infirmary, and how far the Infirmary might be inclined to speculate on getting rid of the Society at some future time. Should the Society yield to lower terms at present ? The exact statement of the Society's case to the Infirmary and the announcement of the Society's intention to add another storey were likely to obviate the two last considerations. How much was the Medical Hall an impediment to the Infirmary ? The blocking up of its windows was the least annoyance. But the Hall prevented the Infirmary from enclosing Surgeons' Square with benefit to itself. To protect itself, if the Society were to remain where they were, the Infirmary would have to establish a system of gates and walls which would completely cut off its eastern territory from the rest of its possessions. The Society obliged all this district to be kept free from building, and to be kept in repair, of which the Infirmary had to pay by far the major part of the expense. What then would be an equitable demand by the Society, independently of the plea of inability to meet heavy expenses ? It would be that the Infirmary should give the Society a good and sufficient site, and a sum of money to erect a Hall like the present one, in lieu of the present site and Hall ; and, in addition, it should provide a sum of money to enable the Society to build an additional storey in lieu of the Society's servitudes and common right.

The sub-committee and Mr. Gifford had examined various other sites in addition to the two corners of the Infirmary ground, and Mr. Tweedie's Church, which had been shown to Professor Simpson. These were the York Hotel in Nicolson Street, the site of the present Empire Theatre ; a church in Roxburgh Place, which runs, to the south, off Drummond Street ; a church in South College

Street, opposite the south side of the University buildings ; the upper part of houses in front of the University ; houses on the north side of Argyle Square, where the Heriot-Watt College in Chambers Street now stands ; houses in Brown Square, the site of the present Dental Hospital at the top of Chambers Street ; Nicolson House, Nicolson Street, opposite the present Hall of the Royal College of Surgeons ; and houses on the south side of Nicolson Square. They viewed also the building occupied by the School of Arts in Adam Square, at the foot, and on the north side of what is now Chambers Street. When Chambers Street was made, Adam Square was demolished, and the School of Arts was removed to its present site, where it became the Heriot-Watt College.

None of those sites, however, could be chosen : in two instances the proprietors declined to sell ; and in the others eligibility was vitiated by one circumstance or another. Brown Square appears to have found favourable consideration, although the building in Adam Square was still under consideration in March ; and it was the immediate cause of bringing George IV Bridge within the scope of enquiry. On 10th January 1851 Mr. Gifford wrote to Mr. Wolley and he enclosed a plan of the City Improvements, issued in 1850, to illustrate two sites at the south end of George IV Bridge which he thought worth considering.

It was clear that the Society could take no decisive step until they received a definite offer from the Managers of the Royal Infirmary ; and this offer was soon received. At a meeting of the New Hall Committee on 6th February, Professor Syme, on behalf of the sub-committee, gave in the following letter :

" 119 Princes Street,
28 January 1851.

" Sir,

" With reference to the various conferences which have taken place with the Committee of the Medical Society, of which I believe you are the Convener, I have now, on the part of the Managers of the Royal Infirmary, to make you the following offer for the premises in Surgeons' Square, belonging to the Society, with all rights attached thereto, and in lieu of the site which it was proposed the Managers should give to the Society for the purpose of building a New Hall etc., viz. :—The sum of One Thousand Seven Hundred Pounds payable when the Disposition by the Society is delivered to the Managers, whose Entry and possession is to be held to have been at the term of Martinmas last, or at the date of the Disposition ; and also liberty to the Medical Society to occupy the House as at present until they can find accommodation elsewhere, provided that such free occupation is not to extend beyond a period of Five Years from the period of the Entry of the Managers of the Royal Infirmary.

" The Managers calculate that the above offer will be equivalent to £2000 to the Medical Society, and the above is the extreme limit to which the Managers are prepared to go for the purpose of acquiring this property.

I am, Sir,

Your most obed. St.,

James Hope.

" Professor Syme,
Convener of the Committee
of the Medical Society."

On the motion of Dr. F. D. McCowan (1838), seconded by Mr. A. F. Turner, an ordinary member, the Committee agreed unanimously that the offer should be approved and recommended to the Society for adoption. When the Society met on the following day, the treasurer, seconded by Dr. F. D. McCowan, moved : " That the Report of the New Hall Committee be taken into consideration at the next Ordinary Meeting, and that notice of the Meeting be sent to the Honorary and Extraordinary Members at present in town ". The motion was unanimously adopted.

On 14th February the Society met to consider the offer of the Managers of the Royal Infirmary to purchase the Medical Hall. Among the ninety-three members present was a large number of honorary and extraordinary members, including James D. Forbes, Professor of Natural Philosophy at Edinburgh, and Dr. Conolly of Hanwell, who was a president of the Society in 1820–21, and who had come to Edinburgh, at the request of his friends in England, to sit for his portrait to Sir John Watson Gordon. Most of the medical professors and extra-academical lecturers at Edinburgh were present, and among them were Professors Syme, J. Y. Simpson, Christison, Goodsir, Hughes Bennett and Hutton Balfour, and Drs. Douglas Maclagan, Thomas Anderson, J. D. Gillespie and P. D. Handyside.

Proceeding to the Report of the New Hall Committee, Dr. Alexander Christison, the President in the chair, said : " It is well to give a short account of what has been done, that everyone may have a clear notion on the subject. As to the history of proceedings like the present, I may remark that from the year 1737, when the Society was instituted, until the year 1775 the Society met in a room in the Royal Infirmary, and that, in point of fact, the Society is entirely indebted for its existence at that period to the Managers of the Royal Infirmary. On this account alone we are bound to act in a liberal manner towards that body. The foundation of the present Hall was laid by Dr. Cullen in 1775, and, until 1819 no proposal can be found relative to alteration of the premises. At that period changes were proposed. An architect was consulted. Questions were laid before counsel relative to ' alienation ' of property. The Town Council was petitioned for accommodation on the High School grounds ; and the purchase of Dr. Barclay's house was likewise contemplated. But in the end no alteration resulted. Again, in 1831, a committee for a similar purpose was formed. They reported in January 1832 that it was inexpedient to alter the Hall, as there was a want of funds, and as they could not find a proper site. Lastly, in 1837 and 1838, the proposal of altered accommodation was renewed but not carried out. It thus appears that the propriety of a change of accommodation was long ago thought advisable. The proceedings more particularly before us refer to the date of

1 February 1850, little more than a year ago. I shall run over the minutes of the Committee to show the exact position of affairs."

Professor Christison, seconded by Dr. Conolly, then moved : " That the Society approve the Report of the Committee appointed to treat with the Managers of the Royal Infirmary concerning the disposal of the property in Surgeons' Square, and adopt its conclusions ".

A report of the speeches and proceedings at the meeting was written by Professor Christison in the form of a pamphlet : " Professor Christison observed that it had become a matter of necessity that the Society should remove to a more eligible situation. They were about to be hemmed in altogether by the Infirmary improvements ; the access had become intolerable ; and there was no longer space for their admirable library. It was fortunate, in these circumstances, that another body was equally interested in their removal. The Managers of the Royal Infirmary, who, since the institution of the Society, had repeatedly befriended them, now made a liberal offer, which, along with other resources, would enable them to build a new hall on a much better site, and with all modern conveniences. No one could doubt that a large sum, in aid of the building fund, might be raised by a subscription among the extraordinary members, now scattered over the whole world, and constituting a great proportion of the practitioners, not merely of this city, but likewise of the country towns, as well as the metropolis of the empire, and who looked upon the Society with affectionate regard as the scene alike of instruction and happiness, when they were students of the University and ordinary members. As the sum, however, which would be thus raised, might not prove sufficient, it would be advisable to make the accumulated fund, now amounting to £1300, available for the purpose to the extent of £600. There could be no more appropriate application of a portion of a fund which had been set aside by their predecessors expressly for ' repairing, altering, and improving the Hall '. It was true that the interest of the fund had some years ago maintained the efficiency of the

Society, and saved it from debt, when the income from other sources fell short of the ordinary expenditure ; and a part of it should still be reserved for annual repairs. But the sum proposed to be made available might be safely withdrawn if found necessary. They must commence with a certainty of being supplied with the requisite building-fund. It was to be hoped that the little capital of the Society might not be seriously encroached on. But although it were to be so, the Society might trust to a considerable accession of new members as soon as the Hall was placed in a respectable site, and with full accommodation for the library, now amounting to 14,000 volumes, selected with a care unexampled in any other institution."

Dr. Christison concluded with moving that the sale be effected in terms of the offer of the Managers of the Royal Infirmary ; that the committee be instructed to carry this resolution into effect, and empowered to purchase a site for the new hall and obtain plans for the Society's consideration ; that a subscription be set on foot among the members and friends of the Society ; and that the accumulated fund be made available for the new hall to the amount of £600.

Dr. Conolly expressed his hope that, as a member of more than thirty years' standing, and one who had taken an active interest in the business of the Society while he was an attending member, he might be allowed the pleasure of seconding the motion. At the time to which he referred, the Society's Hall was surrounded by famous schools of anatomy, and by the Hall of the College of Surgeons, which had been all gradually removed. The site and access were now greatly deteriorated ; and the state of the Hall itself showed that they had not in this respect advanced with the times. He hoped, if he should be spared to revisit Edinburgh, he should find the Society in a new hall, situated in a more desirable locality.

Dr. Andrew Wood was of opinion that it was desirable for the Society to remove from their present Hall. But it was better for them to remain than to move at the risk of sacrificing the accumulated fund. He, therefore, moved as an amendment that the accumulated fund should not be encroached on for the purpose of building a new hall, and that the offer of the Managers should not be decided upon till November next ; and that the necessary steps be taken for obtaining a subscription and looking out for sites for a new building.

Dr. William S. Carmichael seconded the amendment.

Professor Syme urged the immediate acceptance of the offer of the Managers. After many delays they had got a definite offer, which ought to receive a definite answer. All agreed as to the necessity for moving. No one could doubt the liberality of the offer made them. The adjoining house was bought by the Managers for £600. Their own Hall was now not worth £400 to anybody except the Managers, to whom it was valuable on account of important servitudes which they required to obtain possession of. He deprecated delay, and had no doubt that the requisite funds would be forthcoming. After a lengthy discussion, it was then agreed that the first part of the motion should be put, viz. : That the Society approve the Committee's Report, accept the offer of the Managers, and appoint the following committee to carry the sale into effect :—Ordinary Members : *Presidents*—Mr. Wolley, Dr. Alexander Christison, Mr. Scott Sanderson, Mr. Charles Murchison. *Curator*—Mr. James M'Grigor Maclagan. *Secretaries*—Mr. J. A. Currie, Mr. W. M. Calder. Extraordinary Members : Professors Christison, Syme, Simpson, Goodsir, Hutton Balfour, Hughes Bennett ; Drs. Conolly, Craigie, Simson, Douglas Maclagan, Thomas Anderson, Newbigging, Alexander Wood, Handyside, Donald Mackenzie, J. D. Gillespie, Mackenzie, McCowan ; Hugh Cleghorn, H.E.I.C.S., Archibald White, H.E.I.C.S. ; Messrs. Cuningham, Broadbent, Turner ; Mr. J. F. Macfarlan, *Convener*—with power to add to their number.

The amendment of Dr. Andrew Wood being then balloted for was negatived by a majority of 73 to 20. The President next intimated that the laws of the Society, relative to alienation of property, required that at least six honorary and sixteen ordinary members of nine months' standing should concur in such a motion as that of Dr. Christison, otherwise the meeting could not agree to it. Thereupon nineteen such ordinary members, and the following honorary members : Professors W. P. Alison, R. Christison, James Syme, J. Y. Simpson, John Goodsir and J. D. Forbes, and Mr. J. F. Macfarlan declared their concurrence by signing a declaration. " We the undersigned, consent to the alienation of the Medical Society's property as moved by Dr. Christison and seconded by Dr. Conolly." The ballot was then taken on the motion, which was declared to be carried by a majority of 73 to 10.

On 19th February the New Hall Committee met. There were present : Mr. J. F. Macfarlan, Convener ; Professors Christison and Hughes Bennett ; Drs. Thomas Anderson, Conolly, Douglas Maclagan, McCowan and A. Christison ; and Messrs. Wolley, Scott Sanderson, Charles Murchison, J. M. Maclagan ; and the honorary secretaries. The Committee instructed the honorary secretaries to communicate to Mr. Hope the Society's acceptance of the offer of the Managers of the Royal Infirmary. At a meeting of the Society a couple of days later, Professor Christison, seconded by Dr. Andrew Wood, moved the second clause of his motion of 14th February : " That the same Committee be empowered to purchase a site, and to obtain plans and estimates for the consideration of a full meeting of the Ordinary and Extraordinary Members of the Society ". This clause was carried unanimously. Professor Christison then moved, and Dr. Balfour seconded the third clause : " That a subscription be commenced forthwith among the members and friends of the Society for an additional fund for building the new hall ; and that the same Committee, with Mr. J. F. Macfarlan as treasurer, shall superintend the subscription ". This motion was also carried unanimously. The remaining clause, relative to the appropriation of a part of the accumulated fund of £1300 was postponed at the mover's request.

On 26th February the New Hall Committee appointed a sub-committee, consisting of Mr. Wolley, Convener, Professor Christison, Drs. Douglas Maclagan, T. Anderson, and

A. Christison, and Mr. J. F. Macfarlan, to make arrangements about the site of the New Hall. They appointed also a sub-committee for procuring subscriptions. The members of this sub-committee were : Professor Christison, Convener ; Professors Syme, Simpson, Hutton Balfour and Hughes Bennett ; Drs. Conolly, H. Cleghorn, James White, Simson, Giraud ; the four presidents and the honorary secretaries. The Committee agreed unanimously, on a motion by Professor Hughes Bennett, seconded by Dr. James Simson, an eminent Edinburgh practitioner and later P.R.C.S.E., that Mr. Bryce should be appointed architect of the New Hall. And at this meeting, Mr. Gifford, S.S.C., legal adviser to the Society, presented the letter of acceptance of the offer of the Managers of the Royal Infirmary which he had prepared at the request of the honorary secretaries.

A circular, inviting subscriptions, was written by Professor Christison, chairman of the subscription sub-committee. It ran : " I have the honour to transmit to you, in name of the Royal Medical Society of Edinburgh, the enclosed account of a late Meeting, at which it was resolved to dispose of the present Hall, and to solicit subscriptions for a new one. The debate which took place at the Meeting may explain the present circumstances of the Society, to those who distinctly recollect how it was formerly situated. I may mention more explicitly, however, that the Managers of the Royal Infirmary had previously purchased all the other houses of Surgeons' Square, except the Medical Society's Hall ; that the Hall is now closely hemmed in by the new Infirmary buildings, and will be more so in a short time ; that the access and neighbourhood have become objectionable ; and that, in consequence, the removal of the Hall had become a matter of strong necessity.

" I have further the satisfaction to inform you, that the Society continues to be supported, as formerly, by the highest class of students of the University ; and that its business is conducted with the same zeal and regularity, and to the very great advantage of this School of Learning, of which it has been from the first so prominent a feature. I hope that nothing more needs to be said, to revive the pleasing associations connected with the Society in the recollection of all its members, and to induce you to aid in promoting its usefulness, and perpetuating the singular success which has hitherto attended it throughout its whole history."

Professor Hughes Bennett supported the subscription in a practical way by announcing in a circular : " In aid of Building Fund of Royal Medical Society, Dr. Bennett will deliver Two Lectures on Somnambulism, and the Facts of ' Animal Magnetism ', with reference to their Explanation according to the laws of Physiological Science, in Queen Street Hall, March 20th and 22nd, Half-past Eight p.m."

The medical professors at Edinburgh, including James Miller, Professor of Surgery, who was not a member of the Society, subscribed generously. Among the honorary members who subscribed were Sir James M'Grigor, Bart., and Professors James D. Forbes and W. P. Alison. And among many distinguished old members who subscribed were : Andrew Fyfe, a former treasurer of the Society, Professor of Chemistry at Aberdeen ; William Sharpey, Professor of Physiology at University College, London ; W. B. Carpenter, Professor of Medical Jurisprudence there ; Thomas Anderson, Professor of Chemistry at Glasgow ; and George Edward Day, Professor of Medicine at St. Andrews.

The presidents during the session 1851–52, when the Society removed to their present premises, 7 Melbourne Place, were Thomas Spencer Cobbold, senior president ; William H. Broadbent, James M'Grigor Maclagan, and William Murray Dobie, house-surgeon with Syme in 1852–1853 and a friend of Lister, junior presidents.

On 8th March 1852 Dr. M'Grigor Maclagan presided over an extraordinary meeting of the Society, which was held at the instance of the New Hall Committee to receive their Report recommending the immediate purchase of 7 Melbourne Place. Mr. Gifford's suggestion of a site on George IV Bridge based upon the plan of the City Improvements of 1850 would appear to have been the deciding factor leading up to the Society's final selection. Mr. Gifford was present at this meeting and explained the proposed terms and conditions of purchase. Dr. Cobbold, seconded by Mr. John Taylor, proposed : " That the proceedings of the Committee in regard to the purchase of the house, 7 Melbourne Place, be approved of, and the Committee authorised to complete the transaction ". Dr. Handyside, also a member of the Committee, seconded by Mr. George Birdwood, moved " That the proposal to purchase the four upper floors of the tenement, No. 7 Melbourne Place, for the use of the Royal Medical Society, be not entertained, on the ground that the proposed purchase is not an entire tenement ". After a discussion, Dr. Handyside withdrew his motion. No other objection was made. The president then declared that Dr. Cobbold's motion was carried. On 26th March the Committee reported to the Society that the purchase had been completed. A committee was appointed, which included Professors Christison and Hughes Bennett, and Drs. Warburton Begbie, Douglas Maclagan and Charles Murchison, to consult Mr. Bryce, the architect, regarding alterations in the premises.

On 12th November, the last meeting of the Society in the Medical Hall in Surgeons' Square was held. Dr. W. H. Broadbent, seconded by Dr. W. M. Dobie, moved " That the next meeting of the Society be held in the New Hall, No. 7 Melbourne Place ".

A week later the Society held their first meeting in the New Hall. At public business Dr. Cobbold, the president in the Chair, delivered an Address, and Professor J. Y. Simpson communicated to the Society the results of a series of experiments on living animals, with a view of ascertaining the true nature of uterine contractions in the parturient female.

After a discussion on Professor Simpson's paper in which Professor Hughes Bennett and Drs. Matthews Duncan and W. T. Gairdner took part, the treasurer " proposed a vote of thanks to Dr. Simpson for his valuable paper, which afforded another instance of that kindness of feeling and that disinterested generosity which always characterized his actions ". Professor Simpson expressed, on behalf of himself and his colleagues, the willingness with which he and they would be at all times ready to advance the interests of the Society. He regarded the Society as a school of learning which formed a great class room, far superior to any in the University, and he had no hesitation in affirming that had it not been for the advantages derived from the Society, he would never have occupied a Chair in the University of Edinburgh.

When the hall in Surgeons' Square was being demolished, the workmen came upon the foundation-stone, in which were found a glass bottle and a leaden case hermetically sealed. The bottle was taken to Mr. J. F. Macfarlan, in an opened state, and containing only a small silver medal, on which was engraven, " Medicinae Sacrum April 20 "; and on the reverse, " Societate Medica Conditum A.P.C.N. 1775 ". This medal was mounted ; and it now stands on the mantelpiece at the north end of the Society's Hall. The bottle contained nothing else " except some rotten stuff like paper, which is said to have had a very fetid smell ". The leaden case contained two of the original diplomas granted to members of the Society, one of parchment, the other of paper, and both blank. The foundation stone was covered by a carved slab, bearing the inscription, " Sacred to Medicine ; Founded April 21st 1775 By Thos. McInnes *Mason* ". The stone was built into the wall below the staircase facing the entrance door to the Society's premises at 7 Melbourne Place.

The old clock was found, on removal, to be too big for the debating hall, and was placed above the central entrance door of the library.

The Society's records do not refer to the details of the alterations made to the Melbourne Place premises according to the plans of Mr. Bryce. It is clear, however, from the minutes, that he was responsible for using the whole breadth of the building and the height of the third and fourth storeys to make the finely proportioned hall the main feature of the building with its double row of windows and timbered ceiling.

Above the hall on the fifth storey is the librarian's house. The small rooms behind the hall on the fourth storey were both used as a museum until 1936, when one of them was furnished as a writing-room. The rooms below these on the third floor accommodated some of the books until 1931. Since then one has been used to display the original paintings for the illustration of Sir Byrom Bramwell's *Atlas of Clinical Medicine*, which were presented by his sons to the Society in May 1931. In 1938 the other was furnished with new shelves to preserve some of the old books in the library. On the second floor are the north and south libraries and the secretaries' and librarian's rooms. The adequacy of the premises to the Society's needs after more than eighty years' use testifies to the wise choice of site and architect in 1851.

Throughout the negotiations in connection with the sale of the Medical Hall and the purchase of the present premises, Doyle Money Shaw was a conspicuous and able secretary. Shaw was elected a president in 1852. He began his Inaugural Address by saying that a few months previously he had received from a former schoolfellow, then studying at Cambridge, a letter which contained only the following words :

> DEAR SIR,
>> I'm all in a flutter
>> I scarcely can utter
>> " I'm Senior Wrangler ".

The writer was P. G. Tait, afterwards Professor of Natural Philosophy at Edinburgh. Shaw went on to speak of his being in a flutter at being raised to the office of a President of the Royal Medical Society.

Melbourne Place was a recent City improvement when the Society removed there. Professor Daniel Wilson, brother of that distinguished member of the Society, Dr. George Wilson, has described in his *Memorials of Edinburgh in the Olden Time*, the Old Bank Close which was demolished in 1834 to make way for it. The Old Bank, now known as the Bank of Scotland, which gave the ancient alley its name, carried on all its business in the Close. " But all other objects of attraction to the local historian, within this district, must yield before those of the Old Bank Close, the site of which was very nearly that of the present paving of Melbourne Place. The antique mansion, that formed the chief building in this close, excited very great and general attention from the time that it was exposed to view in opening up the approach to George IV's Bridge, until its demolition in 1834, to make way for the central buildings of Melbourne Place, that now occupy its site. . . . This ancient building was curiously connected with a succession of eminent and influential men, and with important historical events of various eras, from the date of its erection until a comparatively recent period. ' Gourlay's House ', for so it continued to be called nearly to the last, was erected in 1569, as appeared from the date on it, by Robert Gourlay, burgess, on the site, and, partly at least, with the materials of an old religious house. Little further is known of its builder than the fact that he had been a wealthy and influential citizen, who enjoyed the favour of royalty, and made the most of it too, notwithstanding the pious averment sculptered over his door, ' O LORD IN THE IS AL MY TRAIST '." [1] The mansion was " alternately prison and palace ".[2]

The building of Melbourne Place was begun in 1835 ; and the first address there was that of Alexander Ferguson, confectioner, formerly in the Lawnmarket, which appeared in the Edinburgh Directory for 1836–37. Messrs. James and John Gray, the owners of the building purchased by the Society, who were previously in Bank Street, were also established in Melbourne Place towards the end of 1837, as an advertisement in their paper, *Gray's Monthly Record*, shows. Messrs. J. & J. Gray were the proprietors and publishers of *The North British Advertiser*, and the short-lived *Gray's Monthly Record*, followed by *Gray's Weekly Record*, which had an equally brief career. Professor Wilson's description appears to show that the Society's premises occupy part of the site of " Gourlay's House ".

[1] *Memorials of Edinburgh in the Olden Time* (1848), i, p. 172.
[2] *Ibid.* p. 175.

When the property was purchased, Mr. Gifford, the Society's legal adviser, made sure there would be no objection, in the future, to the title. There had been some trouble with Messrs. Hope & Oliphant, W.S., the Agents for the Royal Infirmary, regarding the Society's title to the property in Surgeons' Square. In 1852 Mr. Gifford wrote to the treasurer of the Society : " No difficulty can occur with regard to the New Hall such as occurred with regard to the old one, because I have made Mr. Gray's Trustees dispone the property primarily and expressly to the Medical Society as an Incorporation holding a Royal Charter, and only secondarily to the Presidents and their successors in office for behoof of said Incorporation. In the case of the Medical Hall, there was no Disposition in favour of the Society at all, but only to the Presidents and their successors in office, and hence the objection was made by the Agents for the Royal Infirmary that the title was defective."

In the Disposition by Messrs. Gray in favour of the Society there was a clause which removed the objection put forward by Dr. Handyside, that the premises did not consist of a complete tenement. " It is hereby declared that in case we or our foresaids shall at any time hereafter resolve to sell the street and lower flats and back area of said tenement, or any part thereof, or in case our said disponees or their foresaids shall be inclined to sell the said four upper flats of said tenement or any part thereof, in either of these cases the party inclining to sell shall be bound previously to make an offer of the subjects, so intended to be sold, in writing to the other party, and to allow fourteen days for returning an answer thereto ; and should the said offer not be accepted of, the subjects so proposed to be sold may then be sold to a stranger, but not sooner, or at any lower price or prices than those at which they were first offered to the other party to these presents as hereinbefore provided." This clause referred to the portions of the tenement in which the Society's premises are situated, which do not belong to the Society, and which now consist of two shops, one on the north and the other on the south side of the Society's door and entrance passage. In

1855, and again in 1866, the Society waived their right of pre-emption in favour of a third party. Through no fault of the Society, these decisions deprived them eventually of the exercise of their right, and therefore of getting possession of the entire tenement unless they were prepared to pay for the said portions any price that might be asked.

CHAPTER XIII

Joseph Lister—J. Matthews Duncan—Joseph Bell—J. Crichton-
Browne—A. Crum Brown—Dyce Duckworth—Local Anaesthesia
—R. B. Finlay

On 10th March 1854 Joseph Lister petitioned for a seat in the Society. A week later his petition was balloted for and granted. On both occasions Dr. Heron Watson, a fellow-resident in the Royal Infirmary of Edinburgh in the ensuing summer, and later a colleague there, was president in the chair. At the meeting on 24th March, over which George Birdwood presided, Lister signed the Obligation and became a member.

Lister had arrived in Edinburgh in the autumn of 1853, armed with an introduction to Professor Syme from his teacher, Dr. Sharpey, Professor of Physiology at University College, London. During a part of his active membership of the Society, the summer of 1854 and the winter of 1854–55, he was house-surgeon to Syme, whom he was assisting in private practice as well. It is not surprising, therefore, that in November 1854 he appealed for permission to be excused from the fines he might have incurred from occasional non-attendance, caused by professional engagements. A motion, " That Mr. Lister's petition for exemption from his fines be accepted ", was carried by a majority of one vote.

The period of Lister's active membership was one of great prosperity in the Society. Among contemporary members were Dr. Matthews Duncan, afterwards a lifelong friend ; Joseph Bell, one of his students, and later a colleague in the Royal Infirmary of Edinburgh ; R. Peel Ritchie, afterwards

P.R.C.P.E., and author of *The Early Days of the Royall Colledge of Phisitians, Edinburgh*; A. Crum Brown and T. Grainger Stewart, future colleagues on the Senatus of the University of Edinburgh; Thomas R. Fraser, successor in 1877 to Sir Robert Christison in the Chair of Materia Medica; and James Crichton-Browne and Dyce Duckworth.

Early in 1855 Lister showed his deep attachment to his former teacher by requesting permission from the finance committee, as required by the laws for such a motion, to propose Dr. Sharpey as an honorary member. The request was granted. On 23rd March Professor Sharpey was elected an honorary member.

In connection with a dissertation which Lister delivered before the Society, he manifested a trait which was apparent during his whole career and especially in a later appearance in the Society when he was at the height of his fame as Professor of Clinical Surgery at Edinburgh. It has been described by his nephew: " When at work his whole energies were concentrated upon it regardless of the lapse of time, of meals or other engagements. This virtue often postponed the beginning of the next duty, so that he was apt to be unpunctual, and seldom completely ready even for his public addresses, the final preparation for which was generally put off to the last possible moment." [1] The circumstances were these. A member, Mr. James Turnbull, had not sent in his dissertation on the appointed date, and he was, therefore, according to the laws, liable to expulsion unless he could give a satisfactory excuse. Mr. Turnbull stated that he had only arrived from the White Sea on the day on which his dissertation was due, and that he was quite unable to finish it in the proper time. This excuse was deemed satisfactory by the Society; and an intimation was made later at the same meeting that Mr. Lister's was the next dissertation. A week later, 7th December 1855, it was intimated that Mr. Lister had failed to send in his dissertation, which was due that evening. Lister had recently taken over the lecture-

[1] *Six Papers by Lord Lister* (with a Short Biography by Sir Rickman J. Godlee, Bt.), p. 22. Medical Classics Series (1921).

ship in surgery to the Royal College of Surgeons of Edinburgh, of which he had been elected a Fellow, formerly undertaken by Dr. R. J. Mackenzie, who had died on active service in the Crimea ; and that accounts for the address above the letter which he wrote to excuse the failure to give in his dissertation. The petition for another week was granted unanimously, and at the meeting a week later Lister read his dissertation, " On the Mode in which External Applications act on Internal Parts ". The president in the chair was A. R. Simpson, afterwards successor to his uncle, Sir J. Y. Simpson, in the Chair of Midwifery. Lister was twenty-eight years of age at this time, several years above the average age of an active member.

In 1857 Lister became a life member of the Society. Two years later he took part in a debate, in a manner that revealed the firm gentleness which was a main element in his noble character. A member was accused of soliciting two votes for the election of a president. The accusers and the accused were heard, and then ordered to leave the room. The treasurer moved, " That the Society, having heard the charges against Mr. S——, and his reply, find that the charges have not been proved, and that Mr. S—— be assoilzied from them ; but find, at the same time, that the accusers acted with perfect honour, and are entitled to the thanks of the Society ". A further motion was proposed by Mr. Lister, " That in the opinion of the Society, Mr. S—— has not been found guilty of such solicitation as the law prohibits, but that the accusers are entitled to the thanks of the Society for undertaking so unpleasant a duty ". The treasurer put the first clause of his motion as an amendment against Mr. Lister's motion : the amendment was lost. Mr. Lister's motion, being objected to, was put to the Society, and was accepted.

Lister was, at this time, an assistant-surgeon to the Royal Infirmary of Edinburgh ; in a little over a month, he was appointed Regius Professor of Surgery in the University of Glasgow. Nine years later, he was elected to the Chair of Clinical Surgery at Edinburgh, in succession to Professor

Syme. He occupied the Chair for eight years—" the most brilliant period of his career ".[1]

In 1870 he was elected an honorary member of the Society. These are impressive words, therefore, that Dr. Murray Lyon, later Professor of Clinical Medicine at Edinburgh, spoke in his Inaugural Address as president in 1912 : " We must not forget that our Society was one of the first to honour Lister ". A year after his election to honorary membership, Lister wrote :

" 9, Charlotte Square
Edinburgh
9 March 1871.

" To the President of the Royal Medical Society.
" Dear Sir,
 " I should be glad, if convenient to the Society, to read at the meeting of the 17th inst., a communication on ' The Antiseptic System of Treatment in Surgery '.

Believe me,
Sincerely yours,
Joseph Lister."

The Society unanimously accepted the offer. At the meeting on 17th March Dr. Alexander Macdougall was the president in the chair. (It may be mentioned that he died during his term of office, whilst a Resident in the Royal Infirmary. There is a portrait of him in the Society's Rooms.) Professor Lister commenced by saying that he was labouring under the great disadvantage of having to fulfil an engagement to write on " Antiseptic Surgery " for Mr. Holmes' *System of Surgery*. He apologised for a somewhat hurried preparation, and begged the Society to accept an unwritten communication on " The Anomalous Healing of certain Wounds ".

On the conclusion of Professor Lister's Address before the Society the vote of thanks was proposed by Mr. J. Knowsley Thornton (1870), " who took up the study of medicine because on a visit to Edinburgh he was deeply im-

---

[1] *Six Papers by Lord Lister, etc.*, p. 11.

pressed with Lister's personality, and who became his ' almost perfect house surgeon ', and later his strong supporter and friend. On Lister's recommendation he left a rough country district in the wilds of Northumberland and came to London to help Spencer Wells in his large and fashionable practice. Wells, as we have seen, had recognized the importance of the germ theory even before Lister ; and now with Thornton's assistance carried out the antiseptic treatment in every detail. Thornton in time gained a very wide reputation as an operator both in private practice and at the Samaritan Hospital. A clear writer, a good debater, and a keen fighter, he did much to familiarize both the profession and the public with Lister's work." [1]

The story of Lister's removal to London in 1877 is well known. " Lister had stipulated that he should be allowed to bring with him from Edinburgh four men whom he had himself trained, to form the nucleus of his staff at the hospital. Two were graduates : Watson Cheyne, now senior surgeon to King's College Hospital, and John Stewart, of Halifax, Nova Scotia . . . the other two were unqualified, W. M. Dobie [W. H. Dobie] and James Altham, who afterwards practised at Chester and Penrith respectively." [2]

Among the members of the Society who were dressers, clerks or house surgeons to Lister during his Professorship at Edinburgh, besides the four who accompanied him to London, were T. R. Ronaldson (1870), George T. Beatson (1871), F. Le M. Grasett (1872) and James Baker (1874). Of the last-named, Dr. Douglas, who was then an active member, writes in a letter to the Society : " The most interesting of our Presidents was James Baker, who was a Resident with Lister. Like him he was a ' Quaker ' and a man of very high principle. As a teetotaller he could not subscribe to the expenses of the Dinner, where wines are served. To balance this omission he presented to the Society the clock which you have on the mantelpiece. I saw it there when I attended the Bicentenary meeting last year. He was the most eloquent speaker I have ever heard in Medicine ; and he had a beautiful,

---

[1] Sir Rickman J. Godlee, *Lord Lister*, p. 326.   [2] *Ibid.* p. 409.

soft and fluent voice. He died when on duty in the Residency." On his death in 1877 an extraordinary meeting of the Society was held, at which it was resolved to place an inscribed silver plate, as a memorial, on the clock which he had presented. John Bishop (1869), who married Isabella Bird, the explorer, was a private assistant of Lister during this period.

After Lister removed to London, John Chiene (1862), Professor of Surgery at Edinburgh, and John Duncan (1859), surgeon to the Royal Infirmary there, continued to carry out the antiseptic treatment : in the words of Sir Rickman Godlee, they " did their best to keep the flag flying amidst many difficulties ".[1]

Pasteur was elected an honorary member of the Society in 1875. Speaking at a Reception of Delegates at the Tercentenary Festival of the University of Edinburgh in 1884, he said : " Vous surtout, étudiants en médecine de la célèbre Université d'Edimbourg, qui, formés par des maîtres éminents, avez des droits aux plus hautes ambitions scientifiques, inspirez-vous de la méthode expérimentale ! C'est à ces principes que l'Ecosse doit les Brewster, les Thomson, et les Lister." [2]

In 1897 Lister was elevated to the Peerage.

Although weighed down by illness in his latter years, he retained his interest in his life's work. As late as 1906 he wrote to J. F. Macfarlan & Co. :

> " 12 Park Crescent
> Portland Place
> 8 June 1906.

" Lord Lister would be much obliged to Messrs. Macfarlan if they would kindly inform him what is about the percentage of the double cyanide of mercury and zinc in the cyanide gauze supplied by them."

During the Great War 1914–18 very large quantities of this gauze were ordered for use in the East.

---

[1] *Lord Lister*, p. 328.
[2] *Records of the Tercentenary Festival of the University of Edinburgh celebrated in April 1884*, p. 162.

In 1908 Sir Thomas Chavasse of Birmingham, who had joined the Society in 1875, and clerked under Lister in the old Royal Infirmary of Edinburgh, was invited to deliver the Inaugural Address at the commencement of the session 1908–1909. The Address was the story of the evolution of Listerian surgery. On the occasion, Lord Lister wrote to him :

> " Brook Cottage,
> Walmer.
> 28 Sept. 1908.

" Dear Sir Thomas,

" I cordially wish all success to the inaugural address which you tell me you are about to deliver to the Royal Medical Society.

" I always look back with peculiar pleasure on my relations with the students of Edinburgh.

> Believe me,
> Very sincerely yours,
> Lister."

When the earthly career of—to quote the words of his old house surgeon, Professor John Stewart,—" the greatest man on earth " had closed, the Society expressed their sympathy with the relatives. " The secretary read a letter from Mr. Arthur Lister acknowledging the letter of sympathy which the Senior President and Senior Secretary had sent to the relatives of the late Lord Lister."

In the Society's Rooms there is an autograph photogravure, from the portrait of Lord Lister by Lorimer, which was presented in 1908 by Sir Thomas Chavasse.

Lister's friend, Matthews Duncan, had been an assistant to Professor J. Y. Simpson before he joined the Society in 1852, and had taken part in Simpson's experiments in search of a more convenient anaesthetic than ether.

Matthews Duncan was an extra-mural lecturer on diseases of women when he read his dissertation before the Society in 1854, " Reflections on the Duration of Pregnancy with Remarks on the Calculation of the Date of Confinement ".[1]

---

[1] *Dissertations of Royal Medical Society* (1892), pp. 300-316.

In the same year he became a life member of the Society. In 1861 he was appointed a physician for diseases of women to the Royal Infirmary, and was for some time a colleague of Sir James Y. Simpson in that position. He rapidly became, in the words of Sir Rickman Godlee, " the great gynae-cologist ".[1] He took a close interest in the Society throughout his career, and, in 1872, he was elected an honorary member along with Sir James Paget.

Thomas Grainger Stewart (1855) was a physician to the Royal Infirmary when Lister returned to Edinburgh in 1869 ; and he was later, as Professor of Practice of Physic, a colleague of Lister's on the Medical Faculty.

The dissertation which he read before the Society was " On Reflex Action ". In 1857 he was elected a president. In 1858 he seconded the treasurer's successful motion, " That an Honorary Member's Diploma be conferred upon David Livingstone, LL.D., D.C.L., Fellow of the Faculty of Physicians and Surgeons, Glasgow ". Livingstone had already a tie with the Society, as he was a friend of Dr. George Wilson, already mentioned as a distinguished senior member. " The same year [1837], Dr. Graham went to London as Professor of Chemistry in University College, and Livingstone, who also went to London, had the opportunity of paying occasional visits to his class. In this way, too, he became acquainted with the late Dr. George Wilson, after-wards Professor of Technology in the University of Edin-burgh, who was then acting as unsalaried assistant in Dr. Graham's laboratory. . . . Livingstone showed his friend-ship in after years by collecting and transmitting to Wilson whatever he could find in Africa worthy of a place in the Edinburgh Museum of Science and Art, of which his friend was the first Director." [2] In 1860 Grainger Stewart became a life member of the Society. In the same year, when he was a house physician in the Royal Infirmary under Professors Hughes Bennett and Laycock, he wrote : " With the per-mission of the Society I shall be glad to read a communication

---

[1] *Lord Lister*, p. 254.
[2] W. G. Blaikie, D.D., *The Personal Life of David Livingstone*, p. 23

next Friday evening on a case of chronic pleurisy, with waxy degeneration of the liver, kidneys and spleen ". His work on certain forms of Bright's Disease brought him into notice, and led to his appointment as pathologist to the Royal Infirmary, and to an extra-mural lectureship in pathology. In 1864 he presented to the Society a copy of his " Observations on the Waxy or Amyloid Form of Bright's Disease " ; and in the same year he described the saccharometer before a meeting of the Society. As a professor, he continued to show his interest in the Society's welfare. At the Dinner in 1886, in replying to the toast of " The Scottish Universities ", he said : " The Universities owe a great deal to the Royal Medical Society, which is the oldest students' Society in Great Britain, and probably in the world ". He received the honour of knighthood from his Sovereign, to whom he was Physician-in-Ordinary in Scotland.

Joseph Bell (1857) was a great-grandson of Benjamin Bell (1769) who, as an early member of the Society, became an honorary member by rotation. Benjamin Bell was an eminent surgeon in Edinburgh. He resided at Newington House, later the residence of Duncan McLaren, at one time Lord Provost, and later Member for the City. Newington House is now the Scottish National Institution for Blinded Sailors and Soldiers. " When Newington was laid out in streets, the road where the mansion-house stands was called ' Blacket Place ' in honour of the old estate of the Bells in Dumfriesshire." The Bells were " an ancient Dumfriesshire family who could trace their lineage back many centuries. . . . They were a fighting race, their name occurring in many a Border incident." [1]

Joseph Bell became a member during a brilliant period in the history of the Society. There was intense activity which lasted without a break for ten years. Some of the members combined strong mental endowments with outstanding physical characteristics which, in later years, attracted the notice of passers-by on the streets of Edinburgh. Such were William Turner, afterwards Principal of the University of Edinburgh,

[1] W. P. Anderson, *Silences that Speak* (Edinburgh, 1931), p. 538.

James Crichton-Browne, A. Crum Brown, Thomas R. Fraser, John Duncan, R. B. Finlay, Thomas Annandale, John Chiene, John Wyllie and Byrom Bramwell. Other active members during these years were Dyce Duckworth, W. Mitchell Banks and T. Lauder Brunton. Considering the future eminence of these members, it is good to read that at the annual extraordinary meeting in 1863, after Mr. Finlay had moved a vote of thanks to Dr. A. J. Macfarlan, the treasurer, " A very stormy discussion arose regarding an interval in the business, during which the whole Society spoke at once ".

In 1858 Bell read his dissertation on " Epithelial Cancer ". In 1859 he was president in the chair at the legislative meeting when J. F. Macfarlan, seconded by his son A. J. Macfarlan, proposed " That Extraordinary Members may have the privilege of designating themselves Fellows of the Royal Medical Society ". The proposal was rejected. It was not until 1887 that the words " Extraordinary Member " were altered to " Fellow " in the laws. Yet in 1858 there appeared a small work entitled " *On Health. What preserves, what destroys, and what restores it.* In Ten Letters to a non-medical Friend. By Jonah Horner, M.D., Fellow of the Royal Medical Society of Edinburgh." Apparently the volume escaped the Society's notice, as there is no evidence in the minutes that the author, who was an active member in 1818, was challenged for calling himself " Fellow ". At the same meeting A. J. Macfarlan, seconded by Joseph Bell, proposed " That Resident Licensed Practitioners, of not less than three years' standing, Resident Physicians and Surgeons in the Royal Infirmary, if holding their appointments for not less than six months, Demonstrators and Teachers in the University, and the College of Surgeons, if elected members of the Society, shall be exempted from compulsory attendance at the Meetings of the Society, and from service on Committees, but in all other respects shall be subject to the Laws affecting Ordinary Members ". The proposal, amended to include resident physicians and surgeons in Chalmers', Maternity, and Sick Children's Hospitals, was incorporated into the laws, where it remained, with later modifications, upwards of sixty years.

In 1860 Dr. Joseph Bell was house-surgeon to Professor Syme. In December of that year he wrote to the president in the chair : " With the permission of the Society I shall have great pleasure in reading a communication on ' A Case of pulsating tumour of the Orbit, with remarks ' at the first meeting of the Society after the Christmas recess ". At the meeting in January when he read his communication, J. Crichton-Browne was the president in the chair. In 1871 Bell was appointed a surgeon to the Royal Infirmary : his colleagues were P. Heron Watson and Thomas Annandale. " Rapidity was his keynote, swiftness in operating ; ' get the patient off the table and into bed ' was his sound dictum ; yet his work in plastic surgery, harelip and cleft palate, work needing most careful and delicate handling, was a strong point with him ; while in the management of urethral stricture he was perhaps the most dexterous on the staff. He had the eye of a Red Indian brave for minute indications, not only of disease but of race, locality, occupation, or what not, applicable it might be for diagnostic use. . . . That Bell was the prototype of Conan Doyle's ' Sherlock Holmes ' was the Nemesis which befell him, and in his last days it used to grieve him that he would be remembered as such, and not as he really was, the brilliant teacher, the acute observer, the well-read, cultured gentleman who for his living practised the art and craft of surgery." [1]

In March 1858 a conversazione was held at the Society's Room when Dr. Alison, Professor Emeritus of Practice of Physic, read a paper " On the Science of Life ". Of the medical professors, Drs. J. Y. Simpson, Hughes Bennett, Hutton Balfour and Laycock were present; and the Senatus of the University was represented also by Professors J. Stuart Blackie, Campbell Fraser, G. J. Allman and George Wilson, who filled the Chairs of Greek, Logic, Natural History and Technology, respectively. Also present were Mr. James

---

[1] " Lister and His Contemporaries in Edinburgh ", by C. E. Douglas, *Edinburgh Medical Journal*, vol. xlv, No. XI, p. 812.

Spence, the successful candidate against Lister, in 1864, for the Chair of Systematic Surgery at Edinburgh ; Mr. Lister ; and Dr. W. T. Gairdner. " Dr Alison commenced by reminding the members of the Royal Medical Society of the observation of the late Dr. Gregory, that the Hall of their Society, and the free discussion there carried on a century ago, had been the seat and the instrument of the overthrow of the humoral pathology, previously taught by Boerhaave and all the great schools of medicine in Europe. . . . He quoted the words of one of the first living philosophers of France, Victor Cousin, that the correct views of psychology, and the high rank assigned to that study in the Universities of Scotland were what chiefly distinguished them ' in the presence of the European public '." [1] At the ordinary meeting on the following evening, the treasurer moved " That a special vote of thanks be given to Professor Goodsir for the very great interest he manifested in the Society by sending for exhibition at the conversazione so great a number of splendid anatomical preparations ".

Towards the close of this session the treasurer made a somewhat belated allusion to " the balance remaining over from the subscription for the picture of the Medical Hall ". The picture, now in the Society's Rooms, was painted three years before. In the minutes of that session it is mentioned twice. " 5th January 1855. A picture of the Old Hall was painted about this time. It is not the property of the Society. But it was the intention of the subscribers, from the first, to present it to the Society. The president ruled that as the picture was not the property of the Society, the consideration of its disposal appeared to be entirely a private matter." A few weeks later the picture was the property of the Society. " 16th March 1855. Mr. Aitchison laid before the Society the picture of the Medical Hall, and read a letter from the artist, Mr. Dallas, apologising for the length of time he had taken to execute it." The treasurer's allusion to the picture in 1858 was followed by the unanimous adoption of a motion, " That the balance in the treasurer's hands,

[1] *Edinburgh Medical Journal* (1857–58), vol. iii, p. 955.

INTERIOR OF THE SOCIETY'S HALL, 7 MELBOURNE PLACE

after the acquisition of the picture of the Medical Hall, be handed to the aquarium committee to be expended at their discretion ". This is the first allusion to the aquarium which provided R. B. Finlay with an opportunity, in 1862, of displaying those powers which later made him so formidable a cross-examiner at the English Bar.

In 1861 the minutes mention another picture of the Medical Hall which now stands on the north mantelpiece of the room in which the Society hold their meetings. It is actually a small engraving of an illustration, in Grant's *Old and New Edinburgh*, of the south-west corner of Surgeons' Square, where the Medical Hall stood. The minutes state : " Mr. Crichton-Browne, the senior president, presented a picture of the Medical Hall which had been entrusted to his care at the Annual Dinner of the Society by Professor Hughes Bennett. He proposed ' That the Finance Committee should attend to the framing of this interesting donation '. A vote of thanks was moved to the donor ; and the secretaries, Messrs. T. R. Fraser and John Duncan, were instructed to inform Professor Hughes Bennett of this vote."

James Crichton-Browne was a son of Dr. W. A. F. Browne (1825), who was twice a president of the Society, and who had a distinguished career as a psychotherapist. The outset of that career is described by George Combe in the Memoir of his brother, Dr. Andrew Combe. " On the 22d March 1834, Dr. Combe wrote to his brother George as follows : ' You will see an advertisement in to-day's Advertiser about the Lunatic Asylum at Montrose, which offers a liberal salary, &c., to " a medical gentleman " ; application to be made to your friend, Mr. James Leighton. I should like you to write to him. . . . The reason . . . is, that I have a hankering after some such charge, as better suited to my present condition of body and mind than general practice, for which I do not feel that I have adequate stamina.'

" The same advertisement attracted the notice of Dr. W. A. F. Browne, who had studied Phrenology under George Combe, and afterwards the subject of insanity in Paris, under Esquirol, and who, moreover, had practically devoted himself to that branch of the profession ; and he wrote to Dr. Combe and his brother, soliciting their influence in procuring the appointment for him. As Dr. Combe, from personal intimacy with Dr. Browne, entertained a high opinion of his merits, he immediately gave up all idea of himself applying for the situation, and cordially supported the pretensions of his young friend." [1] " Dr. Browne gave such high satisfaction as resident medical superintendent of the Montrose Asylum, that he was subsequently chosen to fill the corresponding office in the Crichton Royal Institution for the Insane, near Dumfries ; and in public estimation he now stands in the first rank in this branch of the medical profession." [2] Dr. W. A. F. Browne was an eloquent writer.

Crichton-Browne inherited his father's gift of eloquence, although his was rather that of the spoken word. In 1859 he read before the Society his dissertation on " The Psychical Diseases of Early Life ". And in the same year he enhanced the value of the Society's records by successfully proposing, " That the Society provide an album in which the photographs of the annual presidents shall be inserted ". In 1924 a new album, to contain groups of the four annual presidents, was presented by the presidents of session 1922–23, who included their photograph in the gift. Now, a group of the presidents is taken each year ; and the presidents, when obtaining their copies, present one to the Society. This is a special copy for the album, and is put in by the photographer.

In 1860 Crichton-Browne was elected senior president.

An account of his career is given by Dr. C. C. Easterbrook, a president in session 1894–95.[3] " After Edinburgh he continued his studies in London, where he qualified L.S.A. in 1863, and in Paris. Having decided to specialise in psychological medicine, and to do in England what his father had done for the insane in Scotland, he received his training as assistant medical officer in Devon, Derby, and Warwick County Asylums, and soon thereafter his promo-

[1] G. Combe, *Life and Correspondence of Andrew Combe, M.D.* (1850), pp. 228-229.
[2] *Ibid.* footnote, p. 229.
[3] *Edinburgh Medical Journal*, N.S. (IVth), 1938, vol. xlv, p. 294.

tion. In 1865 he was appointed medical superintendent of the New Borough Asylum at Newcastle-on-Tyne, and gave a course of lectures on mental diseases at the College of Medicine in that city.

" In 1866 he was promoted to the large West Riding Asylum at Wakefield as its medical director, and during the nine years of his great and assiduous work there, when he also lectured on mental diseases at the Leeds School of Medicine, he made ' Wakefield ' famous, not only as a model of administration and demonstration centre for asylum reforms, and as regards the enlightened methods of treatment which he introduced and extended, but also as the recognised centre of investigation in the country into the pathology of mental and nervous diseases. This he effected by the establishment of a research laboratory in neuropathology, the first of the kind in the Kingdom, which soon attracted the notice and visits of neurologists ; and by the publication of the historic ' West Riding Asylum Medical Reports ', edited by himself and first appearing in 1871, containing the results of the clinical and pathological investigations of the wealth of material available, and including many contributions by distinguished physicians and neurologists, and in particular the accounts of Sir David Ferrier's classic experiments (following those of Fritsch and Hitzig) on cerebral localisation, which were carried out at the laboratory on dogs and monkeys, and laid the basis of our knowledge of the localisation of function in the human brain cortex. The ' West Riding Asylum Medical Reports ' were the first English journal of neurology and neuropathology.

" In 1875 Crichton-Browne was appointed Lord Chancellor's Visitor in Lunacy, and the duties of that very responsible post, carried out with scrupulous care and understanding sympathy as in all his work for the mentally afflicted, engaged his activities for nearly half a century, till 1922, but by no means absorbed his abounding energies. He soon became a feature of London social and public life, and no gathering of medical or scientific men seemed complete without him. In 1878, along with Hughlings Jackson, Sir

John Bucknill, and Sir David Ferrier, he founded and co-edited ' Brain ' as a special journal devoted to neurological research. . . . In 1886 he was created a Knight Bachelor by Queen Victoria."

In 1904 Sir James delivered the Inaugural Address before the Society. Those who are privileged to remember the occasion will doubtless agree that he was " the Orator of Medicine ". The Address, " Past and Present " was partly reminiscent of his early days in the Society. It may be that he recollected the passage in his Valedictory Address as president in 1861 where he said : " The debates of the past winter have been, I can truly say, more brilliant and profound than those of many previous years ; and that they have been more prolonged no one will dispute. So marked have they been in this respect, that the librarian, in his anguish of spirit, has been heard exclaiming, on Friday evenings, in the words of Macbeth,—' Methought I heard a voice cry, Sleep no more ! ' "

As regards scientific speculation and discovery the period of his active membership was a stirring one. " Darwin's ' Origin of Species ' was published in 1859, and Virchow's ' Cellular Pathology ' (dedicated to John Goodsir) in the same year. Berthelot's ' Organic Chemistry Founded on Synthesis ' and Fechner's work on ' Psycho-Physics ' appeared in 1860. Pasteur's work on ' Microbes ' and Claude Bernard's on the ' Mechanism of Sensation ' followed in 1861. And with the gist of all these epoch-making works we were promptly made acquainted in the Society. . . . But it was not merely a theoretical knowledge of science in all its branches that we cultivated here. When it was possible we had demonstration and experiment. . . . A physical problem having arisen, an expedition of which the late Dr. Alexander Dickson, Professor of Botany, and Professor Crum Brown were members, was fitted up and sent forth from this building, to determine by direct experiment the effect of a flask of olive-oil in smoothing the troubled waters of Dunsappie." [1]

In 1889 Sir James was elected an honorary member, along

[1] Inaugural Address, 1904, by Sir James Crichton-Browne.

with Hughlings Jackson, Sir Victor Horsley, Oliver Wendell Holmes and Sir Henry Littlejohn. The last-named was the first Medical Officer of Health for Edinburgh, and he was acting in that capacity at the time of his election. Eight years later he succeeded Sir Douglas Maclagan in the Chair of Medical Jurisprudence. His son, Dr. Harvey Littlejohn, who succeeded his father in both appointments, was senior president in 1889; and to him Sir James addressed his letter of thanks for his election : " I can truly say that no professional distinction that could be conferred on me could give me half as much pleasure as this one. The approbation of grave and reverend seniors is delicious, but the homage of clear-eyed, generous, and uncalculating youth is more exquisite still."

At the Bicentenary Dinner of the Society in 1937 a telegram of greetings was sent to Sir James. The following reply was received : " Sir James Crichton-Browne is highly gratified by the greetings which you have so kindly sent him from the Bicentenary Dinner of the Royal Medical Society of Edinburgh. A Senior Member, he has deeply grateful, if somewhat pathetic remembrance of what the Society did for him more than seventy years ago."

At the time of his death in January 1938, in his ninety-eighth year, he was senior Fellow of the Society.

Two of Sir James's fellow-presidents were Alexander Crum Brown and James Bell Pettigrew.

Pettigrew was a very distinguished student. The dissertation which he read before the Society was " On the Presumption of Survivorship ". In the year in which he was elected a president he had the honour of delivering the Croonian Lecture before the Royal Society : the subject was his researches on the muscular structure of the heart. And at his graduation in 1861 the Senatus of the University of Edinburgh conferred on him a gold medal for his dissections of the nerves of the heart. For a short period he lectured on physiology in the extra-mural school at Edinburgh. " His most outstanding contributions to physiology were concerned with the subject of motion in animals, and especially of flight in birds, and some of the points to which he drew attention were of importance in the development of aeronautics. His first communication on this subject was made to the Royal Institution of Great Britain in 1867, and for these researches he was awarded the Godard Prize of the French Academy of Sciences and was laureated by the Institute of France."[1] In 1875 he became Professor of Anatomy at St. Andrews.

Crum Brown, like many of his scientific contemporaries, would appear to have taken up the study of medicine because it was at that time an almost indispensable preliminary to a career in science. The subject of his dissertation was " Chemical Types ". He was an outstanding active member. In 1860 he figured in an incident, unique in the history of the Society, when Mr. James Miller, Professor of Surgery at Edinburgh, who was not a member, attested a petition for a seat in the Society. Crum Brown's name was substituted. Nine years later he succeeded Lyon Playfair in the Chair of Chemistry at Edinburgh. In 1896 he delivered the Inaugural Address before the Society. Recollecting his own experiences, he said : " I have always thought the private business of the Society an excellent school of common-sense. You have here the world in little, and if you learn to work harmoniously with your fellow-members here, you may hope to work harmoniously with your fellow-citizens in matters of wider importance. You may fail to carry your scheme for the ventilation of the hall ; that perhaps does not matter much, but you will have learned at all events some of the things to avoid when you set about trying to persuade a Local Authority to carry out some scheme of sanitary improvement."

In 1911 the Society received a letter from Dr. Leonard Dobbin, who had been senior assistant to Professor Crum Brown, and was acting as treasurer of the Crum Brown Portrait Presentation Fund, offering to the Society a photo-reproduction of the portrait. This generous offer was gladly accepted, and the secretaries were instructed to incorporate the thanks of the Society in the minutes.

Another indefatigable member during this prosperous

---

[1] John D. Comrie, *History of Scottish Medicine* (2nd ed.), vol. ii, p. 578.

period was Alexander Dickson who was a president in 1859–1860, and who later became Regius Professor of Botany at Edinburgh, and Regius Keeper of the Royal Botanic Garden there. He, like Crum Brown, showed early " awakenings of latent scientific impulses ". " Engrossed in natural science, he took, it would seem, comparatively little interest in the purely professional departments of the medical curriculum. He, however, appreciated differentiation as a means of promoting advancement in the art as well as in the science of medicine. In his inaugural address, as a president of the Royal Medical Society, he supposes the questions, ' Of what use is it for . . . a student of medicine to know that the cranium is composed of vertebral elements—that such and such bones of the face correspond to costal arches ; and that certain bones and muscles of the upper extremities correspond to other bones and muscles in the lower ? Why should ' . . . his memory be burdened with ' *apophysis* ' and ' *epiphysis* ', when ' there is so much else to be learned of more direct importance ? ' And he goes on, ' To such objections it may be answered, that although morphological anatomy in its present state may be of little *practical* importance to the medical man, yet this is no reason why he should not study it. It must be at once apparent that, from the nature of homological anatomy, one of the great ends which it is destined to accomplish is a simplified teaching of descriptive anatomy. . . . The medical man, while he performs his duties to his suffering fellow-creatures, ought never to forget at the same time what he owes to medical science and to posterity.' " [1] When Professor Dickson delivered the Inaugural Address in 1881, his concluding words were : " I cannot too strongly recommend to the students of our great Medical School the advantages of a society such as this. There are many, I am sure, who look back upon their association with the Royal Medical Society as the turning-point in their lives, as having been the stimulus which first urged them forward to a successful career."

[1] Obituary Notice of Professor Dickson, 1889. By T. R. Fraser, Professor of Materia Medica at Edinburgh.

Thomas R. Fraser and John Duncan were the secretaries during the session 1860–61 ; and in the following session they were fellow-presidents. Duncan's Inaugural Address, as president, on " Medical Language and Style " was in conformity with the high standard prevailing at the time. A point on which he laid particular stress was, that " members of the Society have joined a profession where all knowledge should be common property ". In 1863–64 he was house-surgeon with Syme. In 1877 he became a surgeon to the Royal Infirmary where Heron Watson and " Joe " Bell—to give Joseph Bell his sobriquet—were his colleagues.

Thomas R. Fraser was a very active member—he even served on the aquarium committee. He was an able secretary, and the minutes in his handwriting are a pleasure to read. The dissertation which he read before the Society was, " The Physiology of Sleep ". His Inaugural Address as president was a review of " The Present Condition of Medical Science " ; and he dedicated it " To my Fellow-Presidents, with Feelings of the Highest Respect, and Happy Remembrances of Pleasant Co-operation in the Discharge of Honorary Duties ". In 1863 he presented to the Society a copy of his Graduation thesis, *On the Characters, Actions, and Therapeutic Uses of the Ordeal Bean of Calabar*, for which he was awarded a gold medal by the University of Edinburgh in 1862. In 1868, when he was assistant to Sir Robert Christison, Professor of Materia Medica, he collaborated with Crum Brown in an essay on " The Connection between Chemical Constitution and Physiological Action " which attracted considerable notice. He " was one of the pioneers of experimental pharmacology through his original work on physostigmine (1863–67), strophanthus hispidus (1873–95), which he added to the Pharmacopoeia, and his investigations of arrow-poisons and serpent venoms ".[1] In 1877, on the resignation of Sir Robert Christison, he succeeded to the Chair of Materia Medica. In 1900 he delivered the Inaugural Address before the Society. His subject was, " The Work of the Plague Commission in India ". For his

[1] Garrison, *History of Medicine* (3rd ed.), p. 706.

work on the Commission he had received the honour of knighthood. In the same year Sir Thomas was elected President of the Royal College of Physicians of Edinburgh. In a photograph of the Fellows of the College, which was presented to the Society in 1902 by Dr. Kenneth M. Downie, who was a president during the session 1866–67, Sir Thomas is seen occupying the chair.

Sir Dyce Duckworth's lifelong interest in the Society may be compared with that of Professor Hughes Bennett. Twice he delivered the Inaugural Address before the Society; in 1906, when he recalled memories of his active membership before proceeding to his subject, " The Dignity of Medicine ", and when his old fellow-president, Sir Thomas Fraser, seconded the vote of thanks; and in 1921, when he spoke on " Art in relation to Modern Medicine ", and Sir Byrom Bramwell moved the vote of thanks.

He joined the Society in 1859. In the following year he read his dissertation " On the Physiological and Thera- peutical Actions of the Alkaloids ". Among the members who took part in the discussion of the paper were Crum Brown, Andrew Smart, a former president, who became a well-known medical practitioner in Edinburgh, and John Berryman, a native of New Brunswick, who was later an assistant to Sir James Y. Simpson, and whose name appears in the biography of Simpson by Professor Duns. A month after reading his dissertation Duckworth wrote to the Society begging leave, in accordance with the laws, to make further use of it. In the same month he was elected curator of the museum committee. This committee had long ceased to be a standing one, for the library committee had charge of the museum and apparatus. Duckworth resolved to bring about its restoration to its former status. He succeeded. Three minutes written by him appear in the " Minute Book for Occasional Committees ", and they show the thoroughness with which he discharged the duties of curator. At a meet- ing of the committee on 1st February 1861, " Mr. Arthur Gamgee, seconded by Mr. Duckworth, moved that Mr. Crum Brown, President, be requested to bring in a new law or set of laws at the Extraordinary Legislative Meeting of the Society to the effect that the museum committee, as now constituted, be finally established and put on the same footing as the finance and library committees ". On 8th February, " Mr. Gamgee's motion, that the general report be made up, and presented at the next meeting of the Society, was unanimously adopted ". A week later Mr. Duckworth presented his report. " Mr. Crichton-Browne, seconded by Mr. T. R. Fraser, moved a vote of thanks to the Curator and Members of the temporary Museum Committee for their elaborate Report. Mr. Crum Brown, President, expressed, on behalf of the Society, the thanks which had been voted, and instructed the Secretaries, Messrs. T. R. Fraser and John Duncan, to place the Report on the Library table." In 1906, the Report, in the form of a draft, was again laid on the library table. Sir Dyce Duckworth had enclosed it in the following letter to the Society : " I have been rummaging in some of my recesses lately, and destroying various papers. Amongst them, I came upon the enclosed rough draft of a Report to the Royal Medical Society of Edinburgh which is rather curious to reperuse in 1906. This document may interest you, and if there is no minute of such a Report being handed in, it might be saved in the Society's archives as indicating the ideas of 1861. Some of the members may like to see it."

In 1861 he was elected a president. In the following year, he and Richard Davy (1861), M.R.C.S., read a communication before the Society on " Observations on some Local Anaesthetics ". This was shortly after the first introduction of local anaesthesia. The paper was published in the *Edinburgh Medical Journal*, July 1862.

In 1863–64 Dyce Duckworth was house-physician in the Royal Infirmary with Professors Hughes Bennett and Laycock. He settled in practice in London, and became a physician at St. Bartholomew's Hospital. At the Tercentenary Festival of the University of Edinburgh in 1884 he was the delegate from St. Bartholomew's Hospital Medical School. In 1909 he was made a baronet.

In 1888 Sir Dyce was elected an honorary member of the Society. In a letter of thanks he wrote : " It is a source of pride to me, and of extreme satisfaction, that my affection for the Edinburgh great Schools of Medicine should be, thus, so agreeably reciprocated ".

Drs. John Duncan and Douglas Argyll Robertson were elected to honorary membership on the same day as Sir Dyce Duckworth. " In 1863 Argyll Robertson associated his name with the discovery of the remarkable properties of Calabar bean as an ophthalmic agent. . . . A few years later he had the good fortune to add another stone to his own cairn, by associating his name with the eye symptoms in certain spinal lesions, and the ' Argyll Robertson pupil ' is now as much a classic name as either Bright's Disease or Pott's fracture. . . . He was a man of splendid physical powers ; as a young man every form of manly sport came easily to him." [1]

Robert Bannatyne Finlay entered the Society in 1861 ; and among those who attested his petition for a seat were Dyce Duckworth, John Duncan and T. R. Fraser. The new member soon showed his intention to acquire the art of public speaking by steady practice in the Society. Indeed, the minutes testify that his record in this respect has never been surpassed. In his first session he stood for the curatorship of the library, but was defeated by John Berryman. He was compensated by election to the finance committee, where one of his colleagues was William Rutherford, afterwards Professor of Physiology in succession to Dr. Hughes Bennett. Throughout his active membership his name appears regularly as a speaker in the discussions on dissertations, along with other well-known names : Thomas Annandale, John Wyllie, Mitchell Banks, John Chiene and, occasionally, Dr. Joseph Bell. But his special subject was the aquarium. His motion, seconded by Arthur Gamgee, " That the committee appointed to carry out the conversion of the aquarium into a Wardian case should consider the

---

[1] *Quasi Cursores*, Portraits of the High Officers and Professors of the University of Edinburgh at its Tercentenary Festival, 1884, pp. 282-283.

propriety of such conversion, and report thereon " was carried unanimously. Later, the legal trend of his mind appears, and continues to show itself in his demeanour in the Society. " Mr. Finlay moved, ' That the secretaries be instructed to give legal notice to the members of the Royal Medical Society that an Extraordinary Meeting will be held on 14th March to consider the propriety of selling the aquarium.' " Again, " Mr. A. J. Macfarlan proposed that the proceeds from the sale of the aquarium should be placed to the credit of the ordinary account of the Society. Mr. Finlay stated that Mr. Macfarlan's remarks were premature, as the aquarium was not yet sold." This is the last reference to " the monsters of the deep, ending their days, not offensively, in the aquarium ".[1] Next, the delay in purchasing an album for the photographs of the presidents called for animadversion. " Mr. Finlay proposed, ' That the Finance Committee be instructed at once to provide an album suitable for the preservation of the photographs of the presidents '." His tenacity of purpose could not be called in question. The foregoing motion was made at the close of a session. At the commencement of the following session, seven months later, " Mr. Finlay asked if an album for the photographs of the presidents had been provided ". His regard for sanctions was strict. When a member was expelled because he had failed to deliver his dissertation, " Mr. Finlay moved ' That the secretaries forthwith inform Mr. A—— of his expulsion ; and of the amount of his fines ; and that the Society possesses the power of instituting legal proceedings for their recovery '."

The foregoing extracts from the minutes reveal qualities of a youthful mind which, in course of time, enabled their possessor to reach the highest eminence in the profession of his ultimate choice.

In 1862 Finlay was elected a president. In 1863 he read his dissertation on " Hippocratic Surgery " before the Society. And in the same year he graduated M.D. at the University of Edinburgh. In 1864 Dr. Finlay became a life

---

[1] Inaugural Address, 1904, by Sir James Crichton-Browne.

member of the Society. His photograph, when he was twenty-one years of age, is in the presidents' album. Looking at it, no one who saw him in later middle age can fail to appreciate how strikingly he had retained the appearance of his youth.

Soon after obtaining his degree he forsook medicine for law, and in 1867 he was called to the English Bar. He became Q.C. in 1882, Solicitor-General in 1895, when he was knighted, and Attorney-General in 1900. He was member of Parliament for Edinburgh and St. Andrews Universities when, in 1916, he was appointed Lord Chancellor and elevated to the peerage with the title Baron Finlay of Nairn. Three years later, on his retirement from office, he became a Viscount.

It is gratifying to record his distinguished association with the University of Edinburgh. In 1902 he was elected Rector. In 1910 he was elected parliamentary representative for Edinburgh and St. Andrews Universities. The three chief figures in the latter event were distinguished senior members of the Royal Medical Society. Principal Sir William Turner was the returning officer, and Sir Robert Finlay's unsuccessful opponent was Sir A. R. Simpson, who had retired from the Chair of Midwifery in 1905. Finlay's speech and appearance on the occasion were alike unforgettably impressive.

" In 1920 Lord Finlay became a member of the Permanent Court of Arbitration, and in 1921 one of the first judges of the Permanent Court of International Justice at The Hague. In spite of his years he possessed incomparable qualifications for this post. In a speech made after his death by M. Anzilotti, the president of the court, who referred to him as the most beloved and respected of its judges, stress was laid upon the unique combination in Finlay's experience of the study and application of both municipal and international law, upon his knowledge of languages, and his classical and literary culture. . . . Quite apart from the advantage to the newly established court of Finlay's learning and high character, it was widely recognized as being of the greatest value to Great Britain to have sent there as its first representative a personality of so much culture and distinction." [1]

Early in 1861 J. F. Macfarlan died. He had been honorary treasurer for thirty-three years. In reply to a message of sympathy with the family from the Society, his son wrote that his father was deeply interested in the Society to the very last. " Even on his deathbed he often expressed his satisfaction at the success which has attended it this winter ".

In 1936 Sir James Crichton-Browne, when he was ninety-six years of age, wrote to the senior president that he remembered J. F. Macfarlan well, as a personal friend. Therefore the words he used to express the feelings of his fellow-members and himself in his Valedictory Address as senior president in 1861 may fitly conclude the story of J. F. Macfarlan's connection with the Society. " I would express the deep sorrow felt by every member of the Society on the removal from amongst us of our venerable and esteemed Treasurer, John Fletcher Macfarlan. I shall not attempt to pronounce any eulogy, nor to estimate the character of him whose loss we deplore. For it would be an injustice to give a few minutes to the consideration of a stirring life, like his, spent in the manful discharge of duty, and in vigorous efforts for the maintenance of what he thought right. J. F. Macfarlan rejoiced at the Society's prosperity, he stood by it in its adversity, and I may safely say, that he was known to, and is now regretted by, such as remain of those of our predecessors who for the last forty years have constituted this Society, and carried with them its name and fame to the highest positions in the profession, and throughout the world."

[1] *Dictionary of National Biography*, 1922–30. Article on " Viscount Finlay ", by Sir Sidney A. T. Rowlatt (Judge of High Court, King's Bench Division, 1912–1932).

CHAPTER XIV

Professor Laycock's Proposal—Thomas Annandale—John Chiene
—Mitchell Banks—Lauder Brunton—Byrom Bramwell—Professor Hughes Bennett's Committee, 1868

AT the Graduation Ceremonial in Medicine at Edinburgh in the summer of 1862 the Promotor, Professor Laycock, paid a high compliment to the Society. There were no tutorial classes in the Faculty of Medicine at Edinburgh in those days ; and the Promotor, in his Address, advocated the establishment of a tutorial system of instruction. He proposed that the Royal Medical Society should undertake the task. The proposal was mentioned appreciatively by Dr. Robert Blair Cunynghame in his Inaugural Address to the Society, on taking the chair as president at the commencement of session 1862–63.

Professor Laycock's magnanimous proposal has some pathos attaching to it, for a few months previously a motion to elect him an honorary member of the Society was rejected. Evidently, the reason was that " as a teacher he was not popular, as his lectures were not of the matter-of-fact nature desired by students preparing for an examination ".[1] It may be noted that the unsuccessful motion was moved by James Crichton-Browne ; and that in it, Laycock, who had introduced a course of lectures on medical psychology, was designated Lecturer on that subject, as well as Professor of Medicine, in the University of Edinburgh.

On the death of J. F. Macfarlan his son, Dr. A. J. Macfarlan, who was a president during the session 1859–60, was elected treasurer. Dr. Macfarlan had introduced a

[1] Robert Thin, F.R.C.P.E., *College Portraits*, p. 88.

235

fresh subject of scientific enquiry to the Society when he read before it his dissertation on " Photography and its Applications to the Microscope, with a few remarks on taking Stereoscopic Illustrations of Bones, etc." He stated : " We come now to consider an application of photography to our medical studies which, were it rightly introduced, might very materially assist us in those departments where it is desirable to have drawings of solid objects. More especially in our text-books upon anatomy and surgery, botany and natural history, stereoscopic illustrations would be of great use, as not a few of the drawings are almost unintelligible from the fact, first pointed out by Leonardo da Vinci, that ' A painting though conducted with the greatest art, and finished to the last perfection, both with regard to its contours, its lights, its shadows, and its colours, can never show a relievo equal to that of the natural object, unless those be viewed at a distance and with a single eye '." He pointed out that although Sir Charles Wheatstone, then Professor of Experimental Philosophy at King's College, London, must be justly considered as the discoverer of the stereoscope, Sir David Brewster must be regarded not only as the inventor of a much more useful form of the instrument by the introduction of lenses, but as the true exponent of the theory upon which it is constructed. Sir David Brewster became Principal of the University of Edinburgh in 1859.

In 1862 Thomas Annandale and John Chiene joined the Society. Their entry marked the commencement of a friendship which lasted for forty-five years, until Annandale's sudden death in 1908 severed the tie. In becoming a member Annandale followed a family tradition, for his father, a surgeon in Newcastle-on-Tyne, was admitted to membership of the Society in 1824.

Annandale commenced his career by serving an apprenticeship to his father. In later years he recalled how, at the age of fifteen, he was already working as a surgeon with his father, and attending a hospital. In 1856 he came to Edinburgh to sit his preliminary examination. In 1859 he became M.R.C.S. " I remember ", he said, " running up to London to pass the examination, and of course I need scarcely say that I borrowed the train fare ". A year later he graduated M.D. at Edinburgh, gaining the highest honours, and a gold medal for his thesis on " The Injuries and Diseases of the Hip Joint ". He was private assistant as well as house-surgeon to Mr. Syme. Soon after he was elected a president, in 1863, he read his dissertation before the Society on " Diseases of the Fingers ", which he enlarged later into one on " Injuries and Diseases of the Fingers and Toes " for which he was awarded the Jacksonian Prize by the Royal College of Surgeons of England : " An honour ", wrote Mr. Syme, " so far as I know, not hitherto conferred on any one north of the Tweed ". In 1865 he became a life member of the Society.

Admitted F.R.C.S.E. in 1863, he became junior demonstrator of anatomy under Professor Goodsir, and later a lecturer on surgery in the extra-mural school. After holding the appointments of assistant surgeon, and surgeon to the Royal Infirmary, he was elected Regius Professor of Clinical Surgery when Lister left Edinburgh for London in 1877. He occupied the Chair for thirty years. " The Annandale Gold Medal in Clinical Surgery ", awarded annually by the University of Edinburgh, was founded in his memory.

Professor Annandale was a very clear lecturer. As an operator he had great manipulative skill and manual deftness. " His coolness and resource in emergencies always excited the admiration of his assistants and students. He never showed hesitation, and we believe that he never knew what it was to be nervous. An instance may be quoted : when the *élite* of surgeons of both worlds met at Philadelphia, the operation on an aggravated case of retropharyngeal tumour was offered to and declined in turn by Esmarch and the late Sir William MacCormack ; Annandale accepted with alacrity, and successfully carried out the operation under difficulties which few men in these days would have faced and surmounted." [1]

His slight compact figure, cheerful face and good-

[1] *Edinburgh Medical Journal*, N.S., 1908, vol. xxiii, p. 2.

humoured eyes [1] were known to all Edinburgh citizens. He had a charming personality ; and he was especially beloved by his hospital patients.

As a sportsman Annandale was a keen angler. And he took great pride in his connection with H.M. the King's Bodyguard for Scotland, the Royal Company of Archers. Joining as an Archer in 1870, he became Surgeon-General to the corps in 1900.

At the close of 1907 Professor Annandale and Sir Patrick Heron Watson passed away within a few hours of each other. The following entry appears in the Society's minutes of meeting on 17th January 1908 : " The Society have heard with deep regret of the deaths of Professor Annandale and Sir Patrick Heron Watson, past presidents, and they desire to express their deep sympathy with the relatives ".

Two of Annandale's colleagues during his term of office as a president of the Society, 1863–64, were Dr. David James Simpson, senior president, eldest son of Sir J. Y. Simpson, and Dr. William Rutherford, who became Professor of Physiology in the University of Edinburgh.

Dr. D. J. Simpson is said to have borne, in many respects, a great likeness to his father.[2] Certainly, as an active member of the Society he resembled his illustrious father, for he carried out with thoroughness any task he undertook. He was, without question, one of the ablest secretaries in the history of the Society. His handwriting, large, firm, and clear, indicates the care which he took in writing the minutes, and which was in accord with the high traditions of the Society.

The dissertation which Dr. Simpson read was on " Syphilization " ; and the speakers in the ensuing discussion included his father's assistant, Dr. John Berryman, Dr. R. B. Finlay and Dr. John Duncan, who, as a surgeon to the Royal Infirmary, has been described as " That philosophic surgeon whose clinical lectures, with their wide grasp of

---

[1] This life-like description appeared in the *Evening Dispatch* on the day of Professor Annandale's death.

[2] J. Duns, D.D., *Memoir of Sir James Y. Simpson, Bart.*, p. 444.

principles, will ever remain a fond memory amongst his pupils ".[1] Towards the close of his period of office Dr. D. J. Simpson showed his appreciation of the historical, as well as the practical, value of the Society for students at the University of Edinburgh. He moved : " That a committee, consisting of three members, be appointed to draw up a prospectus containing a short history of the Society, with a statement of the advantages which the Society offers to students, together with some mention of the names of the most illustrious men who have been connected with it ; and that the Medical Professors be requested to distribute the pamphlets by giving one to each gentleman who entered their class list ". The motion, which was supported by Thomas Annandale and John Chiene, was carried unanimously. Dyce Duckworth and William Rutherford were appointed members of the committee, and D. J. Simpson, the chairman, in accordance with the law that the proposer of a motion for the appointment of an occasional commmittee shall be nominated by the president to be chairman of the committee.

In 1865 Dr. D. J. Simpson, who had been studying in Vienna for some time, returned to Edinburgh to succeed his cousin Dr. (afterwards Professor Sir) A. R. Simpson, in assisting his father in his private practice. " Patients grumbled if the assistant came, but when the assistant proved to be Dr. ' Davie ', with the voice so like his father's, and the same blending of cheerfulness and determination graven on his face, he was accepted as a substitute."[2] This promising career was cut short by death, after a few days' illness, at the beginning of 1866. Sir James had just received, through Earl Russell, the offer of a baronetcy from Queen Victoria, and, in a letter to his son Walter, he wrote : " When God sent this terrible affliction upon me, I thought of not taking out the Baronetcy patent. But Mr. Pender, and all else, I hear, think that idea wrong, and almost, if not now quite, impossible."[3]

[1] Professor Chiene, *Looking Back, 1907–1860*, (2nd reprint), p. 24.
[2] Eve Blantyre Simpson, *Sir James Y. Simpson* (Famous Scots Series), p. 129.
[3] J. Duns, D.D., *Memoir of Sir James Y. Simpson, Bart.*, p. 447.

239

On the death of Dr. D. J. Simpson, the Society adopted a resolution, " That the secretaries be empowered to write to Sir James Y. Simpson expressing the deep regret and sorrow felt by members of the Royal Medical Society for him in his late sad affliction which he has sustained in the loss of his son ".   At a meeting of the Society, a week later, over which Dr. John Chiene, then a president, presided, Sir James's reply to the Society's message of condolence was read :   " 52 Queen Street, Edinburgh.   Jany. 25th 1866.   My dear Sirs, I beg to acknowledge, through you, from the Royal Medical Society a kind letter of condolence regarding the death of my dear son.   Believe me, I feel most deeply touched by this warm and eloquent expression of sympathy on the part of my son's personal friends and acquaintance— the members of the Royal Medical Society.   During the last years of his life, in few things did he take a deeper interest than in the prosperity of that Society over which he once had the honour of presiding.   I am, My dear Sirs, Very gratefully yours, J. Y. Simpson.   To Messrs. Lauder Brunton and Lowe, Hony. Secretaries of the Royal Medical Society."

The first mention of William Rutherford in the minutes is on 20th December 1861, when he supported a motion : " That in consideration of the death of H.R.H. the Prince-Consort, the Royal Medical Society be adjourned forthwith to 10th January 1862 ".   It must not be forgotten that His Royal Highness had honoured the Society by presenting it with an addition to the library.

A month later Rutherford gave in his dissertation on " Cellular Pathology ", which, owing to his illness, was read for him by John Duncan, president in the chair.   He is thus a notable example of the truth of Sir James Crichton-Browne's statement that the Royal Medical Society kept its members in touch with every advance in the healing art,[1] for Virchow's *Cellular Pathology* was published only three years earlier.   Moreover, the Society may claim a share in

[1] " Past and Present," Inaugural Address delivered to the Royal Medical Society, Edinburgh, October 1904, by Sir James Crichton-Browne.

the advance to pathological bacteriology, for the first lecturer on the subject in the University of Edinburgh was the present Professor Emeritus of Pathology at Glasgow, Sir Robert Muir, who joined the Society in 1888. This epochal advance in the science of medicine has been impressively referred to by Sir William Osler. As Sir William was deeply interested in the history of the Society, of which he was an honorary member, and whose guest he was at the Annual Dinner in 1907, his words may be warrantably interposed here: " Each generation has its own problems to face. Men of the present generation grow up under influences very different from those which surrounded my generation in the seventies of the last century. Which of you knows the ' Cellular Pathology ' as we did ? To many of you it is a closed book,—to many more Virchow may be thought a spent force. But no, he has only taken his place in a great galaxy. . . . It is one of the values of lectures on the history of medicine to keep alive the good influences of great men even after their positive teaching is antiquated. Let no man be so foolish as to think that he has exhausted any subject for his generation. Virchow was not happy when he saw the young men pour into the old bottle, cellular pathology, the new wine of bacteriology. . . . Knowledge evolves, but in such a way that its possessors are never in sure possession. ' It is because science is sure of nothing that it is always advancing ' (Duclaux)." [1]

During Rutherford's curatorship of the library, 1862–63, Sir James Paget's *Lectures on Surgical Pathology*, edited by William Turner, was admitted. The original work is " amongst the classics in medicine which might still be read with advantage and profit ".[2] The subsequent appearance of Virchow's *Cellular Pathology* necessitated this second edition, which was undertaken by William Turner, later Principal Sir William Turner, who was then Senior Demonstrator of Anatomy to Professor Goodsir. Goodsir and

[1] Sir William Osler, Bart., M.D., F.R.S., *The Evolution of Modern Medicine*, pp. 218-219 (chapter vi. " The Rise of Preventive Medicine ").
[2] A. Logan Turner, M.D., *Sir William Turner*, K.C.B., F.R.S., p. 82.

Turner "doubtless . . . talked the matter carefully over, and Goodsir's valuable material would be placed at the disposal of his assistant ".[1]   Mention of the names of Virchow and Goodsir recalls the tribute paid by the former to the latter's memory at the banquet held during the Tercentenary Festival of the University of Edinburgh in 1884, when these two great honorary members of the Royal Medical Society, Pasteur and Virchow, sat next to each other.   In a brilliant speech, Virchow said, " I myself, if I turn my eyes around me, I see immediately before me, and after our great Schwann, the much lamented Goodsir ".[2]

Rutherford had graduated M.D. with honours, obtaining a gold medal for his thesis before he was elected a president of the Society in 1863 ; and during his period of office he was house-physician in the Royal Infirmary to Dr. D. R. Haldane, an extra-mural lecturer on medicine, who was, in Professor Chiene's opinion, " the best systematic lecturer I ever listened to ".[3]   He spent the following year on the Continent studying at the schools of Berlin, Vienna and Paris.   On his return to Edinburgh he was appointed assistant to Professor Hughes Bennett " who first taught Practical Histology in this country ".[4]   His predecessor in the post was Dr. Argyll Robertson, the celebrated ophthalmologist, who began his career in the physiological laboratory in the University.   " Douglas Argyll Robertson was the first in Great Britain to give a course of what we would now term Practical Physiology, in which were included Histology, the elements of Physiological Chemistry, the Volumetric analysis of urine, the elements of electro-physiology, and the physiology of muscle and nerve." [5]   At the age of thirty, Rutherford became Professor of Physiology at King's College, London.   He held that post for five years, 1869–74, during

[1] A. Logan Turner, M.D., *Sir William Turner, K.C.B., F.R.S.*, p. 83.
[2] *Records of the Tercentenary Festival of the University of Edinburgh celebrated in April 1884*, p. 133.
[3] *Looking Back, 1907–1860*, (2nd reprint), p. 23.
[4] W. Rutherford, M.D., Professor of Physiology at King's College, London, *Notes on a Course of Practical Histology* (1872).
[5] *Annals of The Round Table Club*, p. 18 (ed. Professor J. G. M'Kendrick).

the last three of which he was Fullerian Professor of Physio
logy in the Royal Institution, London. In 1874 he was
elected to the Chair of Physiology at Edinburgh on the
retiral of Professor Hughes Bennett on account of ill health.
" Prior to the time of Hughes Bennett and during his tenure
of the Chair, the professors of Physiology had also been
professors of Clinical Medicine in the Royal Infirmary. . . .
Rutherford did not act as a physician in charge of wards,
but confined himself entirely to teaching and to research in
physiology."[1] "Rutherford", wrote Professor M'Kendrick,
" largely developed the course of instruction and gave it
more systematic form. He was a brilliant experimentalist,
and he was the first to demonstrate in Edinburgh a large
number of physiological phenomena, such as those of blood
pressure, the innervation of the heart and vessels, respiration, and the production of voice ".[2] " Latterly, he occupied
himself mainly in the preparation of his lectures. . . .
The habit gradually grew up among students of attending
the lectures in Physiology both in the second and third
year of study ; in consequence, there was a very large class,
numbering usually between 400 and 500, although there was
no compulsion to take two courses of lectures."[3]

In his introductory lecture, on his election to the chair,
he paid a tribute to two of his Continental teachers, the great
Leipzig physiologist, Carl Ludwig, and Du Bois-Reymond
of Berlin. " Most of the present physical aspect of physiology is owing to Ludwig, who introduced into biological
study the graphic method of recording movement invented
by Thomas Young ; to Carpenter, who applied to physiological phenomena Grove's principle of the correlation of
force ; and so, much about the same time as Mayer, and
independently of him, paved the way to the application to
physiology of Joule and Helmholtz's great principle of the
conservation of energy : much of it, too, is owing to Du

[1] *History of the University of Edinburgh, 1883–1933* (ed. A. Logan Turner, M.D.),
Article " Physiology ", by J. D. Comrie, M.D., p. 108.
[2] *Annals of The Round Table Club*, p. 18.
[3] *History of the University of Edinburgh, 1883–1933* (ed. A. Logan Turner, M.D.),
Article " Physiology ", by J. D. Comrie, M.D., p. 108.

Bois-Reymond on account of his researches on animal electricity. Physiology is indebted to these and many others, principally because they have brought a profound knowledge of physics to bear on the phenomena of life."

Professor Rutherford had considerable musical talents : he frequently sang at Symposia Academica, and similar festivities ; and he was one of the founders of the Edinburgh University Musical Society, to which he acted as secretary for three years.[1]

He died in 1899. At a meeting of the Society in October 1900, over which Dr. J. D. Comrie presided, Mr. Carnegie Dickson announced that he desired, on behalf of the Rutherford Memorial Committee, to present to the Society an enlarged, framed photograph of the late Professor Rutherford. He asked the Society to accept the gift from the Committee. The president requested Mr. Carnegie Dickson to convey the thanks of the Society to the Committee for the presentation portrait which would ever be highly prized by the Society.

John Chiene's entry into the Society was followed within a few weeks by that of John Wyllie. And there is no finer story in the records of the Society than the close association of those two men in the Society, and afterwards, as distinguished members of the profession. Chiene's petition for a seat was attested by, among others, Dr. Joseph Bell, and Dr. John Duncan who became his lifelong friend : two attestors of Wyllie's petition were Dr. Joseph Bell and John Chiene. They served together on committees ; they were secretaries together during the session 1864–65 ; they graduated together, with honours in 1865, Wyllie obtaining a gold medal for his thesis ; and together they were Residents in the Royal Infirmary when they were fellow-presidents of the Society during the session 1865–66. In later years they were colleagues on the Medical Faculty in the University of Edinburgh, Wyllie in the Chair of Medicine, " the blue-ribbon position in British Medicine ",[2] and Chiene in the Chair of Surgery. A delightful picture of the two men,

---

[1] *Quasi Cursores* (1884), p. 212.
[2] Harvey Cushing, *Life of Sir William Osler*, vol. i, p. 515.

capital types of a robust generation, and one that will especially appeal to all members of the Society, is presented before the mind's eye by these few words, written in 1907, by John Chiene : " I thought of Oliver Goldsmith at Leyden the other day when I visited Boerhaave's tomb with Professor Wyllie ".[1]

Among other members of the Society who graduated with honours, along with Chiene and Wyllie, were Lachlan Aitken, "who died a comparatively young man of an illness contracted at his work, when assistant to Sir J. Y. Simpson " ; Andrew James Duncan, later consulting physician to the Royal Infirmary, Dundee ; John Aymers MacDougall, who became *facile princeps* the surgeon of the Riviera, and resided in Cannes ; and William Allan Jamieson, long a teacher of diseases of the skin in the Royal Infirmary of Edinburgh, and ultimately a consulting physician to that institution.[2] Allan Jamieson, who always rode a bicycle when making professional visits, was a well-known figure in Edinburgh in the days before the introduction of the motor car. He was a most dignified man.

Mention of dermatology is a reminder that Robert Willan, " the father of the father of dermatology ",[3] was, like his famous son, a member of the Society. He joined it on the same day in 1740 as Francis Home, who became the first Professor of Materia Medica at Edinburgh, and shortly before Mark Akenside and John Roebuck signed the Obligation. He was afterwards a practitioner at Hull.

An attractive feature of Chiene's record in the Society is the constant evidence of unselfish readiness to serve its interests : a typical instance is given in the minutes of 9th January 1863 : " Mr. Chiene was found to be the only member willing to serve on the Finance Committee ". And in 1871, when he was assistant surgeon to the Royal Infirmary, he not only consented to act as chairman of a committee appointed to consider the election of a sub-librarian, but,

[1] *Looking Back, 1907–1860*, (2nd reprint), p. 38.   [2] *Ibid.* p. 20.
[3] Sir William Osler's Speech at the Annual Dinner of the Society, 2nd February 1907.

after the election, he expressed his willingness, with the help of one or two members, to return the testimonials to candidates living at a distance. As there were upwards of 180 candidates, the task of addressing envelopes was not a light one, and might have deterred a less busy man from accepting. He was a member of the finance committee, 1862–63, which successfully recommended the proposal of Professor Huxley for honorary membership; and in the following year he served on the library committee at which Mitchell Banks presided; the meetings being occasionally attended by Thomas Annandale, *ex officio*, as a president. Chiene's dissertation was on " Diseases of the Mamma "; and Annandale, John Duncan and Wyllie took part in the discussion. He did not hesitate to rebuke a friend who failed on any occasion to rise to the standard of duty demanded by the Society. Thus: " Mr. Wyllie did not give in his dissertation but promised to do so some day next week. Mr. Chiene lamented and deprecated the fact that during this session, almost all the members who have written dissertations had not sent them in at the proper time. Dr. D. J. Simpson asked Mr. Wyllie to say definitely when his dissertation would be laid on the Society's table. Mr. Wyllie said, ' Tuesday '." It may be noted that Wyllie's dissertation on " Larynx and Laryngoscope " was written in 1864, only a few years after Manuel Garcia's invention of the modern laryngoscope, and its adoption into laryngology. About this time the medical professors gave valuable support to the Society by taking part in the discussions at public business. Thus, " Professor Laycock opened a discussion on a communication which was read by Dr. Dyce Duckworth "; and Professor Spence, who filled the Chair of Surgery, showed similar interest. Mention also should be made of Professor J. Y. Simpson's presentation of his book on *Acupressure*. Lauder Brunton, who was a member of the library committee, was requested by the president to thank Professor Simpson.

On 8th December 1865 " Dr. Chiene in the Chair delivered his Inaugural Address ". His subject was, " The

Difficulties a Student of Medicine has to contend against ; and how, in my opinion, these Difficulties have to be overcome ". He said : " I shall always look back in after years with feelings of the deepest veneration on this time-honoured, time-worn institution, and I am sure I shall never forget for a single moment the many happy and profitable hours I have spent within these walls ". He recommended to his fellow-members an hour's daily walk. And he continued : " There is another recreation, with regard to which—as far as my present audience is concerned—advice is superfluous. I refer to joining the Royal Medical Society. I have spoken to many of my fellow-students, and tried to impress on them the benefits and advantages of our Society. The general excuse for not joining our ranks was want of time. They would tell me, ' I cannot afford a night in the week '. Now this is no argument at all. The subjects here discussed are not foreign to our studies, but rather, I apprehend, the hours spent here will be directly useful as directing our attention to many important matters which will be of great use to us in after life."

A distinguished past senior president of the Society has stated [1] that John Chiene, who had been his chief, and had left him a lasting inspiration, had a great aversion to the use of the word " student " with reference only to undergraduates—" When a man ceased to be a student he became intellectually dead ".

The story of Professor Chiene's career is told by himself in a pamphlet entitled *Looking Back, 1907–1860*, which had its origin in an introductory lecture to his class. On the suggestion of his resident, Dr. Mark Fraser, a past president of the Society, the editor of *The Student* agreed to publish the lecture. So warm was its welcome that it was issued as a separate publication ; and it soon reached a second edition.

" Forty years ago, in the end of February 1867, my dear master, John Goodsir, sent for me, his Junior Demonstrator

[1] Inaugural Address to the Society, 12th October 1934, by W. J. Stuart, M.A., F.R.C.S.Edin.

of Anatomy, to his house at South Cottage, Boswell Road, Wardie. . . . I found him lying on a camp bed in a narrow room . . . a small table at his side, and on the table his Bible and Quain's ' Anatomy '. He asked me how his students were getting on, and bade me farewell. His last words were, ' Teach *my* students, Dr. Chiene. Good-bye.' He died shortly afterwards . . . and I have taken these words as my life-motto. . . . Today, when I celebrate my silver wedding as Professor, I take as my subject, ' Looking Back '."

The allusion to Claud Muirhead in *Looking Back* calls for some mention of that fine gentleman and eminent physician in connection with the Society. Admitted a member in 1862, he read before the Society a dissertation on " Medical Meteorology " ; and in 1864 he was elected a president. Early in 1865 he wrote a letter to the president in the chair offering his resignation of the office of president. The esteem in which he was held is reflected in the entry in the minutes : " The Society unanimously express regret that Dr. Claud Muirhead should have considered it necessary to send in his resignation. If Dr. Muirhead were informed how much the Society desired him to remain in office, he might reconsider the matter. On the other hand, there was the question of the delicacy of interfering with Dr. Muirhead's resolve. His resignation was accordingly accepted."

To return to Mr. Chiene's narrative : " The turning-point in my surgical training was in the spring of 1866, when I was introduced by Mr. Syme to his son-in-law, Joseph Lister, who was then Professor of Surgery in Glasgow. He shook me cordially by the hand, and that grasp—I still remember it—fixed me. From the day he came to Edinburgh in 1869 as Mr. Syme's successor in the Clinical Chair until he went to King's College, London, in 1878, I spent daily two hours in his wards—on Sunday afternoons often three or four hours. Lister went to Church in the morning, and visited the Infirmary in the afternoon. I have repeatedly, in season and out of season, spoken of those days when I saw him at his daily work, elaborating with zeal and patience and doggedness that imperishable system which he has been privileged to see an accepted fact. When I knew him he could count his disciples on the fingers of both hands. Don't mind that red herring drawn across the path called aseptic surgery. Boiling water is as much an antiseptic as carbolic acid. . . . In October 1871 I was elected Junior Assistant Surgeon in the Royal Infirmary in succession to my lifelong friend the late John Duncan. . . . In November 1877 Mr. John Duncan got wards, and I was elected Senior Assistant Surgeon. In March 1878, when Mr. Lister went to London, I was appointed Junior Surgeon. I worked in the Old Infirmary until October 1879, when the New Infirmary was opened. I had twenty-two beds in Ward 4, with side-rooms, until July 1882, when I went to Wards 13 and 14, where I have since remained. . . . In those years each professor had to pay his assistants, and at first I had several assistants, because I started (1882) what I believe to be the first teaching Bacteriological Laboratory in the United Kingdom. When the new regulations became law in 1892 the teaching of Bacteriology passed very properly into the hands of my friend, the Professor of Pathology."

Mr. Chiene has mentioned several members of the Royal Medical Society in *Looking Back*, besides those who graduated with honours along with him. Among those are: Dr. John Smith (1844), the founder of the Edinburgh Dental School; Alexander Struthers (1850), brother of Sir John Struthers, the anatomist; Dr. Archibald Dickson (1859), brother of Alexander, Professor of Botany at Edinburgh 1879–87; his " close friend ", Sir George Thomas Beatson, chief founder of the St. Andrew's Ambulance Association, who was senior president of the Society in 1873–74; his " dear friend ", Dr. Robert Milne Murray (1879), lecturer on midwifery, who introduced the axis-traction forceps; [1] A. A. Scot-Skirving (1891), consulting surgeon to the Royal Infirmary, 1928–30; and Dr. J. G. Cattanach, who was a president in 1894–95. Cattanach was well known to many generations of Edinburgh students of medicine as assistant successively to Sir Thomas Grainger Stewart and to John

---

[1] John D. Comrie, *History of Scottish Medicine* (2nd ed.), vol. ii, p. 691.

Wyllie in the Chair of Medicine. He was in business before he began to study medicine ; and he was over forty years of age when he graduated M.B., C.M. with distinction in 1893.[1]

Professor Chiene was a cautious surgeon. As a lecturer he was noted for his fund of Scotch sarcasm. His favourite philosopher, whom he quoted frequently to his class, was Lao-tze, the Emperor of China's chief librarian, who was born in 604 B.C. And his famous triangle must be mentioned : it appears on the back of the cover of *Looking Back*. On the left and right sides are the words " Audi " and " Vide " respectively, and on the base, " Tace ". There was a good deal of the old Roman about Chiene.

In *Looking Back* he gave a list of " Books that may have influenced me " ; and he included the works of Robert Burns. When he was President of the Royal College of Surgeons of Edinburgh he was a subscriber to a work entitled *Robert Burns and the Medical Profession*, by William Findlay, M.D. The volume shows that three members of the Society had close associations with the poet. They were the celebrated Dr. James Gregory, Dr. James M'Kittrick Adair, who was a president in 1788–89, and Dr. Samuel Hughes, who joined the Society in 1792.

Dr. Gregory first met Burns at the house of the Scottish judge, Lord Monboddo. His high character and powerful mind made a deep impression on the poet, who inscribed a translation of Cicero's *Select Orations*, which the doctor had presented to him, in glowing terms : " This book, a present from the truly worthy and learned Dr. Gregory, I shall preserve to my latest hour, as a mark of the gratitude, esteem, and veneration I bear the Donor. So help me God ! " [2] Dr. Adair accompanied Burns on a tour, in 1787, by Stirling, the Devon and Dunfermline. He married a sister of Burns's bosom friend, Gavin Hamilton of Mauchline.[3] Dr. Hughes was a student when he met Burns. In 1795, the year in which he graduated, he visited the poet at

[1] *British Medical Journal*, 9th May 1936.
[2] Dr. W. Findlay, *Robert Burns and the Medical Profession*, p. 23.   [3] *Ibid.* p. 31.

Dumfries and received from him a manuscript copy of " Scots Wha Hae " with an account of the circumstances on which the song was founded. The manuscript is now in the Municipal Museum of Edinburgh.[1]

The Society has yet another link with Burns. For William Nicol, the poet's close friend, joined the Society in 1772. He studied first theology, and then medicine, at the University before he became a master in the High School of Edinburgh. Like his contemporary and rival, Dr. John Brown of Brunonian fame, he assisted students of medicine in the Latin translation of their graduation theses.[2]

Professor Chiene was a prominent Rugby footballer in his undergraduate days and was the first president of the Scottish Rugby Union on its formation in 1873.

In 1911 Professor Chiene's House Surgeons' Committee presented to the Society a bronze medallion of the Professor. In the Society's rooms there is a photogravure of the presentation portrait of Professor Chiene which was later presented to the Royal College of Surgeons of Edinburgh by his son, George L. Chiene, F.R.C.S.E., who was a president of the Society in 1897–98.

Mitchell Banks joined the Society during this brilliant period in its history. In 1863 he was elected curator of the library committee. This was the only office he held, for his chief interest lay in the discussions on the dissertations, in which he was frequently joined by his old schoolfellow, R. B. Finlay. Both men received their early education at the Edinburgh Academy, where Finlay was " dux " of the school, and Banks was, as he took pride in relating, always " dux " of his class. In 1864 Mitchell Banks graduated M.D. with honours at Edinburgh, and received a gold medal for his thesis on the Wolffian bodies. Like Annandale and Chiene he early came under the influence of those great men, Syme and Goodsir. During the summer of 1865 he was a resident physician in the Royal Infirmary of Edinburgh. In 1869

[1] *Ibid.* p. 67.
[2] Dr. J. Currie, *Works of Robert Burns, with an Account of his Life*, p. 177.

he became F.R.C.S. England, without being required to pass the examinations for fellowship.

The scene of his life's work was Liverpool, where he settled in 1868. He joined the staff of the Infirmary school of medicine and became lecturer on anatomy ; and, when the school was incorporated into University College, he filled the Chair of Anatomy until his resignation in 1894. Largely through his efforts and capacity for organisation the Infirmary school developed into a medical college, and ultimately the medical faculty of a university. He was a distinguished surgeon, and was successively assistant surgeon, full surgeon, and consulting surgeon to the Royal Infirmary of Liverpool. He is best remembered for his pioneer work in developing the operations for the radical cure of hernia and of cancer of the breast. The William Mitchell Banks lectureship in the University of Liverpool was founded in his memory.[1]

On 4th March 1808 he was elected an honorary member of the Society. A week later he was the guest of the evening at the Annual Dinner of the Society. In proposing the toast of " The Royal Medical Society " he said : " I never was a member of any society—and I have been in many— where the whole arrangements and the business were conducted with more order and regularity than they are in the Royal Medical Society."

In 1899 he received the honour of knighthood.

Early in 1904 he presided at the last Kitchen Concert in the old Royal Infirmary of Edinburgh, and at the Annual Dinner of the Residents' Club. " A great event in the history of the Club was the holding of the ' Last K.C.' in the kitchen of the old Royal Infirmary, before it was taken over for rebuilding by the University authorities. On 11th March 1904 the old walls rang once again with the voice of song and story. . . . A more crowded and enthusiastic audience surely never was pressed into that kitchen before. Sir William Mitchell Banks presided, and the charm of his

---

[1] *Dictionary of National Biography*, " Sir W. Mitchell Banks ", by Sir D'Arcy Power, F.R.C.S. *Edinburgh Medical Journal*, N.S., vol. xvi, p. 199.

oration still lingers in the memories of those who heard it." [1]

A few months later Sir Mitchell Banks sought the advice of his old fellow-member in the Society, Sir Dyce Duckworth, who was attending the functions in connection with the laying of the foundation stone of Liverpool Cathedral. Three weeks later he succumbed to an attack of angina pectoris. [2]

At the meeting of the Society in December 1863, when Mitchell Banks was elected curator of the library, Thomas Lauder Brunton, who became a member only a fortnight earlier, was appointed to serve on the finance committee. In one respect Lauder Brunton's record in the Society is unique, for he was senior president and a resident physician in the Royal Infirmary when he made " his greatest single contribution to practical medicine ". [3] In an unpublished series of experiments with the sphygmograph and haemodynamometer Dr. Arthur Gamgee had discovered that nitrite of amyl greatly lessened the arterial tension in animals and man. Observation of those experiments induced Lauder Brunton to try amyl nitrite in angina pectoris. He tried it in the wards, with the sanction of the visiting physician, Dr. Hughes Bennett, and his hopes were completely fulfilled. [4] It is worthy of mention that the vote of thanks accorded him for his Inaugural Address, as senior president of the Society, was seconded by Arthur Gamgee. The dissertation which he read before the Society was on " Mercury ".

In 1866 Brunton graduated M.B. with honours at Edinburgh. The following three years he spent on the Continent studying in various schools. In Carl Ludwig's laboratory at Leipzig he conducted experiments on the action of nitrite of amyl on the circulation. [5] And in Kühne's laboratory in Amsterdam he repeated that physiologist's

[1] Preface to List of Residents 1838–1937, Edinburgh Royal Infirmary Residents' Club.

[2] *Lancet*, 20th August 1904.

[3] *Dictionary of National Biography*, 1912-21, " Sir Lauder Brunton ", by J. A. Gunn.

[4] *Lancet*, 27th July 1867.

[5] *Journal of Anatomy and Physiology*, vol. v.

observations on the chemical composition of the nuclei of blood corpuscles.[1] On his return to England he became lecturer in materia medica at the Middlesex Hospital. In 1871 he commenced his long connection with St. Bartholomew's Hospital with a similar appointment. In 1885 he published his *Text-book of Pharmacology and Therapeutics*, which was the first complete text-book written from a physiological standpoint.[2] " He became a master in the application of the physiological findings of pharmacology to internal medicine." [3] He was successively casualty physician, assistant physician, and physician to St. Bartholomew's. And he was a widely known consultant in London.

In 1889 he was a member of the Hyderabad Chloroform Commission which issued its Report in an elaborate volume, along with another on *Selected Tracings of Experiments with Chloroform and Ether* to accompany the Report.

In 1908 he was made a baronet.

Sir Lauder Brunton, like Sir Dyce Duckworth, his colleague at St. Bartholomew's, retained a lifelong interest in the Society as these extracts from the minutes show : " 28 October 1898. A letter was read from Dr. Lauder Brunton in which he enclosed a cheque for the benefit of the Society " : " Two members of the library committee were appointed a sub-committee with powers to arrange for the purchase of the microscopical specimens referred to in the Report of the special committee appointed to consider the disposition of Dr. Lauder Brunton's gift to the Society. Arrangements are being made with regard to the inscription for the books purchased with the same gift."

Professor Chiene in *Looking Back* mentions his old fellow-member in the Society in these words : " Lauder Brunton . . . graduated in 1866, now a very well-known consulting physician, but that is nothing : his strength is his simplicity : any ' wisdom of the serpent ' which he may possess (we all have some—we are told to have it) is only

[1] *Journal of Anatomy and Physiology*, November 1869.
[2] *Dictionary of National Biography*, 1912–21, " Sir Lauder Brunton ", by J. A. Gunn.
[3] Garrison, *History of Medicine* (3rd ed.), p. 705.

superficial : get at the real man and Brunton is as he was in our student days, doing good—his left hand not knowing what his right is doing."

In 1865 Dr. George F. Etherington (1838), who was, at one time, vice-president of the Cuvierian Natural History Society of Edinburgh, resolved to keep fresh in the minds of members of the Royal Medical Society the memory of Georges Cuvier by presenting to the Society a medallion in memory of the great comparative anatomist.

About this period, and indeed for some years later, the grave risks which still attended hospital work are shown by a number of deaths of members of the Society from typhus fever. One of the victims was Dr. John Baddeley (1866), who was the chief founder of the Edinburgh University Athletic Club. At the time of his death he was president of the Club.[1] He was a man of fine physique, and a great athlete. The entry in the minutes, on his death, is briefly impressive : " The Royal Medical Society record with the deepest regret the untimely death from typhus fever caught in the arduous pursuit of his professional duties in the Royal Infirmary of John Baddeley, M.B., one of its most esteemed and promising members ".

A prominent active member during the session 1868–69 was Charles Edward Underhill, who was elected a president in 1869. Soon after he graduated in 1870, he became associated with Dr. Matthews Duncan ; and the departure to London of that celebrated gynaecologist enabled Underhill to acquire a large practice. In the extra-mural school of medicine he lectured in midwifery and diseases of children. In 1906 he was elected President of the Royal College of Physicians of Edinburgh in succession to another senior member of the Society, Dr. John Playfair. He died in 1908 during his tenure of that office. Among his more immediate successors in the Presidential Chair of the Royal College was his old fellow-member in the Society, Sir Byrom Bramwell, who was elected in 1910.

[1] *Transactions of the Botanical Society* (1867–68), vol. ix. Obituary Notice by J. Hutton Balfour, Professor of Botany, Edinburgh.

Byrom Bramwell is, in one respect, the most outstanding figure in the history of the Society, for upon him alone was conferred the dignity of Honorary President. He joined the Society in 1867, and in the following year he became curator of the library. In 1869 he read before the Society his dissertation on " The Germ Theory of Organization ". He was a sportsman as well as a distinguished student. In a debate in the Society, " Should Athletic Exercises be encouraged in our University ? " he moved the affirmative. He was a member of the University Rifle Corps ; and he has related how he made Professor Sir Robert Christison's personal acquaintance through the Corps. " Christison was captain of the University Rifle Corps. He was in the habit of driving down to the drills in his carriage and pair and picking up the first two or three privates whom he overtook on his way to the Queen's Park. One summer I lodged with two dear friends, William Cleaver, who was the handsomest man in the University, and Frederick Page, who for many years was professor of surgery in the University of Durham, in Dundas Street ; one window of our sitting-room commanded the west end of Heriot Row, and Darnaway Street, where Christison resided. Cleaver and I, who were members of the Rifle Corps, used to wait till Christison's carriage appeared in Darnaway Street ; we then nipped down the stairs and walked with our rifles along Abercromby Place ; when Christison saw us he used always to take us up. In this way I got several lifts down to the Queen's Park and became personally acquainted with Christison."[1]

Bramwell sprang from a medical family : his father and grandfather were members of the profession. After a brilliant career as a student, he graduated M.B. with honours at Edinburgh in 1869. In 1877 he graduated M.D. there, and obtained a gold medal for his thesis. In the Inaugural Address, which he delivered to the Society in 1922, he has bequeathed to posterity a vivid and invaluable picture of

[1] Inaugural Address to the Society delivered by Sir Byrom Bramwell on 20th October 1922, published in the *Edinburgh Medical Journal*, vol. xxx (1923), pp. 133-156.

" The Edinburgh Medical School and its Professors in my Student Days, 1865–1869 ". " There was no Students' Union ; there were no hostels ; the Infirmary, situated in a hole, was a dingy, dirty, insanitary building ; the dissecting-room was deplorable (all the medical classes were then held in the old University, and the dissecting-room was at the top of the stairs in the north-west corner of the quadrangle). Sir William Mitchell Banks, in writing to congratulate Sir William Turner on his election as Principal, in the year 1903, termed it ' that terrible old dissecting-room at the top of the stair '. There were at that time no beautiful permanent dissections to study from ; the bodies were often imperfectly preserved—sometimes, before we had done with them, in an advanced state of decomposition. Let me illustrate this point by a little incident. One beautiful summer morning in June 1866 I went with my dear old friend, Edward Harriman Dickinson, and another friend, Dods, by an early train to fish the Clyde. We were alone in the carriage. We had not gone far when Dickinson began sniffing about, poking his head under the seats, and said, ' There is a beastly smell in this carriage '. Dods, who was a somewhat stolid man, replied, ' I think it must be the maggots in my creel ' ; then he added, ' *I got them from " my part " '*. In my day there were no practical classes, except in physiology ; there were no clinical tutors ; we had to work out the cases for ourselves ; that was perhaps not a disadvantage, for we had more time to think ; we had, too, more clinical material to work with—the proportion of students to beds in the hospital was smaller than it is now ; further, we had the Royal Medical Society ; then, as now, it was a flourishing institution. I was elected a member on 15th November 1867. I well remember the reverence with which I regarded the Presidents, more particularly, the Senior President, and the feeling of nervous trepidation with which I got on my feet for the first time to make a few disjointed and incoherent remarks. I was never a President ; the winter I would certainly have been a President, I had gone into practice. . . . The medical professors of the University, some of their assistants, and many of the extra-mural lecturers and teachers were very remarkable men ; indeed, I speak advisedly when I say that, so far as my knowledge enables me to judge, there was never any medical school in the world at any period of its existence which, at any one time, had such a number of extraordinarily able and distinguished men as the Medical School of Edinburgh had when I became a medical student in November 1865."

In 1869 Bramwell acted for six months as house-surgeon in the Royal Infirmary to James Spence, the Professor of Surgery. He has described Spence as "a fine and most successful surgeon, a very skilful lithotomist ; he was so fond of the operation of lithotomy, that we students used to say that Jimmy Spence's idea of Paradise was 'to be perpetually employed cutting the damned for stone ' ".

Soon after his house-surgeoncy in the Infirmary, Bramwell removed to North Shields, where he was in general practice for a few years. On his return to Edinburgh he was appointed pathologist to the Royal Infirmary. In 1880, the year in which he was elected a Fellow of the Royal College of Physicians of Edinburgh, he commenced to lecture on medicine in the extra-mural school. He rapidly established his reputation as a very distinguished teacher of medicine. He was successively assistant physician and full physician to the Royal Infirmary, where his Wednesday out-patient clinics in the " duck-pond "—as the room was known to students—were famous. Those clinics were published later as *Clinical Studies*. He was so lucid in his lectures that it was almost unnecessary to take notes. He had an attractive voice and a good manner. As an investigator, " He was specially celebrated for investigations into diseases of the nervous system and did much to clear up such intricate subjects as those of intracranial tumour and aphasia. His manuals on *Diseases of the Spinal Cord* and *Diseases of the Heart and Thoracic Aorta* were popular text-books in the last twenty years of the nineteenth century, while his *Intracranial Tumours*, published in 1888, contained many new facts on this subject drawn from his own observations, and is generally regarded as a medical classic. His *Atlas of Clinical Medicine* was a more comprehensive work, of which three volumes appeared during the 'nineties." [1]

Sir Byrom Bramwell placed the Society under a deep debt of gratitude to him when in 1922 he delivered the Inaugural Address : a real contribution to medical history. His opening remarks were : " Allow me, in the first place, to thank you for asking me to give this address : to be asked to follow in the footsteps of the many distinguished men who have given the Inaugural Address to the Royal Medical Society is an honour which I assure you I fully appreciate. It is always a great pleasure to speak in this hall : it recalls many memories ; and I thought it might be interesting to you to hear something of my student days and of the men who were my teachers." And he concluded : " Mr. President and Gentlemen, I must apologise for speaking at such length ; my only excuse is my extreme interest in the subject. I hope I have interested you ; but, what is much more important, I trust that what I have said of these great men will stimulate you, to do what in you lies to maintain and, if possible, increase the credit and renown of our great University, of our celebrated Medical School, and of this venerable Royal Medical Society of Edinburgh." Here, the words of Sir William Osler, who claimed Sir Byrom as a " warm personal friend ",[2] may be quoted : " History is the biography of the mind of man, and its educational value is in the direct proportion to the completeness of our study of the individuals through whom this mind has been manifested ".[3]

Mention has been made of Sir Byrom's vote of thanks to Sir Dyce Duckworth, when that brilliant clinician delivered the Inaugural Address to the Society in 1921. On three similar occasions he performed this duty : in 1910, when Sir Clifford Allbutt delivered his Address on " Blood Pressures

[1] *History of the University of Edinburgh, 1883–1933* (ed. A. Logan Turner, M.D.), p. 130.

[2] Harvey Cushing, *Life of Sir William Osler.*

[3] Sir William Osler, Bart., M.D., F.R.S., *The Evolution of Modern Medicine*, p. 219 (chapter vi, " The Rise of Preventive Medicine ").

and Arterial Diseases "; in 1917, when that distinguished senior member of the Society, Sir James Mackenzie, founder of the Institute for Clinical Research at St. Andrews, read his Address on " The Aim of Medical Education " ; and in 1924, when Sir Ronald Ross spoke on " Thoughts on Medical Discovery ".

In 1927, at the unanimous request of the active members, Sir Byrom Bramwell presented his portrait to the Society.

The unique distinction of Honorary President was conferred on Sir Byrom in 1923. In a letter of thanks to the Society for his unanimous election, he wrote : " Dear Mr. President, Please convey to the Royal Medical Society my warmest and most grateful thanks for electing me an Honorary President—the first Honorary President of the Society. I regard this as one of the greatest and most pleasing honours I have ever received during my long life."

In 1868, William Turner, who had succeeded Goodsir in the Chair of Anatomy at Edinburgh in the previous year, was elected an honorary member of the Society. He had already made contact with the Society for, in 1866, when he was senior demonstrator of anatomy in the University, he delivered a lecture at the request of the members in their Hall. The lecture was " an elaborate study of the surface arrangement of the convolutions of grey matter of the cerebral cortex, based upon a series of dissections of the brains of apes and man ".[1] Shortly after his election to honorary membership he read before the Society a communication on " An enormous tumour recently presented to the Anatomical Museum of the University ".

In 1901, the year in which he was made K.C.B., his name appears in the minutes of the Society as mover of a vote of thanks to D. J. Cunningham, then Professor of Anatomy at Trinity College, Dublin, afterwards Turner's successor in the Chair of Anatomy at Edinburgh. The occasion was the Inaugural Address to the Society ; and Professor Cunning-

[1] A. Logan Turner, M.D., *Sir William Turner, K.C.B., F.R.S.*, p. 191.

ham's subject was, " The increase of the Cortical Districts of the Human Cerebrum considered especially in connection with Facial Expression and Speech ".

In 1903 Sir William Turner was appointed Principal of the University of Edinburgh.

In 1922, a framed copy of the engraving of Sir James Guthrie's portrait of Sir William Turner was presented to the Society by his son, Dr. A. Logan Turner, who was a president of the Society during the session 1889–90.

Early in 1868 the state of the Society appeared to give cause for serious consideration. In the previous session, 1866–67, a decrease in the number of students joining the Society was attributed by some members to the system of Saturday class examinations in the University : such a system, they maintained, was bound to influence students against joining a Society whose meetings were held on Friday nights. Accordingly the secretaries were instructed to send a communication to the Dean of the Faculty of Medicine proposing an alteration in the system. The Dean was Hutton Balfour, a senior member, who was deeply interested in the well-being of the Society. His reply was not favourable to any change. In March 1868 Dr. A. J. Macfarlan successfully moved " That it be remitted to the office-bearers of the Society to consider in what way the prosperity of the Society can be best promoted ". This committee rendered great service to the Society, for one outcome of their deliberations was the proposal, " That some distinguished member of the University be asked to read a paper on some interesting subject, on the first or second ordinary meeting of next session ". This was the origin of a practice which the Society has ever since observed. And it commenced under favourable auspices, for the first man of eminence to deliver an Inaugural Address to the Society, after the proposal of 1868, was Professor Hughes Bennett who " had a high opinion of the Royal Medical Society ; he regarded it ' as one of the most valuable adjuncts to medical education and culture in Edinburgh, and a session rarely passed without the Society having the benefit of his powerful advocacy from the professorial chair ' ".[1] Professor Hughes Bennett took as the subject of his Address, which he delivered on 6th November 1868, " Physiology as a Branch of General Education ". Dr. Macfarlan, who had proposed the appointment of the committee of March 1868 with such a fruitful result, proposed a vote of thanks to Professor Bennett. The proposal was expanded in 1871, when a motion was carried, " That the Public Business of the first Ordinary Meeting of next session be set apart exclusively for the delivery of an Inaugural Address by some man of eminence ". For a considerable number of years, even after the expansion, in 1871, of the proposal of 1868, invitations to deliver the Inaugural Address were confined to senior members of the Society, resident in Edinburgh, who had risen to eminence in the profession. About 1890 the Society adopted a broader policy ; and from time to time thereafter distinguished men in other schools of the United Kingdom were invited to give the Inaugural Address.

Meanwhile, the state of the Society in 1868, despite the recommendations of the committee appointed in March of that year, was not satisfactory. In the following May an extraordinary meeting was held for the purpose of considering further the adoption of such measures as were likely to counteract the falling off in the number of new members. Professor Hughes Bennett, seconded by Professor Hutton Balfour, moved " That the office-bearers of this Society, together with Professor Douglas Maclagan, and Drs. Matthews Duncan, P. D. Handyside, Heron Watson, Crum Brown, T. R. Fraser, and Arthur Gamgee, with power to add to their number, form a Committee to consider the best steps to be taken to promote the prosperity of the Society, and to deliver their Report to the Society at the first ordinary meeting in November ". The motion was carried unanimously. Professors Hughes Bennett and Hutton Balfour were added to the committee. If the committee had examined the minutes they would have straightway discovered the cause of the unsatisfactory state of the Society,

[1] Inaugural Address to the Society, 1922, by Sir Byrom Bramwell.

and saved themselves much deliberation, for it was revealed, in summary fashion, in the preceding January, when " Dr. Haddon called attention to the fact that, during this session, the Presidents had not been so regular in their attendance at the meetings of the Society as had been the case in former sessions ". However, after setting forth a number of irrelevant, though well-intentioned proposals, they reached an understanding of the cause of the depressed condition of the Society as the bulk of their Report shows. They stated : " So far as your Committee is enabled to learn, it would appear that there is a misunderstanding on the part of the Presidents as to their duties, and the obligations they are under to attend the meetings, and take part in the debates. The Presidents should exhibit, by the regularity of their attendance, and the evident interest they take in all the proceedings of the Society, an example to the members generally. The laws of the Society everywhere show a strong determination to insist upon the fulfilment of these obligations on the part of the Presidents. Past experience has sufficiently demonstrated that, when the Presidents are all active in bringing forward communications, in constantly studying and criticising the dissertations, and nightly taking part in the debates, the discussions are conducted with vigour. Such efforts show a proper estimate of the duties which are owed to the Society. Your Committee, therefore, are decidedly of opinion that the Society should be very careful, not only in selecting its most talented members as Presidents, but also such as will undertake to fulfil their obligations to the Society." The Report was signed by the chairman of the committee, Professor Hughes Bennett.

In 1869 Dr. A. J. Macfarlan, treasurer of the Society, died at the early age of thirty-one. It was unfortunate that only three weeks before his death he had asked and received permission from the Society to re-gild the metal representation of a serpent which formerly adorned the cupola on the roof of the Medical Hall in Surgeons' Square. This symbol of Aesculapius was not restored to the Society. Dr. Macfarlan was for some years a partner in his father's firm, J. F.

Macfarlan & Co. As treasurer of the Society, delicate health prevented him from the regular discharge of his duties. His offer to resign office on that account was not accepted by the Society. During his long absence on the Continent in quest of health, the duties of treasurer were undertaken temporarily by Dr. Dyce Duckworth.

CHAPTER XV

ON the death of Dr. Macfarlan, James Robertson Young was appointed interim treasurer. The proposal for his election was moved by Edwin Thompson, a secretary, whose manuscript notes, in eight volumes, of the lectures of Professors Hughes Bennett, Christison, Henderson, Laycock, J. Y. Simpson, Spence, and William Turner, and Dr. Rutherford Haldane have an honoured place on the shelves of the Society's library. Thompson, like John Baddeley, died from an attack of typhus fever whilst a Resident in the old Royal Infirmary.

The terms of Thompson's successful motion were, " That Mr. J. R. Young, who is not a member of the Society, be appointed interim-treasurer ". This is the only instance of the election of a non-member to the office. The honour conferred on J. R. Young was, in all likelihood, owing not only to his high character but also to his long association in business with J. F. Macfarlan. Through this connection, J. R. Young had been conversant with the affairs of the Society for many years. His handwriting appears in the New Hall subscription book in 1851. He was held in esteem by many of the senior members, particularly by Dr. Warburton Begbie.

In 1879 he tendered his resignation because he felt convinced that the Society should have a treasurer who had

265

both voice and vote in matters affecting its interests : as a non-member he had neither. A committee, consisting of Dr. Charles W. Cathcart, the senior president, and his junior colleagues, and the secretaries, was appointed to confer with him. J. R. Young held to his opinion that the treasurer could not discharge his duties satisfactorily unless he were a member. And he pointed out that, according to the laws of the Society, membership was unattainable by him. The Society declined to accept his resignation, and removed his disability by electing him an extraordinary member. Dr. Fowler Scougal, seconded by Dr. Sims Woodhead, moved " That henceforth the Honorary Treasurer of the Royal Medical Society shall *ex officio* be an Extraordinary Member of the Society, without having entailed upon him the usual duties attached to that position ". The proposal was accepted.

Fowler Scougal was a president during the session 1879–80. As a life-member he continued to take a close interest in the proceedings of the Society ; and when he wrote to the secretaries in 1891, enquiring if he were eligible for election to the order of " Fellows ", instituted in 1887, he gave expression to his loyal sentiments by stating, " I never fail to visit the Society's rooms when I am in Edinburgh ".

Sims Woodhead entered the Society in 1875. He served on the museum committee, and, in 1878, he became a president. The Annual Dinner, in his term of office, was made memorable by the speech of Principal Sir Alexander Grant in reply to the toast, " The Edinburgh and Scottish Universities ", in which he announced the proximate date of the opening of the New University Buildings adjoining the Royal Infirmary. This addition to the Medical School of the University was vitally important, for although the School " still held its place in the first rank of the Medical Schools of the world . . . it began to be felt that its tenure of that place would be in jeopardy unless better appliances could be given to it ".[1]

Woodhead commenced his career as a teacher in 1881,

[1] Sir A. Grant, *The Story of the University of Edinburgh*, vol. ii, p. 208.

when W. S. Greenfield, who was then appointed to the Chair of Pathology at Edinburgh, chose him to be his assistant. His *Practical Pathology*, which appeared in 1883, was founded on his lectures in practical pathological histology, a new course which was committed to his care by Professor Greenfield, who had introduced it. In 1889 he was appointed Superintendent of the Laboratory for the prosecution of Original Research, which the Royal College of Physicians of Edinburgh instituted in that year. He was an original founder of the Pathological Club of Edinburgh; and in 1892 he founded *The Journal of Pathology and Bacteriology*, which intensified research in these developing subjects. In 1899 he was appointed to the Chair of Pathology in the University of Cambridge.[1]

In 1895 the treasurer had to undertake a special duty, for in that year the Society resolved to reprint and publish the catalogue of the library; and the chief consideration, apart from the method to be adopted in preparing a new catalogue, was the financial one. The reasons for the project were clear. There was only one available copy of the catalogue, which was difficult to read owing to a great number of manuscript additions. There was the *Catalogue raisonné*; but this classified arrangement of the books was not convenient for ready reference. The treasurer reported that the scheme was practicable, and would be advantageous to the Society. A committee, which included two presidents, Dr. H. J. F. Simson and Dr. Macrae Taylor, was appointed to prepare a catalogue. Simson was curator of the library in 1895, when several important works were acquired, including a set of the Johns Hopkins Hospital Reports, which were presented to the Society by Professor Osler. Simson became a distinguished obstetrician in London, and, as befitted a member of a medical Society incorporated by Royal Charter, an " accoucheur in attendance at the birth of royal babies ".[2] In 1925 he was created K.C.V.O., and

---

[1] *Edinburgh Medical Journal*, vol. xxviii (1922), pp. 132-133. John D. Comrie, *History of Scottish Medicine* (2nd ed.), vol. ii, p. 697.

[2] *Edinburgh Medical Journal*, vol. xli (1934), " Transactions of the Edinburgh Obstetrical Society ", p. 1.

in that year was in communication with the Society regarding the library which he had helped to systematize when he was a young graduate. The work of preparing a catalogue was accomplished in fifteen months; and the edition, consisting of one thousand copies, appeared in the autumn of 1896. The first copy was presented to Sir Douglas Maclagan who had shared in the laborious task of preparing the *Catalogue raisonné*, which was published in 1837, the hundredth year of the Society's existence. The second copy was presented to Professor Crum Brown at the conclusion of his Inaugural Address to the Society in October 1896.

At the Annual Dinner in 1896, when Sir Watson Cheyne, who was so closely associated with Lister, was the guest of the evening, the treasurer was presented with a handsome silver rose-bowl, which bore the inscription : " Presented to James Robertson Young, Esq., J.P. By Fellows and Members of the Royal Medical Society in acknowledgment of their appreciation of the valuable services he has rendered as Honorary Treasurer of the Society during a long series of years." The presentation was made by Professor A. R. Simpson.

The Annual Dinner is given by the presidents, and is called the Annual Presidents' Dinner. The senior president occupies the chair, and the three junior presidents are croupiers. A croupier at the Dinner in 1896 was Dr. Kenneth MacLean, who died in the autumn of that year from a mysterious illness whilst he was acting as a resident in the Royal Infirmary. On his death, Dr. H. J. F. Simson, seconded by Dr. Edwin Bramwell, moved that a tablet should be erected in his memory in the Society's rooms. The memorial tablet was placed on the south wall of the debating-hall.

In 1902 J. R. Young, who was eighty-four years of age, intimated his resignation. He had been treasurer of the Society for thirty-three years. It is almost certain that he continued to discharge the duties of his office at an advanced age in order to attain the record of J. F. Macfarlan, who was treasurer throughout a similar period, for he regarded that

THE YOUNG ROOM

" This room was furnished during the Bicentenary Session
IN MEMORY OF J. R. YOUNG
Honorary Treasurer of the Society from 1869 to 1902

The expense was met by a donation
given for the purpose by his grandson, JAMES GRAY "

estimable man as his exemplar in the conduct of life. He was succeeded in office by Dr. Macrae Taylor, whose friendship he greatly valued. On his resignation he was elected an honorary member of the Society. He died at the end of February 1907 ; and a legacy, which he bequeathed to the Society, is mentioned in the minutes in the following highly honourable circumstances.

In February 1907 Sir William Osler, then Regius Professor of Medicine in the University of Oxford, was the guest of the evening at the Annual Dinner of the Society. In proposing the toast, " The Royal Medical Society ", he expressed his pleasure at the Society's record in these words : " I had known, of course, in a vague way, about this ancient Society with its widespread affiliations, and I remember with what satisfaction I received its honorary membership a few years ago ; but it was not until I got a few days ago a list of the members that I appreciated the pride that you must all feel in belonging to it. . . . Looking over the list of members since 1737 I was prepared, of course, to find the names of many of the great men of the profession, but I did not expect to find a list of such extraordinary distinction. I doubt if there is any other society in the world, except, perhaps, the Royal Society of London, with such a roll of honour." [1] Professor Osler suggested the formation of a collection of the works and portraits of famous members of the Society.

The Society appointed a committee to report upon this suggestion. The members of the committee were three presidents, Dr. D. P. D. Wilkie, who, as Sir David Wilkie, was afterwards Professor of Surgery at Edinburgh, Dr. Murray Drennan, now Professor of Pathology there, and Dr. T. Graham Brown, who became Professor of Physiology in the University of Wales. In their Report the committee suggested that a list of famous members should be drawn up and submitted for approval and correction to a competent authority, preferably Professor Osler ; that a fund should be instituted for the purchase, as occasion arose, of the works

---

[1] *Scottish Medical and Surgical Journal* (March 1907).

and portraits of such famous members ; and that, in order to place the fund upon a satisfactory basis, the legacy bequeathed to the Society by J. R. Young should be set aside for the purpose. With a slight modification the Report was approved. But the suggestions were not carried out. This is a sequel that occurs from time to time in a Society whose active membership, consisting of students and young graduates, is constantly changing. A faint echo of the committee's suggestions was heard a year later, however, when a portion of the legacy was utilised to defray the cost of framing a number of autotypes from engravings after portraits of famous members of the profession, which were presented to the Society by Sir Jonathan Hutchinson. Sir Jonathan's association with the Society began as far back as March 1886, when he wrote to the secretaries : " I received with great pleasure your letter informing me that I have been elected a corresponding member of the Royal Medical Society. Will you kindly, at the next meeting of the Society, convey to its members the expression of my best thanks for the honour thus conferred upon me." In 1890 he delivered the Inaugural Address before the Society. His subject was, " Integrity of Attention and other valuable Mental Processes in Medicine ".

The Society's collection of portraits of celebrated members of the profession, inaugurated by Sir Jonathan Hutchinson's gift, was enlarged by an engraving of John Rutty, which was presented by Sir Robert Jones of Liverpool, who was the guest of the Society at their Dinner in 1912, and was later elected an honorary member of the Society.

The commencement of the decade 1872–82 in the history of the Society was auspicious, for the Inaugural Address in 1872 was delivered by Dr. Warburton Begbie, whose fine qualities were portrayed by Sir Mitchell Banks in memorable words, which were addressed to students of medicine.[1] " If ever I pictured myself as a great physician ", said Sir Mitchell Banks, " when I looked closely into that picture, it was the portrait of Begbie that I saw. So he became my

[1] An Address to the Students of the Yorkshire College, Leeds, October 1892.

medical hero. As a teacher he had no rival in Edinburgh when I was a student. He was the gentlest and most kindly of men. When he entered a ward a new light seemed to shine in the faces of the sick. It was a great lesson to us young lads. We were full of health and life and hope ; somewhat too apt to think that these sick people were only pathological curiosities, and that we should never have trouble and disease like them. But there stood our master, who had seen much human suffering, who had not a few trials to bear himself ; and every day he taught us not only lessons in medicine but lessons in courteous and considerate demeanour to the poor. I have always thought of him in my own mind as *The Gentle Doctor*, and I have always striven in the hospital ward and in the clinical theatre to imitate his example."

The president in the chair on the occasion of Dr. Warburton Begbie's Address was Lewis Shapter who, on the same night, presented to the Society a reading-desk for use in the debating-hall.

John Halliday Croom was an active member of the Society in 1872. He had already graduated M.D. at Edinburgh, studied thereafter in London and Paris, and acted as Assistant to the Professor of Midwifery in the University of Edinburgh. Early in 1874 he read before the Society his dissertation, " The Presentation of the Fœtus in Twins ". In 1875 he became a life-member. Twice during his distinguished career he was invited to deliver the Inaugural Address to the Society : in 1885, and in 1902 when he had received the honour of knighthood and was President of the Royal College of Surgeons of Edinburgh. Members who heard his Address on the latter occasion will remember his brilliant delivery ; and they may recollect the strange omission of the Latin phrases, such as *per se* and *ipso facto*, with which he loved to adorn his lectures. His natural good taste made it easy for him to combine expressions of wit and solemn words of wisdom in a pleasing manner. His representation of the benefits to be derived from membership of the Society was sufficiently convincing. " No one ", he said, " realises more than I do the important rôle which the Society plays in the School to which we all belong, and during the quarter of a century that I have been a teacher I have never ceased to urge its claims to the utmost of my ability. . . . The Society is, by its name, a witness to itself as one of the serious institutions of our school, connected with the gravest and most responsible of the professions meeting for the promotion of interest in, and the discussion of questions closely related to the life and welfare of our fellow-men."

Halliday Croom was in general practice before he devoted himself exclusively to obstetrics and gynaecology. He commenced to lecture in the extra-mural school on obstetrics and gynaecology in 1878. He rapidly made his reputation as a teacher and clinician ; and no student's course was considered complete if he had not attended Croom. In 1886 he was appointed gynaecologist to the Royal Infirmary. He was the first to institute a course of clinical midwifery in the wards of the Royal Maternity Hospital. In 1905 he succeeded Sir A. R. Simpson in the Chair of Midwifery in the University of Edinburgh.[1] When he retired from the Chair in 1922 he had completed fifty years of teaching in the Edinburgh School of Medicine.[2]

No one who once saw Sir Halliday could forget his commanding presence : it was well said that he impressed his individuality by his mere appearance.

In 1911 the June number of the *Edinburgh Medical Journal* was dedicated to the memory of James Young Simpson, who was born at Bathgate, Linlithgowshire, on 7th June 1811. To this number Sir Halliday Croom contributed an article on " Simpson's Influence on the Progress of Obstetrics ". The article is illustrated by a reproduction of an autograph letter of Simpson's, which is addressed to the members of the dissertation committee of the Royal Medical Society. The letter is in the possession of the Royal College of Physicians of Edinburgh. It is addressed from the " Medical Society Hall " ; and it is : " I was prevented

---

[1] *Edinburgh Medical Journal*, vol. xxx (1923), pp. 604-605.
[2] *Ibid.* vol. xxviii (1922), p. 283.

by a severe indisposition of many weeks' duration from reading my dissertation last winter, and I shall in consequence be placed, I believe, very early on the roll of the ensuing session. The subject, or rather subjects on which I was to write were the Structure, Functions and Diseases of the Placenta. After carefully considering these three topics it appears to me, that to discuss them all in a way in any degree satisfactory would require limits greatly more extended than those assigned to an ordinary dissertation. I would therefore humbly beg of you to allow me to restrict my Dissertation to the Diseases of the Placenta." Simpson read his dissertation at a meeting a week before his election as senior president of the Society. Sir Halliday's final estimate of Simpson's work was : " To my mind, apart from the discovery of chloroform and its application to obstetrics, the greatest, the permanent gift he bequeathed to the profession, was his own keen enthusiasm, which he was able to impart to others. He thus became the founder of a school of obstetricians whose names are indelibly printed on the pages of every obstetric volume." [1]

In 1874 Magnus Retzius Simpson, who was elected a president of the Society in the same year, and who was a son of Sir J. Y. Simpson, read his dissertation on " Acupressure ", a method of arresting surgical hæmorrhage which his father had invented. The storm raised in Edinburgh by the introduction of acupressure had evidently subsided. Sir Byrom Bramwell gave a vivid picture of its fury, in his Inaugural Address to the Society in 1922,[2] when, referring to " Syme and Simpson ", he said : " In the *British Medical Journal*, July 1870, p. 21, it is stated—' Mr. Syme expressed his disapprobation ' of acupressure ' in a very emphatic manner ' at a clinical lecture. After stating that he had not interfered in what he considered useless innovations in obstetric practice, he continues, ' It appears that my example in this respect has not been followed, and that, in a pamphlet recently published, I have been charged,

[1] *Edinburgh Medical Journal*, vol. vi. (1911), p. 523.
[2] *Ibid.* vol. xxx (1933), pp. 133-156.

not only with ignorance of my profession, but with want of good faith in teaching it. Such vulgar insolence I treat with the contempt it deserves.' Then, according to Miss E. B. Simpson's biography of her father, ' with firm hand, teeth compressed, and altogether a most determined and savage expression, he tore the pamphlet [Dr. J. Y. Simpson's *Answer to Objections to Acupressure*] in two, and gave the fragments to his Assistant to be consigned to the sawdust box with other surgical remains.' I was not myself present on this occasion, but my friend, Dr. John A. MacDougall tells me that it created great excitement, and that Simpson's lecture-room the next morning was crowded with students and doctors anxious to hear what reply he would make. Dr. MacDougall tells me that Simpson came into the lecture-room with his usual beaming smile, carrying a copy of Syme's text-book on the *Principles of Surgery* in his hand ; his answer was a single sentence from this text-book. 'Gentlemen,' he said, 'Torn arteries do not bleed, torsion does no harm.' "

Sir Halliday Croom has stated that J. Y. Simpson's reputation as a pure obstetrician rests upon his introduction of anaesthesia into midwifery, which was his outstanding glory, and which overshadows all his other work.[1]

Here, it may be mentioned that another member of the Royal Medical Society, Henry Hill Hickman (1819), has a place in the history of anaesthesia, for he was " the earliest known pioneer of Anaesthesia by Inhalation ".[2] Hickman was distressed by the agonies of patients upon whom he operated, and he resolved to endeavour to find out a method of producing surgical anaesthesia. " In the early part of the nineteenth century several accounts were published regarding the value of gases for the alleviation of pain in certain diseases and it is probable that Hickman's attention had been drawn to the work of another Shropshire doctor— Dr. Thomas Beddoes—who was born in Shifnal in 1760.

[1] *Edinburgh Medical Journal*, vol. vi (1911), p. 532.
[2] Inscription on Memorial Tablet in Bromfield Church, near Ludlow, placed at the initiative of the Section of Anaesthetists of the Royal Society of Medicine.

Another reason in support of this theory is that the Faculty
of the Edinburgh School, including Alexander Monro,
warmly supported Beddoes in his work. As Hickman was
a member of the Edinburgh Medical Society, he may likely
have known all about the current experiments of Beddoes,
Davy, Pearson, Warren, and others of this period. At the
outset of his professional career Hickman performed a number
of experiments on animals. The experiments included semi-
asphyxiation by the exclusion of atmospheric air, and
anaesthesia by carbon dioxide. . . . The success which he
attained after numerous experiments convinced him that
similar experiments on human beings by his methods would
be of inestimable value to mankind by making all surgical
operations painless." [1] As his experiments were disregarded
by the profession in his own country, he decided to appeal
to the Royal Academy of Medicine in Paris. There also he
failed to carry conviction of the value of his experiments ;
and his only defender was Baron Larrey. Deeply dis-
heartened, he returned to England. Soon afterwards he
died at the age of thirty.

John Elliotson,[2] who was a president of the Society
during the session 1809–10, and who later was greatly interested in hypnotism, then known as mesmerism, as a general
anaesthetic, deserves mention, not as a figure in the history
of anaesthesia, but as the individual to whom Thackeray
dedicated *Pendennis*. Elliotson was the first President
of the Medical and Chirurgical Society of London after
its incorporation by Royal Charter in 1834.[3] He was
senior physician to University College Hospital, London,
and Professor of Medicine in University College there.[4]
Thackeray's dedication was a token of gratitude for professional attention. The dedication is : " To Dr. John
Elliotson. My dear Doctor, Thirteen months ago, when it

[1] Souvenir, *H. H. Hickman Centenary Exhibition, 1830–1930*, at The Wellcome
Historical Medical Museum, pp. 21-23.

[2] J. Elliotson, *Surgical Operations in the Mesmeric State* (London, 1843).

[3] Norman Moore, M.D., F.R.C.P., and Stephen Paget, F.R.C.S., *The Royal Medical
and Chirurgical Society of London*, p. 236.

[4] *Ibid.*

seemed likely that this story had come to a close, a kind friend brought you to my bedside, whence, in all probability, I never should have risen but for your constant watchfulness and skill."

The distinction with which Sir Halliday Croom maintained the high position to which Sir J. Y. Simpson had raised the Edinburgh School of Obstetrics and Gynaecology was continued by Berry Hart, Freeland Barbour, Milne Murray and J. W. Ballantyne.

Berry Hart was a president of the Society during the session 1877–78. He was a good active member who appreciated the value of the discipline of mind which the conduct of private business may afford. His dissertation was, "The Justo-Minor Rickety Malacostean Pelves, their Nature, Mechanism of Labour, and Treatment in Parturient Women". It reveals an inclination towards scientific investigation which his career showed to be the distinctive quality of his mind. After he graduated, Berry Hart, like Halliday Croom before him, acted as Assistant to the Professor of Midwifery. His *Structural Anatomy of the Female Pelvic Floor* appeared in 1880. This work was a masterly contribution towards the clarification of ideas upon the behaviour of the pelvic floor in various physiological states, including labour, particularly in respect of the exact description of prolapsus uteri, or, as he preferred to call it, sacro-pubic hernia; it illustrated the mode of action of Sims's speculum; and it was the means of introducing the modern method of cystoscopy. Berry Hart also devised a new method of investigating obstetrical problems by means of frozen sections. He was conjoint author with Freeland Barbour of *A Manual of Gynæcology* which was long the leading text-book throughout the English-speaking world. In 1883 he commenced to lecture on midwifery in the extra-mural school. He was physician to the Royal Maternity Hospital, and gynaecologist, in succession to Halliday Croom, to the Royal Infirmary. He is chiefly remembered as an expert scientific investigator.[1]

[1] *History of the University of Edinburgh, 1883–1933* (ed. A. Logan Turner, M.D.), p. 143.

Freeland Barbour was an active member of the Society during six sessions ; and he was a graduate in Arts, Science and Medicine when, after serving as a secretary, he was elected a president in 1880. His dissertation, " Localization of Function of the Brain ", reflects the great intellectual earnestness that prevailed among students of medicine at Edinburgh at this time. It is an early manifestation of the clear thought expressed in precise language which later characterised his famous *Manual of Gynæcology*, written in collaboration with Berry Hart.

A few years after the *Manual of Gynæcology* appeared, Freeland Barbour published his *Atlas of the Anatomy of Labour*, which laid the foundation for a deal of research into pelvic anatomy and the physiology of labour.[1] He became a highly successful extra-mural lecturer in gynaecology. Later, during Sir Halliday Croom's tenure of the Chair of Midwifery, he lectured in gynaecology, in the midwifery course, for the University. He was gynaecologist to the Royal Infirmary, and obstetric physician to the Royal Maternity Hospital. He was a skilful operator. In 1914 he was elected President of the Royal College of Physicians of Edinburgh.

He showed his devotion to the University of Edinburgh by endowing the Freeland Barbour Fellowship for research in midwifery or diseases of women. And he took an interest in the young graduates who held the Fellowship, and in their work. He was noted for his wide hospitality to students.

At the commencement of the session 1897–98 he delivered the Inaugural Address before the Society. His subject was " Infantile Scurvy ".

J. W. Ballantyne, like Freeland Barbour, was a life-member of the Society. His dissertation, " Oöphorectomy, or Battey's Operation ", opens with an historical survey of his subject, and is an elaborate essay. Accompanying it, in the annual volume of dissertations, is a paper entitled " Some Cases of Clinical and Pathological Interest in the Buchanan Ward under Professor A. R. Simpson, 1883–84. By J. W.

[1] *Edinburgh Medical Journal*, vol. xxxiv (1927), p. 543.

Ballantyne, M.B., C.M., Buchanan Scholar." The Buchanan Scholarship is awarded annually to the graduate most distinguished in midwifery and gynaecology, and entitles the holder to serve as resident in the gynaecological wards of the Royal Infirmary, and in the Royal Maternity Hospital under the Professor of Midwifery. In this way, young Ballantyne came under the influence of Simpson. Thenceforward he devoted himself to midwifery and gynaecology, and especially to literary and laboratory research in these subjects. He was more successful as a writer than as a teacher in the extra-mural school. He worked hard and unceasingly on the subject of pre-natal conditions ; and the fruits of his labour appeared in his volumes on *Diseases of the Fœtus* and *Ante-natal Pathology and Hygiene*, which are standard works. Many years elapsed before he succeeded in persuading the medical profession to accept his views on ante-natal pathology, and on the need for ante-natal care. His unfaltering advocacy of ante-natal care of expectant mothers was rewarded by the establishment, in 1915, in the Royal Maternity Hospital, of an ante-natal department, and by his appointment as physician in charge of it.[1]

Robert Milne Murray had the good fortune to receive his early education from his father, who was a schoolmaster and a cultured man. He graduated in Arts at St. Andrews, and in Medicine at Edinburgh. In 1879 he joined the Society, and three years later he became a life-member. In his dissertation, " A Study of some Relations of Automatic and Reflex Action ", he explained that, as a full account of the two forms of nervous manifestation involved in great measure an exhaustion of the physiology of the nervous system as a whole, he had confined his attention to some special points in the nature of these functions and their relations to the animal economy. The chief feature of the essay is historical, for it reflects the keen interest in physiology which Professor Rutherford, by his original method of instruction by means of elaborate diagrams, had aroused in the minds of his students.

[1] *Edinburgh Medical Journal*, vol. xxx (1923), p. 123.

After he graduated M.B., C.M., he was appointed resident surgeon at the Royal Maternity Hospital, and assistant to Halliday Croom. In 1886 he became an extra-mural lecturer on midwifery. In that department of medicine he is chiefly remembered by his introduction of the axis-traction forceps.[1]

The application of electricity in medicine is another department in which he distinguished himself. He was medical electrician in the Electrical Department of the Royal Infirmary from its establishment in 1896 until 1901, when he became a member of the gynaecological staff.[2] He was succeeded in that position by his assistant in the Electrical Department, Dr. Dawson Turner, who was one of the first in this country to grasp the importance of Röntgen's discovery.

As early as February 1896 Dr. Dawson Turner gave a demonstration of X-rays before the Society in their Hall.

Other active members of the Society during this period who later specialised in obstetrics and gynaecology were Nathaniel Thomas Brewis and James Haig Ferguson.

Brewis became a life-member of the Society in 1880. After graduation, and a spell of general practice in Edinburgh, he rapidly made his mark there, first as an obstetrician, and then as a gynaecologist. Elected a Fellow of the Royal College of Physicians of Edinburgh in 1887, he later obtained, as the development of gynaecology showed to be necessary, the Fellowship of the Royal College of Surgeons there. For many years he lectured on obstetrics and gynaecology in the extra-mural school. From 1906 until 1921 he was gynae-cologist to the Royal Infirmary.[3] His own private nursing home in Cambridge Street, originally the St. Kessog's Home for Diseases of Women, became known far and wide. He is described as one who was a master of operative technique, and who did pioneer work when abdominal and plastic surgery were in their infancy.[4] He had the gift, in an

[1] *Ibid.* vol. xv (1904), p. 287.
[2] A. Logan Turner, M.D., *Story of a Great Hospital*, p, 292.
[3] *Edinburgh Medical Journal*, vol. xxxi (1924), p. 675.
[4] *Ibid.* vol. xxxiii (1926), " Transactions of the Edinburgh Obstetrical Society ", p. 3.

uncommon degree, of inspiring his patients with complete confidence in him.

Brewis had a fine personality : it was always a pleasure to meet him. In his early days he was a notable Rugby footballer, and he represented Scotland in several international matches. In 1885 he was elected President of the Scottish Rugby Union.

Haig Ferguson joined the Society in 1880. During the session 1883–84 he was curator of the library. The subject of his dissertation, " Germs and their Relation to Diseased Action ", which he read before the Society in 1882, was a topic of exceptional scientific interest at the time owing to the important discoveries which had lately been made in this relation, and to the researches which were then going on in various places, and by many eminent men. He was a graduate in Medicine when he was elected a president of the Society at the commencement of the session 1884–85. His senior colleague was Diarmid Noël Paton who became Professor of Physiology in the University of Glasgow. Forty-three years later these two former presidents appeared together in the Society's Hall—Professor Noël Paton to deliver the Inaugural Address and Dr. Haig Ferguson to move a vote of thanks to the speaker.

In all likelihood Haig Ferguson was attracted to that department of medicine, in which he attained eminence, by his early association, as private assistant, with Halliday Croom. Although he was in general practice for a considerable number of years, his aim was to devote himself to obstetrics and gynaecology. Accordingly, in 1902, he successfully sat the examination for the Fellowship of the Royal College of Surgeons of Edinburgh. He was already a Fellow of the Royal College of Physicians there. In 1906 he was appointed assistant gynaecologist, and in 1921 gynaecologist to the Royal Infirmary. From 1915 until 1927 he was obstetric physician to the Royal Maternity Hospital. In 1929 he was elected President of the Royal College of Surgeons of Edinburgh.[1]

[1] *Edinburgh Medical Journal*, vol. xli (1934), p. 455.

He was appointed Chairman of the Central Midwives Board of Scotland, of which he was an original member, in succession to Sir Halliday Croom, who was the first holder of that important office.

In 1926 he delivered an Address before the Society on " The Importance of Gynaecology and Obstetrics in relation to General Practice ". And in 1930, when he held the high office of President of the Surgeons, he was the guest of the evening at the Annual Dinner of the Society.

In concluding this summary of the careers of those seven distinguished senior members, it may be mentioned that when the Obstetrical Society of Edinburgh agreed to disperse their library, some of the books were housed in the library of the Royal Medical Society.[1]

A contemporary of Haig Ferguson in active membership of the Society was John Thomson who became a pioneer in Edinburgh in the development of the subject of diseases of children. In the earlier days of the Edinburgh School of Medicine there was a connection between obstetrics and diseases of children, for the Professor of Midwifery included the latter subject in his course. After the establishment of the Royal Edinburgh Hospital for Sick Children in 1860, three physicians gave regular courses in the extra-mural school on diseases of children ; and they were succeeded by a number of extra-mural lecturers who were physicians to the Sick Children's Hospital.[2] In 1885, a Lectureship in Diseases of Children was instituted in the University ; and in 1913 the appointment was given to John Thomson who had lectured on the subject in the extra-mural school. In the latter part of his career he devoted much time to the difficult subject of mental defect in children. He was physician, and later, consulting physician to the Royal Edinburgh Hospital for Sick Children ; and consulting physician to the Royal Scottish National Institution, Larbert.

[1] *Ibid.* vol. xxxi (1924), " Transactions of the Edinburgh Obstetrical Society ", p. 21.
[2] *History of the University of Edinburgh, 1883–1933,* (ed. A. Logan Turner, M.D.), p. 155.

He was an honorary fellow of the Royal College of Physicians, London, and an honorary member of the American Pediatric Society.

In 1899 he gave a lantern demonstration before the Society of " Diagnosis and Prognosis of Mental Disease in Children ". And in 1905 he delivered an Address before the Society on " Congenital Pyloric Spasm ".

In John Gray M'Kendrick the Society gained a member who was a born physiologist for, on his own confession, in his early years before he commenced the study of medicine, he was attracted by physiology. Although he graduated in Medicine at Aberdeen he pursued part of his medical studies in the University of Edinburgh. There he came under the influence of John Goodsir, the renowned Professor of Anatomy ; and he has left on record his impression of that great man.[1] " Goodsir ", he said, " was one of the first men of his time, and he will always have a place in the front rank of naturalists, using the word in its broadest sense. He was no mere human anatomist, but he took a wide view of organic structure in all its aspects, anatomical, morphological, physiological. He gave the impression of being really a great man, a philosopher, one who saw deeply into things, one whose mind recognised the importance of what to other minds seemed trivial, one who lived for science and the expansion of human thought. To John Goodsir might also be traced the rise of the modern physiological school in Great Britain."

As the years passed, after he graduated, M'Kendrick saw no prospect of reaching " the fairyland of science ". Hospital and dispensary appointments, however, gave him valuable experience ; and later he found that this contact with the phenomena of disease influenced his teaching throughout his career as Professor of Physiology in the University of Glasgow. His opportunity came in 1868, when he was resident surgeon in a small hospital in the vicinity of Ben Nevis. Hughes Bennett, then Professor of Physiology at Edinburgh, had travelled north to see an

[1] Valedictory Address to his Students, Glasgow, 1906.

English gentleman who was dying in a shooting-lodge near Glencoe. There he met M'Kendrick, and probably perceived the inclination of his mind. They corresponded. The outcome was M'Kendrick's appointment in 1869 as assistant in Hughes Bennett's laboratory in Edinburgh. Owing to the failure of Bennett's health, he had to perform all the duties of the Chair throughout the three years he held the appointment.

In 1872 M'Kendrick commenced to lecture in physiology in the extra-mural school. And in the same year he was admitted a member of the Royal Medical Society. The dissertation which he read before the Society in 1874 was " Recent Researches on the Physiology of the Nervous System ". Along with the dissertation, he presented a paper entitled, " On the Physiological Action of Light. Abstract of three communications read before the Royal Society of Edinburgh by James Dewar, Esq., Lecturer on Chemistry, and John G. M'Kendrick, Demonstrator on Practical Physiology, of the University of Edinburgh ". This paper shows how elaborate was the research to which he alludes in the following passage in his dissertation, under the heading, " The Action of External Agents on the Terminal Organs of the Senses " : " The only research which bears upon this point, with which we are acquainted, is one undertaken and carried on in the spring of last year by my friend, Mr. James Dewar, and myself. The specific object of the enquiry was, if possible, to determine the actual change produced by the action of light on the retina. This we have succeeded in accomplishing, and we can now state the fact thus : The specific action of light on the retina is to produce a change in the electro-motive force of that organ and of the optic nerve." M'Kendrick's collaborator was afterwards Sir James Dewar, Jacksonian Professor of Natural Experimental Philosophy in the University of Cambridge.

In 1876 M'Kendrick was appointed to the Chair of Physiology in the University of Glasgow. " When he was appointed Regius Professor at Glasgow, he found the Department of Physiology practically non-existent. His distinguished predecessor, Andrew Buchanan, had done no more than give courses of lectures. . . . No grants from the University were at first obtainable, and from his meagre salary M'Kendrick bore much of the expense of acquiring microscopes and apparatus. When laboratories were provided they consisted of two badly-lighted rooms."[1] His ambition to obtain a proper Department of Physiology was satisfied when, in 1903, the citizens of Glasgow placed the necessary funds at the disposal of the University authorities. The acquisition of a large and valuable collection of apparatus for purposes of research especially gratified him, for he held that great researchers are born, not made, and that when they are discovered they should receive every facility for doing their work. Provision was made in the new laboratories for research in the subject of experimental psychology, or, as he preferred to call it, the physical examination of all those physiological processes that lie at the basis of our mental life. This was a subject in which he took a deep interest. " Since the days of Fechner ", he said, " this subject has become an important branch of science. It is the link between physiology and psychology, and from the latter we pass into mental philosophy. All graduates in mental science should have a thorough grounding in experimental psychology, so that they may understand something of the wonderful physiological mechanism that is at least correlated to mental activity."[2]

Diarmid Noël Paton, a son of Sir Noël Paton, R.S.A., succeeded M'Kendrick in the Chair of Physiology at Glasgow in 1906. He was a graduate in Medicine when he was elected a junior president of the Society in 1883. In 1884 he became senior president. His dissertation was " Jacksonian Convulsions and their relationship to Idiopathic Epilepsy ". In 1885 he became a life-member of the Society.

He became a distinguished extra-mural lecturer in physiology. And in 1890 he succeeded Sims Woodhead as Superintendent of the Laboratory for the prosecution of Original

---

[1] *Edinburgh Medical Journal*, vol. xxxiii (1926), p. 176.
[2] Valedictory Address to his Students, 1906.

Research, which the Royal College of Physicians of Edinburgh had instituted in the preceding year.[1]

Soon after his appointment to the Chair of Physiology at Glasgow, he gave a lantern demonstration before the Royal Medical Society of " The Source of the Allantoic and Amniotic Fluids ". And in 1927 he delivered the Inaugural Address to the Society. His subject was " The Relationship of Science to Medicine ". He referred to his own medical and scientific career, and pointed out that the medical curriculum fully realised the relationship he was discussing. Of the essential qualities of a doctor, sympathy, unselfishness, decision of character, keen observation, and power of reasoning from observation, he considered that the last two qualities should be learned in the elementary classes of biology. Physiology presented an ideal training-ground in the field of observation. Diagnosis necessarily preceded treatment ; and for diagnosis a knowledge of physiological mechanism was essential. Investigators into important subjects were, in many cases, the practitioners ; and, among them, Gull, Addison, Koch, Reverdin, Beaumont and Sir James Mackenzie were notable examples. The essential characteristics for successful scientific research were curiosity, imagination, determination, the critical faculty, and the power of honest observation ; and of these, the first three were probably inborn, while the two latter ones might be cultivated. He pointed out that the Society played an important part in enlarging and training those essential characteristics.

Two active members of the Society during this period, who later gave additional distinction to the School of Medicine of the Royal Colleges of Edinburgh, were G. A. Gibson and Alexander Bruce.

George Alexander Gibson was an Edinburgh graduate in Science and Falconer Memorial Fellow when he joined the Society in 1875. This Fellowship in Natural History as applied to palaeontology and geology was founded in 1869 in memory of Dr. Hugh Falconer, Superintendent of the

[1] *Historical Sketch of the Royal College of Physicians of Edinburgh* (1925), p. 98.

Botanic Garden at Calcutta. Dr. Falconer is already mentioned as a member of the Society (1826). It should be stated here that, although there was no Faculty of Science in the University of Edinburgh in Gibson's student days, the Senatus had established degrees in Science in 1864.[1] The Faculty of Science was created by Ordinance in 1893.[2]

In 1877 Gibson, a graduate in Medicine and, by this time, a Doctor of Science, was elected a president of the Society. In the summer of that year he was house physician to Dr. George W. Balfour in the Royal Infirmary. And this association may account for the dissertation, " Circulatory Phenomena ", which he read before the Society. It certainly aroused in him a devotion to the heart and circulation which, it is said, grew to be the passion of his life. " With boundless, untiring energy he studied the immense literature of circulatory disease, and accumulated a vast store of personal observations. He became one of the best known authorities on cardiac pathology and therapeutics." [3]

In 1890 he commenced to lecture on the Principles and Practice of Medicine in the Edinburgh Medical School. In the same year he presented to the Society a copy of the work *Physical Diagnosis, A Guide to Methods of Clinical Investigation*, which he wrote in collaboration with William Russell who was pathologist to the Royal Infirmary, and an extra-mural lecturer in pathology and morbid anatomy. Russell was the first occupant of the Moncrieff Arnott Chair of Clinical Medicine, which was founded in 1913, in the University of Edinburgh. He was elected an honorary member of the Society in 1925.

Gibson was a fine lecturer. He was physician to the Royal Infirmary when he was appointed by the Royal College of Physicians of Edinburgh to deliver the Morison Lectures. Introducing his subject, " The Nervous Affections of the Heart ", he said: " Founded in 1864 by Sir Alexander

---

[1] Sir A. Grant, *The Story of the University of Edinburgh*, vol. ii, p. 164.
[2] *History of the University of Edinburgh, 1883–1933* (ed. A. Logan Turner, M.D.), p. 241.
[3] *Edinburgh Medical Journal*, vol. x (1913), p. 153.

Morison of Bankhead, a former President of the College, the Lectureship was originally intended to meet a want in the medical curriculum by supplying a series of lectures upon insanity. With the development of medical education during the final quarter of last century, the subject of insanity obtained a recognized place in almost every medical school, and the proposal therefore commended itself to the authorities of the College that the scope of the Morison Lectures might be widened with advantage. During the last twenty years, accordingly, many interesting courses of lectures have been delivered upon other branches of medicine than insanity, the only stipulation now being that their subject shall be in some way connected with the Nervous System. Taking advantage of these recent provisions, it is my intention to devote the lectures of this and the succeeding winter to the Nervous Affections of the Circulation." [1]

In 1908 he gave a lantern demonstration before the Society of " Modern Methods of estimating Arterial Blood Pressure ". The vote of thanks, on the occasion, was moved by Dr. R. A. Fleming, a well-known extra-mural lecturer in medicine, and a life-member of the Society.

In his later years Gibson wrote the *Life* of Sir William Tennant Gairdner, Regius Professor of Medicine in the University of Glasgow, for whom he had long cherished a sincere affection. Although Sir William was not a member, he was for long a warm friend of the Society.

At one time it seemed likely that the scene of Gibson's professional activity would not be Edinburgh; for within two years of graduation, in 1878, he was appointed assistant physician in the Birmingham General Hospital.[2] It may be noted that Robert Saundby, who was senior president of the Society during the session in which Gibson became a member, was appointed a year earlier to a similar position in the same Hospital. Saundby became a distinguished figure in the Birmingham Medical School, and Professor of Medicine in the University there. He gained a wide reputation as an authority upon medical ethics; and in 1902 he published

[1] *Ibid.* vol. xii (1902), p. 9.   [2] *Ibid.* vol. x (1913), p. 152.

his work, *Medical Ethics : a Guide to Professional Conduct*, which was welcomed by the profession. When he was invited to deliver the Inaugural Address before the Society in 1911 he chose as his subject, " Medical Education in Edinburgh in the Past and Present ".

Alexander Bruce was a president of the Society when he read before the members his dissertation, " Localization of Cerebral Disease ". His essay is an illustration of the accuracy of Sir Douglas Maclagan's observation that the dissertations " furnish us with interesting additions to the biographies of men whose memories we delight to honour " ; [1] for it reveals the early bias of his mind towards the subject of neurology, in which he afterwards distinguished himself. He was a life-member of the Society.

Bruce had a distinguished undergraduate career in Arts at Aberdeen, and in Medicine at Edinburgh. He was Simpson prizeman in Greek, and Seafield medallist in Latin at Aberdeen ; and at Edinburgh he won the Ettles Scholarship, which is awarded annually to the most distinguished graduate in Medicine of the year. This Scholarship was founded in 1868 by Miss Mary Ettles of Inverness as a memorial of her brother, John Ettles, Merchant, Havannah, chiefly at the suggestion of Professor Syme. [2]

Early in his career Bruce became pathologist to the Royal Infirmary, and a lecturer in pathology in the extra-mural school. Later he was physician in the Royal Infirmary and lecturer in clinical medicine. Among his contributions to the literature of medicine are *Illustrations of Mid and Hind Brain*, and *Topographical Atlas of the Spinal Cord*. He was the translator of Thoma's *Manual of Pathology*, and of Oppenheim's *Textbook of Nervous Disease*. [3]

His chief interest was in neurology. This was a lifelong interest, as is evident from the concluding passage of the dissertation which he read before the Society when he was

[1] *Dissertations of Royal Medical Society* (1892), Preface.
[2] John Hutton Balfour, *Address to the Edinburgh Medical Graduates* (August 2, 1869), p. 7.
[3] *Edinburgh Medical Journal*, vol. vii (1911), p. 64.

twenty-six years of age : " I shall ", he said, " consider myself amply rewarded for the trouble necessary to writing upon the ' Localization of Cerebral Disease ', if I have succeeded in inspiring some of the members of the Society with the interest that I feel in this fascinating subject."

Bruce was one of the *heroes* in the song, " The Dauntless Three ",[1] which Alexander James composed, and sang with great gusto on many festive occasions at various dining and other clubs in Edinburgh, of which he was a member.

Alexander James was a president of the Society during the session 1873–74. The Annual Dinner during his term of office is worthy of mention, for, on that occasion, Principal Sir Alexander Grant in reply to the toast, " The University of Edinburgh ", paid a graceful compliment to the senior president, and through him, to the Society. James, who was a life-member of the Society, became a successful extra-mural lecturer in medicine, physician in the Royal Infirmary, and a well-known consulting physician in Edinburgh. He devoted much attention to the subject of diagnosis of diseases of the chest.

Sir Robert William Philip was another of the *heroes* mentioned in James's " The Dauntless Three ". He was elected a president of the Society in 1881, and in 1884 became a life-member. Three years later he commenced his work in preventive medicine by establishing in Edinburgh the Victoria Dispensary for Diseases of the Chest. Later, he was the chief founder of the Royal Victoria Hospital for Consumption, and Farm Colony, Edinburgh ; and " his co-ordinated scheme has been adopted as a national system for the administration of the campaign against tuberculosis ".[2] For his work in this department of medicine he received the honour of knighthood in 1913. He was the first occupant of the Chair of Tuberculosis, the first of its kind within the British Empire, which was founded in the University of Edinburgh in 1917. [3]

[1] Alexander James, M.D., *Divagations of a Doctor* (1924), p. 151.
[2] *Scottish Biographies* (1938), p. 618.
[3] *History of the University of Edinburgh, 1883–1933* (ed. A. Logan Turner, M.D.), p. 157.

In 1913 Sir Robert rendered a signal service to the Society by consenting, at less than twenty-four hours' notice, to take the place of Sir Almroth Wright, who was unable to deliver the Inaugural Address as arranged, owing to an accident to his son. In 1937 he was elected an honorary member of the Society.

A fellow-president with Alexander James during the session 1873–74 was Charles Watson MacGillivray, who had read his dissertation, " The Contagious Diseases Acts ", before the Society in 1871. MacGillivray was house surgeon to his uncle, Sir Patrick Heron Watson, in the old Royal Infirmary when he was elected a president of the Society. He commenced to lecture in surgery in 1883, and in clinical surgery in 1894 in the extra-mural School. In 1892 he was appointed surgeon in the Royal Infirmary. His career marked the close of the period when Edinburgh surgeons could combine family practice with surgical work inside and outside the hospital.[1] In 1905 he was elected President of the Royal College of Surgeons of Edinburgh.

J. J. Graham Brown was admitted a member of the Society in 1872. His dissertation was " Antagonistic Actions of Remedies ". In 1876 he was elected senior president ; and in that year he became a life-member. His business-like methods were of great value to the Society.

He belonged to a medical family. His uncle, Dr. Alexander Wood, who was a president of the Society in 1838–39, was the first to use the hypodermic needle. After he graduated, Graham Brown continued his studies in Paris, Berlin, Vienna and Prague.[2] In 1878 he settled in practice in Edinburgh. He became a sound consulting physician. From 1912 until 1919 he was physician in the Royal Infirmary. When the University Court instituted a Lectureship in Neurology in 1912 he was appointed to the post.[3] And in that year he was elected President of the Royal College of Physicians of Edinburgh.

[1] *Edinburgh Medical Journal*, vol. xxxix (1932), p. 691.
[2] *Ibid.* vol. xxxii (1925), p. 263.
[3] *History of the University of Edinburgh, 1883–1933* (ed. A. Logan Turner, M.D.), p. 159.

As long ago as 1831 the Society had supported the claim, unsuccessful at the time, to parliamentary representation on behalf of the Scottish Universities, and the name of Sir George Berry may be mentioned, for he was M.P. for that constituency from 1922 until 1931.

George Andreas Berry joined the Society in 1875. His dissertation was " On the Fundamental Principles of Education, with Remarks on Medical Education ". He was resident house surgeon at Moorfields Eye Hospital, London, when he became a life-member of the Society. While there, he was an original founder of the Ophthalmological Society of the United Kingdom ; and he was afterwards a president of the Society.[1]

He was a lecturer on diseases of the eye in the extramural school of Edinburgh before he succeeded Argyll Robertson as University lecturer on that subject. From 1890 until 1905 he was ophthalmic surgeon to the Royal Infirmary. In 1910 he was elected President of the Royal College of Surgeons of Edinburgh.

He was appointed Honorary Surgeon Oculist to His Majesty the King in Scotland, and in 1916 he received the honour of knighthood.

A contemporary of Berry in the Society was Peter McBride, who became surgeon to the Ear, Nose and Throat Department in the Royal Infirmary of Edinburgh. When a Lectureship in Diseases of Larynx, Ear and Nose was instituted in the University of Edinburgh in 1897, McBride was elected to the post.[2]

In 1879 the Society resolved to contribute to the fund for the University New Buildings in Edinburgh to be erected in proximity to the Royal Infirmary. Charles Walker Cathcart, then senior president of the Society, discussed with Principal Sir Alexander Grant the disposal of the sum. The outcome was a resolution by the Society : " That the amount be handed to the Committee for the University Extension

---

[1] *Edinburgh Medical Journal*, vol. xlvii (1940), p. 576.
[2] *History of the University of Edinburgh, 1883–1933* (ed. A. Logan Turner, M.D.), pp. 148 and 392.

Scheme with a request that, if possible, it be applied to some special purpose commemorating the Society ".

Principal Grant had a high regard for Cathcart apart from his official status, for although he had said [1] that any young man who became president of the Society seemed predestined for success in after life, he particularised him in the Address which he delivered to the students of the University of Edinburgh in the autumn of 1884. " I cannot forbear ", said the Principal, " from mentioning here one name which I have always held in honour—the name of Dr. Charles Cathcart, who procured for the students their cricket ground, and who has been unwearied in working for their welfare, while he himself has always set them an example of manliness and virtue."

Cathcart became an extra-mural lecturer in anatomy, and later in surgery. In 1884 he was appointed assistant surgeon, and in 1901 surgeon in the Royal Infirmary of Edinburgh. He was an ingenious man, and in 1891 he exhibited before the Society an improved form of sterilizing chamber and a new form of handle for surgical instruments, along with an instrument case, all of which he had invented. Cathcart became a life-member of the Society.

His fine personal character deserves mention ; for in this respect he was an outstanding man. It is thus portrayed by one who knew him well : " Its mainspring was an almost quixotic conscientiousness and devotion to duty. A deeply religious man, he carefully thought out his conduct in any special circumstances, and, having decided in his own mind what was right, followed out that course of action relentlessly to its logical conclusion irrespective of the physical trouble or mental pain which it might bring upon himself. This resulted in a tenacity of purpose, which might have been mistaken for obstinacy, but which was really a very different and higher quality in a man essentially gentle and kind-hearted. Those who differed from him might sometimes be unable to understand how he reached his decision, and might even be annoyed by his persistence, but

---

[1] *The Story of the University of Edinburgh*, vol. ii, p. 485.

nobody ever failed to appreciate the invariable honesty of his motives and to respect him for it." [1]

This devotion to what he considered to be right was strongly in evidence in connection with an incident in the Society, shortly after he ceased to be an active member. He greatly disapproved of a decision which the Society had made ; and he expressed his disapproval in a letter to the Society. " I am deeply pained ", he wrote, " at the decision, which will be most prejudicial to the Royal Medical Society ; and as I feel a deep interest in the welfare of the Society, I beg respectfully to enter my protest against its decision." With the letter, he enclosed his fine ; for any member who protests against a decision of the Society must pay a fine for the privilege of having his protest entered in the minutes. The wisdom of his protest was recognised, and the Society annulled its decision.

Cathcart's name is closely associated, in the history of the medical literature, with that of Francis Mitchell Caird, who was Regius Professor of Clinical Surgery in the University of Edinburgh from 1908 until 1919. Their *Surgical Handbook*, known as " Caird and Cathcart ", appeared in 1889, and was a highly successful publication.

In 1925 Professor Caird was elected an honorary member of the Society.

It was largely owing to Cathcart's insistence that Anderson Stuart, who became the chief founder of the Medical School of the University of Sydney, joined the Society.

Thomas Peter Anderson Stuart crowned a brilliant under-graduate career in Medicine at the University of Edinburgh by graduating with Honours and winning the Ettles Scholar-ship in 1880, and he gained a gold medal for his thesis for the degree of M.D. which he obtained two years later.

As a student, his first course in zoology was under Pro-fessor Huxley, who was lecturing in place of Wyville Thomson, the Regius Professor.[2] Thomson had obtained leave of absence when he was appointed Director of the Scientific

[1] *Edinburgh Medical Journal*, vol. xxxix (1932), p. 274.
[2] William Epps, *Anderson Stuart, M.D.* (1922), p. 28.

Staff of the Challenger Expedition.[1] Professor Huxley was then an honorary member of the Royal Medical Society; and Sir Wyville Thomson was elected an honorary member in 1877.

Anderson Stuart became a president of the Society at the commencement of the session 1882–83. About the same time he was appointed Professor of Anatomy and Physiology in the University of Sydney.[2] Early in the winter of 1883 he resigned the office of president as he had to sail for Australia in order to commence his professional career in the following spring. Among his testimonials when he applied for the post in Sydney was one from his lifelong friend, James Crichton-Browne, then Lord Chancellor's Visitor.[3]

Despite a tendency to undervalue opponents and to arouse their anger needlessly he was a great organiser and administrator. " Upon his first arrival ", says his biographer, " he found no school and no pupils ; he took possession of a small four-roomed building, with the roof still missing ; this he managed to equip, in a place far from the centres at which he could expect to find material ; he fought for a nobler home for the teaching of the young medical man ; and he secured this in spite of opposition and some ridicule, with the result that a magnificent structure, erected at a cost of £120,000, now stands as a monument to his capacity and persistence." [4]

He succeeded in gathering round him an efficient staff in the Medical School. " I secured ", he said, " the appointment of Sir Alexander MacCormick as first Demonstrator of Anatomy and Physiology. Indeed, I take to myself a considerable amount of credit for my foresight in bringing out to the School such men as Sir Alexander MacCormick, Professor J. T. Wilson, Sir James Graham, Dr. Scot-Skirving, Dr. C. J. Martin, Sir Almroth Wright, and Professor Chapman, all of whom have risen to eminence in the profession." [5]

[1] Sir A. Grant, *The Story of the University of Edinburgh*, vol. ii, p. 436.
[2] William Epps, *Anderson Stuart, M.D.*, p. 50.
[3] *Ibid.* p. 165.   [4] *Ibid.* p. 7.   [5] *Ibid.* pp. 52-53.

As Dean of the Faculty of Medicine, Anderson Stuart was, *ex officio*, a member of the Board of Directors of the Royal Prince Alfred Hospital ; and for twenty years he was Chairman of the Board.[1] He " recognized that without a great Hospital he could not have a great Medical School, and his interests were almost as much bound up with one as with the other." [2]

It must be mentioned that Anderson Stuart played a leading part in the establishment of the University of Sydney Medical Society. He " was justly proud of his connection with the University Medical Society, which he regarded as of the greatest value to the students, giving them cohesion and experience in discussion before they graduate. As a member (latterly president) of the well-known and ' antient ' Royal Medical Society of Edinburgh, he had seen the value of such an organization ; and soon after his arrival he was instrumental in bringing a similar one into existence in Sydney." [3]

In 1914 he received the honour of knighthood.

In 1907 Viscount Haldane of Cloan, then the Right Honourable R. B. Haldane, Secretary of State for War, delivered an Address, entitled " The Dedicated Life ", to the students of the University of Edinburgh. He was Rector of the University at the time.

The title of the Address may be said to summarise the career of his brother J. S. Haldane, who devoted himself to biological investigation with the tenacity of purpose which had characterised his forefathers.[4]

John Scott Haldane was admitted a member of the Royal Medical Society in 1880. He could claim a family connection with the Society, for his father's stepbrother, Dr. Daniel Rutherford Haldane, whom Professor Chiene described as the best systematic lecturer he ever listened to,[5] was senior president during the session 1846–47 ; and his maternal

---

[1] *Ibid.* pp. 87-89. 　　　[2] *Ibid.* p. 97. 　　　[3] *Ibid.* pp. 124-125.
[4] *Richard Burdon Haldane—An Autobiography* (1929), p. 28.　General Sir J. A. L. Haldane, *The Haldanes of Gleneagles* (1929), Introduction, p. vii.
[5] *Looking Back, 1907–1860* (2nd reprint), p. 23.

uncle, Sir John Scott Burdon-Sanderson, under whom he commenced his life-work in physiology at Oxford, was a president during the session 1850–51.

The dissertation, " Body and Soul ", which he read before the Society in 1883, is an early expression of his views on the philosophical basis of physiology. It is an elaboration on the scientific side of an essay which he had written in collaboration with his brother, R. B. Haldane, earlier in the same year, on " The Relation of Philosophy to Science ". The essay appeared in a volume entitled *Essays in Philosophical Criticism*, edited by Andrew Seth, later Andrew Seth Pringle-Pattison, Professor of Logic and Metaphysics at Edinburgh, and by his brother, R. B. Haldane, with a preface by Edward Caird, Professor of Moral Philosophy in the University of Glasgow, the work being dedicated to the memory of Thomas Hill Green, Whyte's Professor of Moral Philosophy in the University of Oxford. Of this essay he wrote later : " I was still a medical student at the time, after an Arts course in which, owing mainly to my brother's influence, my chief interest was in philosophy ; and I had already seen that mechanistic biology, which was then everywhere in the ascendant, was as radically unsound as vitalistic biology. We said so in our essay, but could only give general reasons for our conclusion that the real axioms of biology are neither mechanistic nor vitalistic. The truth was that in matters of detail many of the available data were so vague and unsatisfactory that mechanistic interpretations of them, though certainly not of the most characteristic data, were at least plausible. I found my opinions extremely unpopular among my scientific brethren when I duly became a physiologist. Knowing, however, the weight of philosophical reasoning behind me, and encouraged by my brother, and other philosophic friends, I went onwards, and gradually got to grips, using accurate quantitative methods, with the physiology of respiration and other bodily activities." [1]

[1] J. S. Haldane, C.H., M.D., etc., Fellow of New College, Oxford, and Honorary Professor, University of Birmingham, *The Sciences and Philosophy*, Gifford Lectures, University of Glasgow, 1927 and 1928, the Preface.

His great moral courage enabled him to uphold the tradition of the Society that, within its walls, " the doctrines of their masters were frequently discussed ". For in his dissertation he said : " Professor Rutherford, in his lectures on physiology, says that sensation, ideation and other psychical phenomena, are produced in the brain by nerve cells, or groups of nerve cells. It is not creditable to science that it should still be necessary to point out the contradiction, evident though it be, which is involved in all such statements as this."

Haldane never altered his early conception of biology. This fact emerges impressively in the Gifford Lectures which he delivered in the University of Glasgow in 1927 and 1928. His subject was " The Sciences and Philosophy ". When he delivered the Donnellan Lectures in the University of Dublin in 1930, he spoke on " The Philosophical Basis of Biology ".

IIis life-work in physiology, especially in that of respiration, was of great industrial as well as scientific value.

When his brother, then Secretary of State for War, made his historic, informal visit to Berlin in 1912, he accompanied him " as private secretary, ostensibly to confer on scientific matters with biologists at the University of the German capital ".[1]

He delivered the Inaugural Address before the Society at the commencement of the session 1933–34. His subject was " Vision of Brightness and Colour ".

In 1936 he was elected an honorary member of the Society.

[1] *Richard Burdon Haldane—An Autobiography* (1929), p. 240.

CHAPTER XVI

Tercentenary of University of Edinburgh—Fellows—Publication of Selected Dissertations—Public Business Committee—Associates—Dr. Macrae Taylor, Treasurer—War Period 1914–18 : Meetings in South Library—Clinical Meetings in Royal Infirmary —Bicentenary Session 1936–37—Bicentenary Celebrations

In April 1884 the Society held a Reception in their Rooms in connection with the Tercentenary Festival of the University of Edinburgh. Among the guests who were present were Sir James Paget, Sir Joseph Lister, Sir Andrew Clark, celebrated physician to the London Hospital, Dr. W. B. Carpenter, Dr. Burdon-Sanderson, and Sir William Bowman, for whose brilliant work in physiology and ophthalmic surgery the Society had shown their high appreciation by electing him an honorary member. Another notable guest was the Right Rev. Dr. Cotterill, Bishop of Edinburgh, whose son, Sir Montagu Cotterill, was for many years a well-known leading surgeon in the Edinburgh School of Medicine. In 1925 Sir Montagu was elected an honorary member of the Society. In the debating hall were exhibited autograph letters by William Cullen, Joseph Black, and John and James Gregory. In the north ante-room were displayed sketches by John Goodsir's friend, Edward Forbes, a man of genius, who died at an early age after a few months' tenure of the Chair of Natural History at Edinburgh. In the same room was shown a collection of photographs and autographs of the chief European scientists of the nineteenth century.[1]

The University authorities presented a silver medal to the Society as a memento of the Tercentenary Festival ; and later, they presented a copy of *Records of the Tercentenary*

[1] R. S. Marsden, lately President of the R.M.S., *Records of the Tercentenary Festival of the University of Edinburgh*, A Short Account of the Tercentenary Festival, p. 107.

Festival of the University of Edinburgh celebrated in 1884, which was published under the sanction of the Senatus Academicus. The volume is inscribed " Presented by the University of Edinburgh ".

Principal Sir Alexander Grant, one of the most cultured men of his time, died towards the close of 1884. In all likelihood the immense amount of work which he undertook in connection with the Tercentenary Festival of the University injured his health.

At the Annual Dinner in 1885 Dr. Noël Paton, the senior president, in the chair, proposing the toast of the evening, " The Royal Medical Society ", said : " I cannot help noticing at this time the sad loss which the Society has sustained during the past session in the death of Sir Alexander Grant. In him we have lost a true friend—one who appreciated the educational importance of this Society in a large medical school such as ours, and one who ever had its welfare at heart."

Between the years 1887 and 1892 the Society agreed to several important amendments of the Laws.

The initial impulse was supplied in February 1887 by Edward Henry Ezard, who became a president in the following session, at the Extraordinary Meeting for the consideration of proposals for the alteration of the Laws, which was then held biennially. Ezard successfully proposed that the words " Extraordinary Member " should be altered to " Fellow ".

At the Meeting in 1887, at which Ezard's proposal became law, it was enacted, " All Fellows shall be elected by ballot " ; and in 1904 the majority was fixed—" and a three-fourths vote of the Society shall be required ".

A few days after the above Legislative Meeting, a Special Committee which had been appointed to examine the question of publication of the *Transactions* of the Society submitted their Report. The Committee considered that the proposal to publish, in abstract form, a portion of the Public Business of the Society was impracticable with regard to the dissertations and discussions. The Society's appropriate medium of publication was the *Edinburgh Medical Journal*. The *Journal* appeared once a month. The Society held its meetings weekly. The accumulation of material would be too great. An abstract of the dissertations would not do them justice ; and a choice of dissertations would be invidious. The case for communications was different, if the Society could secure the privilege of their publication from the editor of the *Edinburgh Medical Journal*. For the number of communications would probably increase, the performance would be on a higher level, and original work among the members would be encouraged.

Another sympton of the prevailing enthusiasm was the consideration of the titles to be used in signing Diplomas and other official documents. It was resolved that the titles of president and former president should remain as *Præses* and *Olim Præses* ; that the treasurer should sign himself *Quæstor* ; secretary, *Scriba* ; chairman of the finance committee, *Ædilis* ; curator of the library, *Librorum Custos* ; curator of the museum, *Musei Custos* ; and Fellow, *Socius*. *Socius Ordinarius* was retained, as of old, as the title of ordinary member. The Society resolved to print the regulation as an Appendix to the Laws ; and the practice continues.

On the occasion of Queen Victoria's Jubilee in June 1887, the Society resolved that an Address of Congratulation should be forwarded to Her Majesty. The Address began : " To the Queen's Most Excellent Majesty. May it please your Majesty, we, your Majesty's loyal subjects, the Presidents, Fellows, and Members of the Royal Medical Society desire to convey to your Majesty our most humble and heartfelt congratulations on the completion of the fiftieth year of your Majesty's reign. These fifty years have indeed been a golden age for every branch of Science and Art, and for none more than for Medicine, in whose progress your Majesty has ever been graciously pleased to take the deepest and most Queenly interest."

In January 1888 Dr. Ezard again came to the front as a successful innovator. He proposed " That a Member shall be elected annually to the Office of Editor of Transactions :

that no one shall be eligible unless he has been a Member of the Society for at least one Session ; and that the Member elected to the Office shall be responsible for the publication of such of its Transactions as the Society may from time to time direct to be published ''. His proposal, in amended form, became law. After consultation with the Professor of Humanity, the Society resolved that the Editor should sign himself *Actorum Redactor*. The Law continued in force up to a comparatively recent period, when the office was abolished in favour of an Editorial Committee of Transactions. It was enacted : '' The Presidents shall *ex officio* constitute the Editorial Committee of Transactions ''.

Early in 1891 the Society resolved to publish a selection of dissertations by members who had risen to the highest eminence in the profession. The work appeared in the spring of 1892 ; and among the first of the senior members to purchase copies were Dr. Claud Muirhead and Dr. C. E. Underhill, both former presidents of the Society.

Sir Douglas Maclagan wrote the preface to this issue of selected dissertations.

With the respect due to the memory of Sir Douglas Maclagan, two errors in the preface may be pointed out. The names of Sir Charles Hastings and Mungo Park are mentioned among those of illustrious members of the Society of whom there are no dissertations extant. Sir Charles Hastings' dissertation has been mentioned. Mungo Park, the explorer, to whom Sir Douglas obviously refers, was a student of medicine at Edinburgh during the two sessions 1789–90–91. He was not a member of the Society. His death in an encounter with natives at Boussa, in the Western Soudan, occurred in 1805. The '' Mungo Park '', whose name appears in the list of members, was the eldest son of the explorer. He joined the Society in 1819. He obtained the appointment of assistant surgeon in the service of the East India Company. But he died of cholera a few days after his arrival at Bombay.[1]

---

[1] *Life of Mungo Park* (Edinburgh, 1835), p. 290. Joseph Thomson, *Mungo Park and the Niger* (1890), p. 244.

The publication of selected dissertations in the spring of 1892 marked the close of a memorable session. At the commencement of this session a brilliant Inaugural Address was delivered by Mr., later Sir, William Macewen, an honorary member of the Society, who, in 1892, became Regius Professor of Surgery in the University of Glasgow. In his Address he discussed some points with regard to the venous system within the cranium. " Pointing out certain physical and anatomical differences between the intra- and extra-cranial veins, he formulated a theory to explain the mechanism whereby the brain is protected from frequent and sudden alterations in its vascular supply during respiration ".[1] In the latter part of his Address he expressed his views on the duties and aims of a scientist, and on the spirit which should animate him in his work. Professor Chiene, who seconded a vote of thanks to the speaker, said that the early part of the Address reminded him of nothing so much as the work of Goodsir. " I have long held ", he said, " that Surgery is simply common sense applied to Anatomy and Physiology, and Mr. Macewen, one of the foremost surgeons of the day, has given a brilliant demonstration of the truth of this dictum."

An outstanding event during the session 1891–92 was the appointment of a standing committee to be called " The Public Business Committee ". The resolution which led to the establishment of the Committee was proposed by Alexander Miles, the senior president, whose subsequent distinguished career as a surgeon and teacher of surgery in Edinburgh is well known. The preamble of the motion explains the urgency of the matter : " Whereas the question of Public Business and the delivery of Dissertations has within recent years been an increasing source of discussion and difficulties in the management of the Society, the Society considers that the time has come when the subject should be authoritatively dealt with by legislation ". The preamble was signed by the senior president, and by Dr. R. J. A. Berry, a junior president, who was afterwards Professor of

[1] *Edinburgh Medical Journal*, vol. xxxvii (1891), p. 570.

Anatomy, and Dean of the Faculty of Medicine, in the University of Melbourne. The chief outcome of the resolution was the Law : " The Public Business Committee shall provide for the Dissertations and all other Public Business of the Society ". Clearly, this was a highly advantageous change. The first ordinary meeting of the committee was held on the 15th of January 1892.

Several proposals to alter Laws regarding dissertations were accepted by the Society at the legislative meeting at which the Public Business Committee was established. Further alterations have since been made. It is sufficient to state that dissertations are no longer compulsory.

Contrary to expectation, few dissertations during this period deal directly with the new and rapidly developing science of bacteriology. This fact, however, can be readily explained. Bacteriology is essentially a post-graduate study.[1] In 1897 a member who wrote a dissertation on " Certain Effects of certain Environments on Bacteria " indicated the difficulties which beset the overworked student of medicine in dealing with the subject. " During the last ten years ", he said, " the science has so rapidly increased that it has now assumed enormous and almost unwieldy proportions."

The rapidity of the advance was clearly described by James Ritchie, who was a president of the Society during 1889–90, in the Inaugural Address which he delivered when he was appointed, in 1913, the first incumbent of the Robert Irvine Chair of Bacteriology in the University of Edinburgh. Professor Ritchie said : " From the time when the antiseptic system was established, the part played by bacteria as originators of human suffering riveted the attention of the world. At first Lister apparently looked on the mere occurrence of putrefaction in a wound as the essential danger to be guarded against, but very soon, under the influence of the work of Burdon-Sanderson, he appreciated the risk following on the actual entrance of a special group of bacteria into the tissues and their multiplication there. The link

[1] Inaugural Address by James Ritchie, M.D., Professor of Bacteriology in the University of Edinburgh, 1913.

which completed the proof of the existence of this risk was supplied when in 1877 Koch isolated in pure culture the anthrax bacillus and reproduced experimentally this septic-aemic disease as it occurs in the natural infection. The discovery was accompanied by others of a still more far-reaching nature, for Koch substituted for the previous elaborate and imperfect technique simple and efficient methods for the isolation and growth of bacteria. It is thus in 1877 that bacteriology as a science took its birth. Shortly thereafter Koch was established as head of the Imperial Board of Health at Berlin, and to his laboratory there flocked workers from all parts of the world. By 1886 tuberculosis, diphtheria, typhoid fever, septicaemia and pyaemia in all their forms, cholera, glanders, and pneumonia had been shown to have a bacterial origin. Furthermore, the group of true bacteria—the cocci, the bacilli, and the spirilla—had been defined, and the canons of evidence to be fulfilled before a causal nexus between an organism and a disease can be established had been laid down and tested. Since that date the causal factors in other diseases—tetanus, plague, Malta fever—have been determined." [1]

Koch's name is on the list of honorary members of the Society. He was elected in 1884.

Two senior members of the Society early distinguished themselves in the literature of the science. In 1897 Professor James Ritchie along with Robert Muir (later Sir Robert Muir and Professor of Pathology in the University of Glasgow) published a *Manual of Bacteriology* which from the first established its position as a leading English text-book on the subject, a position it has since retained. Sir Robert Muir was elected an honorary member of the Society in the session 1920–21.

For his work in tropical medicine the name of Sir Andrew Balfour, who joined the Society in 1892, deserves mention. The late Dr. J. D. Comrie, who was a president during the session 1899–1900, has summarised Balfour's work in his *History of Scottish Medicine*. " In 1902 ", he wrote, " he

[1] *Edinburgh Medical Journal*, vol. xi (1913), p. 390.

was appointed director of The Wellcome Tropical Research Laboratories at Khartoum. Here, as sanitary adviser to the Soudan Government, he carried out for 11 years the great work of transforming Khartoum from a collection of hovels to a modern city, and succeeded in banishing from it all traces of malaria, which had previously been a very fatal malady. The four volumes of Reports of this laboratory, which were issued between 1904 and 1911, formed a magnificent record of research in tropical medicine. . . . In 1913 Balfour returned to London as director of The Wellcome Bureau of Scientific Research. . . . In 1923 he became director of the London School of Tropical Medicine and Hygiene, and was responsible for the organisation of this School in an extended form." [1] Balfour had considerable literary ability, as his successful romance, *By Stroke of Sword*, showed.

The science of bacteriology was the subject of some impressive remarks by Sir William H. Broadbent when he delivered the Inaugural Address before the Society in October 1894. Sir William had then " reached an age at which new ideas do not flow freely ". So he confessed. But he proceeded : " There can, however, be nothing in the history of human knowledge which appeals more to our imagination and admiration, as medical men, or which vindicates more the claim of medicine to a place in the temple of science, than the revelations of bacteriology ".

Prior to the delivery of his Address, Sir William Broadbent, already an honorary member, went over the Society's rooms under the guidance of a former president, Dr. Harvey Littlejohn, who became Professor of Forensic Medicine in succession to his father, Sir Henry Littlejohn, and Dean of the Faculty of Medicine in the University of Edinburgh. Sir William remarked that until then he had not been adequately impressed by the antiquity of the Society, and was not aware of the important part it had played in developing the faculties of success in generations of medical undergraduates of the University. He added : " Nothing could

---

[1] *History of Scottish Medicine* (2nd ed.), vol. ii, pp. 785-786.

be more interesting than to see, in their own handwriting, the early efforts of men whose names afterwards became illustrious ; and I can imagine no greater stimulus to ambition, than to be chosen by fellow-students as worthy to add to the series."

In 1895 the Inaugural Address was delivered by Sir Thomas Clouston, lecturer in mental diseases in the University of Edinburgh, and physician-superintendent of the Royal Edinburgh Asylum, who was not a member of the Society. For a number of years thereafter invitations to deliver the Inaugural Address were chiefly confined to distinguished senior members. In 1905, however, the Society went farther afield and invited Mr. Mayo Robson of Leeds, who selected for his subject, " The Clinical and Pathological Importance of Chronic Pancreatitis ". And in 1907 Sir Charles Sherrington, an honorary member of the Society, who was then Professor of Physiology in the University of Liverpool, opened the session with an Address on " Inhibition ".

The educational value of the Inaugural Addresses is considerable, for they are delivered by men who are distinguished on account of their culture as well as professional eminence. And the attentive and assimilative undergraduate may one day be grateful for such oratory, if and when he finds himself addressing an audience from a public platform.

Here it may be stated that during the last decade of the nineteenth century the standard of speaking in open debate in the Society was very high. Some of the youthful debaters of those days later occupied positions of the highest eminence in the profession. The period was notable also for the energy and unselfish ardour with which the business of the Society was conducted. The names of two members at this time may be specially mentioned : they are Harry Rainy, who was a president during the session 1892–93, and Kinnier Wilson, who joined the Society in 1899, and, three years later, became a president.

As a graduate in Arts and Science, Rainy distinguished

himself in the subjects of mathematics and physics, and worked under Professor George Chrystal in Professor P. G. Tait's laboratory in the University of Edinburgh. Chrystal and Tait held, with the highest distinction, the Chairs of Mathematics and Natural Philosophy respectively. It is not surprising, therefore, that Rainy, the possessor of this special knowledge, was one of the first to use X-rays in medicine in Edinburgh.[1] His *Clinical Methods*, which he wrote conjointly with Dr. Robert (now Sir Robert) Hutchison, is well known. But it is chiefly on account of his innate goodness that he will be remembered : in this respect he closely resembled his uncle, Principal Rainy, the celebrated Scottish churchman. And no sufferer who once felt his gentle touch could ever forget it. He was *The Gentle Doctor* in the manner described by Sir Mitchell Banks.

Kinnier Wilson's outstanding contribution to the science of medicine is his original description of progressive lenticular degeneration. In 1931 he was invited to deliver the Inaugural Address before the Society. He spoke on " The Resurrectionists of Edinburgh and London ". And in 1936 he was the guest of the evening at the Annual Dinner of the Society.

While the chief business of the Society is, of course, the reading and discussion of the dissertation by the active members, the occasional presence of senior members for the purpose of reading Addresses or Communications, of which they are the authors, is a welcome variation.

In the opening years of the present century some such papers of special current interest were read before the Society. Dr. Francis Darby Boyd, who was later Moncrieff Arnott Professor of Clinical Medicine in the University of Edinburgh, gave an Address on his experiences as physician to the Edinburgh and East of Scotland South African Hospital during the Boer war. Other papers were read before the Society by Mr. Francis M. Caird, on " The Surgery of the Appendix ", and Mr. John Wheeler Dowden, on " Shock ", both well-known leading surgeons in the

[1] *Edinburgh Medical Journal*, vol. xxx (1923), p. 70.

Edinburgh School of Medicine, and later, honorary members of the Society.

In 1905 the age-long mutual regard which has dignified the relations of the Royal College of Surgeons of Edinburgh to the Society was further confirmed. For in that year the Royal College celebrated its Fourth Centenary. In reply to the congratulations of the Society, the following letter was received : " Royal College of Surgeons, Edinburgh, 29th July 1905. Dear Sir, I have to inform you that at a Meeting of the Royal College of Surgeons of Edinburgh held on 26th instant, a special vote of thanks was unanimously passed to The Royal Medical Society for the congratulatory Address which the Royal Medical Society were pleased to present to the College on the Celebration of its Fourth Centenary. I am, Dear Sir, Yours faithfully, (sgd.) Francis Cadell, Secy., To the Secretary of The Royal Medical Society, Edinburgh."

In 1907 Lord Kelvin was elected an honorary member of the Society.

Only eighteen years after Sir William Broadbent's Inaugural Address, Dr. Robert Hutchison, who, as senior president, had occupied the chair on that occasion, was himself invited to deliver the Inaugural Address before the Society. This rapid rise to eminence in the profession was maintained, for the distinguished member was elected later to the Presidency of the Royal College of Physicians of London, and was the recipient of a baronetcy. Dr. Hutchison spoke on " The function of the Royal Medical Society in Medical Education ". So far as the Society is concerned, the Address is a piece of medical literature " of enduring power " ; and it should be regarded as an indispensable introduction for every undergraduate who is admitted a member of the Society.

In 1936 Sir Robert Hutchison was elected an honorary member of the Society.

On the outbreak of war in 1914 Dr. Macrae Taylor, the treasurer, was called upon to mobilise with his unit of the Territorial Army. In his Report for the Financial Year ending 30th September 1914 he stated that he would be unable to attend to his usual work until the war had come to an end.   He requested the Society to relieve him temporarily of his office until he should be able to resume it.

Further, in his Report Dr. Macrae Taylor stated that it would be unfortunate if the Society, whose meetings continued to be held during the war of 1745, when battle came as near Edinburgh as Prestonpans, should entirely abandon its work during the war which had begun in August.   He advised that meetings should be held, and that the Society should carry on its work, as far as possible, until happier times should admit of a resumption of its full usefulness.   He pointed out that the strictest economy would have to be observed ; and that the greatest economy might be effected by holding the meetings in a smaller room than the debating hall.   His advice was acted upon as far as possible ; and during the period of the 1914–18 war, many of the meetings were held in the south library.

Dr. Macrae Taylor resigned the office of treasurer in 1919, a decision which was accepted with regret.

On his death in 1930, a resolution was minuted, in which it was truly stated : " The Members of the Royal Medical Society realize that the Society has never had a more loyal and unselfish member, nor a better friend ".

It was fortunate for the Society that during the years 1914–18 the duties of treasurer were willingly undertaken by a succession of eminent senior members.   Indeed the general support given to the Society by the senior members throughout those years is an inspiring fact in the Society's history.

A sign of the return to the normal state of affairs was the election to honorary membership in 1920 of Professor J. C. Meakins, who then occupied the Christison Chair of Therapeutics in the University of Edinburgh.   This was the first election of an honorary member since pre-war years.

The Society was actually in a flourishing condition at the commencement of the session 1920–21, two years after the close of the war. At the opening meeting of the session eighty petitions for seats were presented.

In 1923 the Clinical Section of the Society, which had ceased to function since 1904, was revived. With the support of Professor Edwin Bramwell, who occupied the Moncrieff Arnott Chair of Clinical Medicine, permission was obtained for the use of suitable accommodation in the Royal Infirmary for the meetings. The title " Clinical Section " was altered to that of " Special Clinical Meetings of the Royal Medical Society ". Provisional resolutions governing the constitution of the meetings were passed.

The Annual Dinner of the Society, which was suspended during the war, was restored with its full customary dignity in 1923, when Sir Humphry Rolleston, Bart., was the guest of the evening.

Some years later Sir Humphry Rolleston was elected an honorary member of the Society; and along with him, a former member of the Society, Sir Norman Walker, then President of the General Medical Council, was elected to honorary membership.

A contemporary of Sir Norman Walker in the Society was Dr. George Lovell Gulland, who was a president during the session 1886–87. Dr. Gulland was Professor of Medicine in the University of Edinburgh from 1915 until 1928. He was well known as a specialist in diseases of the blood. When he was Emeritus Professor he delivered an Inaugural Address before the Society on " Retrospect and Prospect ".

Other post-war Inaugural Addresses were those delivered by Sir John Robertson of Birmingham, who selected for his subject, " The Borderland between Preventive and Curative Medicine " ; Lord Moynihan of Leeds, an honorary member of the Society, who spoke on " Ancient and Modern Surgery " ; and Sir Walter Langdon-Brown, Emeritus Professor of Physic in the University of Cambridge, whose subject was " Changing Conceptions of Disease ".

In 1936 the ancient and historic association of the Society with American Medicine was reaffirmed by the election of Professor Harvey Cushing to honorary membership. The

A CORNER OF THE SOCIETY'S LIBRARY

name of another famous Harvard teacher is on the roll of honorary members—Oliver Wendell Holmes, who was Professor of Anatomy there for many years.

A few years before the Society reached its two hundredth session, the unsatisfactory condition of the library was the subject of serious consideration. Many of the older books were in a decaying state, and they were likely to perish unless they were rescued by skilled hands. Nothing, however, was done until the Bicentenary Session, when proper measures for renovation were adopted with vigour and decision. Many valuable books were rescued from a dire state by the best available skill; and improved accommodation for them was provided.

Arrangements for the celebration of the Bicentenary of the Society were made at an Extraordinary Meeting in May 1936. The Society resolved to hold a Dinner some time in the following February, and a Reception in the Society's Rooms on the afternoon of the same day.

The Inaugural Address of the Bicentenary Session 1936–1937 was delivered by the Right Honourable Lord Horder.

The Bicentenary Dinner was held on 25th February 1937. Owing to the unexpectedly large number of requests for seats, the available accommodation in the Hall of the Royal College of Physicians proved inadequate. It was, in consequence, found necessary to transfer the Dinner to a larger Hall. The Dinner was held in the North British Station Hotel, Princes Street, and the toast of " the Royal Medical Society " was proposed by Sir Robert Hutchison.

Public Business at the weekly meeting of the Society on the following evening took the form of an Address by the Right Honourable Sir Auckland Geddes, a former president of the Society, whose services to the State, within the United Kingdom and as Ambassador to the U.S.A., are a part of British history. There is a historic fitness of things in the fact that a British Ambassador to the U.S.A. should have held office in the Royal Medical Society, in whose list of members appear the names of some of the founders of the Faculty of Medicine in the University of Pennsylvania.

At the close of the Bicentenary Session, three former presidents, Dr. A. Logan Turner, Mr. Alexander Miles and Professor Emeritus Edwin Bramwell were elected honorary members of the Society.

Thus the Society reached the two hundredth year of its existence with its vigour unimpaired.

The Society is primarily, but not purely, a student society. There is the senior element, never intrusive, but careful to ensure adherence to sound traditions. With the maintenance of these traditions, the Royal Medical Society of Edinburgh will continue to flourish.

APPENDIX I

JAMES GRAY, M.A., F.R.S.E.

In 1935 Mr. James Gray was introduced to Dr. J. L. Henderson, the Senior President of the Royal Medical Society, by Mr. N. Rainy Brown of the firm of J. F. Macfarlan & Company, with whom Gray and his grandfather, J. R. Young, had worked for many years. Gray made known his desire to obtain material for a history of the firm from the records and minute books of the Society and was given permission and encouragement to do so. The enthusiasm with which he worked showed that he was keenly interested in tracing the growth of medical knowledge and the changing fortunes of the Society through two centuries and in relating them to the historical and literary background. Gray had a deep admiration for his grandfather, and had, in earlier years, been imbued by him with a respect for the Society amounting to veneration.

The first result of Gray's researches was an article on the Society written with Dr. A. M. McFarlan, then Senior President of the Society, for a series which appeared in the *Medical Press and Circular* in 1936 and later in a book entitled *British Medical Societies.*

In the Bicentenary Session Gray presented the Society with £100, which was used, with his approval, to furnish a room to be known as the J. R. Young Room and used for the safe keeping of some of the old books in the Society's library. In the same Session Gray was elected an honorary ordinary member of the Society.

The material which Gray collected from the Minutes and Dissertations grew in amount and interest with additions from many books on the walls of his study and other books borrowed from or consulted in many libraries in the city. The chapters were discussed as they were written with members of the Society, and the whole story was written out in careful longhand. Gray had made arrangements for the publication of his manuscript before his death in 1942. The difficulties of the war years delayed publication by the Society, and many others have had a hand in the work, but these notes show how much reason the Society has to be grateful to James Gray for his devoted labours on its history.

APPENDIX II

THE ANNUAL PRESIDENTS OF THE ROYAL MEDICAL SOCIETY
From their First Election

SESSION XXVIII. 1764–65
Thomas Smith
Alexander Monro Drummond
James Carmichael-Smyth
James Blair

SESSION XXIX. 1765–66
Thomas Smith
Alexander Monro Drummond
James Blair
John Fyshe Palmer

SESSION XXX. 1766–67
Alexander Monro Drummond
James Maddocks
Daniel Rainey
Samuel Goulding

SESSION XXXI. 1767–68
Alexander Monro Drummond
Samuel Goulding
Theodore Forbes Leith
Andrew Duncan

SESSION XXXII. 1768–69
Alexander Monro Drummond
Samuel Goulding
John Bostock
Charles Blagden

SESSION XXXIII. 1769–70
Alexander Monro Drummond
Samuel Goulding

Andrew Duncan
Walter Jones

SESSION XXXIV. 1770–71
Samuel Goulding
Andrew Duncan
William Brown
Louis Odier

SESSION XXXV. 1771–72
Samuel Goulding
Andrew Duncan
Louis Odier
Isaac Hall

SESSION XXXVI. 1772–73
Andrew Duncan
William Ball
Walter Riddell
Robert Freer

SESSION XXXVII. 1773–74
Andrew Duncan
Walter Riddell
Robert Freer
John Brown

SESSION XXXVIII. 1774–75
John Aitken
Robert Freer
Richard Dennison
William Harvey
Gilbert Blane (vice R. Freer, resigned)

315

SESSION XXXIX.   1775–76
John Aitken
Robert Freer
Sylas Neville
Thomas Blackburne

SESSION XL.   1776–77
John Brown
Robert Freer
David Stuart
James Melliar

SESSION XLI.   1777–78
Robert Freer
Andrew Wardrop
Caleb Hilliar Parry
James Melliar

SESSION XLII.   1778–79
Andrew Wardrop
Edward Stevens
John Ford
Stephen Pellet
George Logan (vice A. Wardrop,
  resigned)

SESSION XLIII.   1779–80
John Brown
Edward Stevens
John Ford
William Cleghorn
Charles William Quin (vice John
  Ford, resigned)

SESSION XLIV.   1780–81
James Russell
Archibald Cullen
Ambrose Cookson
William Lister
Andrew Wardrop (vice A. Cookson,
  resigned)
Charles Stuart (vice A. Cullen, re-
  signed)

SESSION XLV.   1781–82
John Winterbottom

Jonathan Stokes
James Hare
Jacob Pattisson
James Fenwick (vice J. Pattisson,
  died)

SESSION XLVI.   1782–83
John Stark
Andrew Fyfe
Thomas Evory
John Henry Englehart

SESSION XLVII.   1783–84
Edward Harrison
Stephen Dickson
Benjamin Kissam
Robert Cleghorn
Samuel Ferris (vice S. Dickson, re-
  signed)

SESSION XLVIII.   1784–85
James Jeffray
Thomas Addis Emmet
James Macdonell
Thomas Skeete

SESSION XLIX.   1785–86
Richard Pearson
Samuel Hinds
Caspar Wistar
Thomas Beddoes

SESSION L.   1786–87
Edmund Goodwyn
William Alexander
James Mackintosh
John Haslam
John Lane (vice J. Mackintosh, re-
  signed)

SESSION LI.   1787–88
James Chichester Maclaurin
Theobald M'Kenna
John Fleming
Benjamin Smith Barton

SESSION LII.   1788–89
George Dunbar

316

ANNUAL PRESIDENTS

Edward Ash
Robert William Disney Thorp
James M'Kittrick Adair

SESSION LIII.   1789–90
Francis Foulke
John Benjamin Jachmann
Joseph Gahagan
Robert Gray
Henry Bowles (vice F. Foulke, died)
John Gahagan (vice J. B. Jachmann, resigned)

SESSION LIV.   1790–91
John Allen
Alexander Purcell Anderson
Thomas Bradley
William Macdougall

SESSION LV.   1791–92
William Russell
John Langford
John Thomson
Richard Fowler

SESSION LVI.   1792–93
James Bruce
John Butt Salt
Hugh Macpherson
Alexander Philip Wilson

SESSION LVII.   1793–94
Andrew Duncan
Patrick Erskine
Caleb Crowther
Thomas Graham Arnold

SESSION LVIII.   1794–95
James Bell
John Haxby
John Foster
Robert Scarlett

SESSION LIX.   1795–96
William Webb
William Woollcombe
John Reid
Robert Cappe

SESSION LX.   1796–97
Robert Cappe
Joseph Bealey
Gaspard Charles de La Rive
John William Bovell

SESSION LXI.   1797–98
George Birkbeck
John Bostock
Patrick Magrane
Joseph Skey

SESSION LXII.   1798–99
George Birkbeck
George Bell
Thomas Emerson Headlam
Charles Skene

SESSION LXIII.   1799–1800
Robert Besnard
Robert Robinson Watson Robinson
William Gordon
James Corkindale

SESSION LXIV.   1800–1801
Thomas Tudor Duncan
Thomas Bateman
James Corkindale
Charles Best

SESSION LXV.   1801–2
William Cullen Brown
William Saunders
Robert Bevan
Henry Reeve

SESSION LXVI.   1802–3
John James de Roches
John Forster Drake Jones
Andrew Stewart
John Murray

SESSION LXVII.   1803–4
George Kellie
James Laird
Alexander Henderson
Jeremiah Kirby

317

Session LXVIII. 1804–5
John Booth
Nicolas Nugent
George Kellie
Henry Herbert Southey

Session LXIX. 1805–6
Henry Fearon
John Barron
George James Gordon
James Sanders

Session LXX. 1806–7
John Thomson
John Gordon
Daniel Ellis
Noel Thomas Smith

Session LXXI. 1807–8
Renn Hamden
Thomas Pender Smith
Hardwick Shute
George Goldie

Session LXXII. 1808–9
Charles Mackenzie
Richard Harrison
John Henry Cutting
Richard Greene

Session LXXIII. 1809–10
John Ranicar Park
Henry Holland
Henry Hawes Fox
John Sanders Shand
John Elliotson (vice J. R. Park, resigned)

Session LXXIV. 1810–11
William Bromet
James Dottin Maycock
George Sanders
George Coventry

Session LXXV. 1811–12
Marshall Hall
Joseph Collier Cookworthy

Henry Stephens Belcombe
Hugh Ley

Session LXXVI. 1812–13
Peter Sandberg
John Davy
Richard Bright
William Crane

Session LXXVII. 1813–14
Thomas Dickson
Anthony Musgrave
Thomas Harrison Burder
William Moore

Session LXXVIII. 1814–15
Andrew Fyfe, Junior
Robert Hamilton
William Hall Gilby
Robert Edmond Grant

Session LXXIX. 1815–16
Henry Evans Holder
John Whiting
Adam Macdougall
George Craigie

Session LXXX. 1816–17
Hananel Mendes Da Costa
Nathan Ludovicus Young
William Caddel M'Donald
Bransby Blake Cooper
William M. Walker (vice W. C. M'Donald, resigned)
Lionel Thomas Berguer (vice W. M. Walker, resigned)

Session LXXXI. 1817–18
Jonathan Garner
Charles Hastings
George Maw
John Sims

Session LXXXII. 1818–19
Matthew Pierpoint
James Robinson Scott

Edward Turner
William Cullen
Jean Charles Coindet (vice M.
  Pierpoint, resigned)

SESSION LXXXIII. 1819–20
William Stroud
David Craigie
George William Stedman
John Barclay Sheil

SESSION LXXXIV. 1820–21
Henry Gaulter
John Conolly
John Burne
John Lane
Robert Herbert Brabant (vice H.
  Gaulter, resigned)

SESSION LXXXV. 1821–22
Merion M. Moriarty
John Birt Davies
Richard Headlam Keenlyside
Frederick Cobb
Benjamin Bell (vice M. M.
  Moriarty, resigned)

SESSION LXXXVI. 1822–23
William Thomas Williams
James Lomax Bardsley
Matthew Scholefield
Ynyr Burges
John Fletcher Macfarlan (vice M.
  Scholefield, resigned)

SESSION LXXXVII. 1823–24
Alexander John Hannay
James Hope
Charles Holland
John O'Donnell

SESSION LXXXVIII. 1824–25
Francis George Probart
George Carr
Charles Lush

Thomas Simpson
George Charles Julius (vice G.
  Carr, resigned)

SESSION LXXXIX. 1825–26
James Phillips Kay
William Charles Henry
William Holt Yates
William Cullen
Thomas Blundell (vice W. Cullen,
  resigned)

SESSION XC. 1826–27
David Boswell Reid
Ferdinand Wilhelm Becker
George Alexander Gordon
Edward Lubbock
William Alexander Francis Browne
  (vice E. Lubbock, resigned)

SESSION XCI. 1827–28
William Frederick Rawdon
Ferdinand Wilhelm Becker
William Lennard
William Alexander Francis Browne
Robert Arrowsmith (vice W. A. F.
  Browne, resigned)

SESSION XCII. 1828–29
Peter David Handyside
Arthur Todd Holroyd
Thomas Stone
George Henry Heathcote

SESSION XCIII. 1829–30
Evan Bowen
Henry Hulme Cheek
Allen Thomson
Arthur Todd Holroyd
James Hunter Lane (vice A.
  Thomson, resigned)

SESSION XCIV. 1830–31
John Paget
John Hutton Balfour
Andrew Wood
Thomas Stone

319

SESSION XCV. 1831–32
Hewett Cottrell Watson
George Benjamin Whitely
William Gregory
John Hutton Balfour
George Glover (vice J. H. Balfour, resigned)

SESSION XCVI. 1832–33
George Paterson
Charles Ransford
Andrew Douglas Maclagan
Robert Newbigging
James Richard White Vose (vice R. Newbigging, died)

SESSION XCVII. 1833–34
George Augustus Frederick Wilks
A. J. Hamilton
William John Irvine
Robert Spittal

SESSION XCVIII. 1834–35
James Patterson
Patrick Small Keir Newbigging
Stephen Charles Sewell
George Chaplin Child
William Collins Engledue (vice J. Patterson, resigned)

SESSION XCIX. 1835–36
James Young Simpson
Martin Barry
John Hutton Pollexfen
John Reid

SESSION C. 1836–37
William Benjamin Carpenter
John Rose Cormack
Edward Charlton
John Hughes Bennett

SESSION CI. 1837–38
William Herries Madden
David Skae
George Stewart Newbigging

Ralph William Shipperdson Hopper
Alexander Wood (vice W. H. Madden, resigned)
John Percy (vice G. S. Newbigging, resigned)

SESSION CII. 1838–39
Samuel Wright
Alexander Wood
Randle Wilbraham Falconer
Thomas Bazett Tytler

SESSION CIII. 1839–40
George Joseph Bell
Donald Mackenzie
William Henry Low
George Atkin

SESSION CIV. 1840–41
George Edward Day
Thomas Anderson
Hugh Francis Clarke Cleghorn
Richard James Mackenzie

SESSION CV. 1841–42
John Goodsir
Henry Lonsdale
Edwin Thorne Wait
William Scott Carmichael
William Mackinnon (vice W. S. Carmichael, resigned)

SESSION CVI. 1842–43
John Goodsir
Henry Reid
Thomas Bevill Peacock
Henry Lonsdale
Alleyne Maynard (vice H. Lonsdale, resigned)

SESSION CVII. 1843–44
Frank Renaud
Alexander Fleming
Joseph William Turner Johnstone
William Sutherland Stiven

ANNUAL PRESIDENTS

SESSION CVIII. 1844–45
Kelburne King
John Shand
Walter George Dickson
Edward Barons Bowman
Robert Thomas Martland (vice K. King, resigned)

SESSION CIX. 1845–46
Edward Waters
Gordon Kenmure Hardie
William Cameron
Richard White Young

SESSION CX. 1846–47
Daniel Rutherford Haldane
Richard White Young
William Gardiner Morris
James Donaldson Gillespie

SESSION CXI. 1847–48
James Warburton Begbie
William Balfour Baikie
William Rutherford Sanders
James Adam Hunter
Hugh Norris (vice W. B. Baikie, resigned)

SESSION CXII. 1848–49
Martin Brydon Lamb
William Reid
Philip John van der Byl
James Warburton Begbie
Robert Anstruther Goodsir (vice M. B. Lamb, resigned)
Alexander Schultze (vice J. W. Begbie, resigned)

SESSION CXIII. 1849–50
William Reid
William Marcet
James Charles Kelly Bond
William Warden

SESSION CXIV. 1850–51
John Wolley
Alexander Christison

John Scott Sanderson
Charles Murchison

SESSION CXV. 1851–52
Thomas Spencer Cobbold
William Henry Broadbent
James M'Grigor Maclagan
William Murray Dobie

SESSION CXVI. 1852–53
William Murray Dobie
Alexander Struthers
Doyle Money Shaw
William Menzies Calder

SESSION CXVII. 1853–54
Patrick Heron Watson
Archibald William Pulteney Pinkerton
Charles Alexander Winchester
Francis Stephen Bennet François de Chaumont
George Christopher Molesworth Birdwood (vice C. A. Winchester, resigned)

SESSION CXVIII. 1854–55
John Jardine Murray
Robert Rhind
Henry Marshall
David Boyes Smith
Alexander Munro Inglis (vice R. Rhind, resigned)

SESSION CXIX. 1855–56
Alexander Groves Duff
John Sibbald
Henry Marshall
Samuel Pearce Spasshatt
Alexander Russell Simpson (vice H. Marshall, resigned)
John Thorburn (vice J. Sibbald, resigned)

SESSION CXX. 1856–57
Samuel Pearce Spasshatt
William Robinson Hill

321

Frederic Gourlay
John Bayldon

SESSION CXXI. 1857–58
Andrew Pow
Thomas Grainger Stewart
David Yellowlees
Alexander Oswald Cowan

SESSION CXXII. 1858–59
Thomas Albert Carter
Francis Gerhard Myburgh
Henry Graham Dignum
Arthur Carrington
Joseph Bell (vice F. Myburgh, re-
signed)

SESSION CXXIII. 1859–60
Henry Season Wilson
Alexander Dickson
Alexander Johnstone Macfarlan
Andrew Smart

SESSION CXXIV. 1860–61
James Crichton Browne
Alexander Crum Brown
William M'Culloch Watson
James Bell Pettigrew

SESSION CXXV. 1861–62
John Duncan
John Anderson
Thomas Richard Fraser
Dyce Duckworth

SESSION CXXVI. 1862–63
Arthur Gamgee
Robert James Blair Cunynghame
Peter Maury Deas
Robert Bannatyne Finlay

SESSION CXXVII. 1863–64
David James Simpson
William Rutherford
Alexander Montgomerie Bell
Thomas Annandale

SESSION CXXVIII. 1864–65
Frederick Skae
Peter Murray Braidwood
James Carmichael
Claud Muirhead
Robert Baker (vice C. Muirhead,
resigned)

SESSION CXXIX. 1865–66
John Wyllie
John Chiene
James Cunningham Russel
James Keith Anderson

SESSION CXXX. 1866–67
Thomas Lauder Brunton
John Wilson Moir
John Rhind
Kenneth Mackenzie Downie
Charles Nicolson (vice J. Rhind,
resigned)

SESSION CXXXI. 1867–68
William Hogg
Richard Caton
Charles Nicolson
Alexander Christie Wilson
Joseph Robert Hardie (vice C.
Nicolson, resigned)

SESSION CXXXII. 1868–69
Francis Pritchard Davies
Andrea Rabagliati
Charles Holden
James Spottiswoode Cameron

SESSION CXXXIII. 1869–70
Alexander Bennett
David Page
Charles Edward Underhill
John Nicholson Fleming

SESSION CXXXIV. 1870–71
Edwin Hinchcliff
Alexander Macdougall
James Muir Howie
William Livesay

SESSION CXXXV. 1871–72
Edward Willis Way
Lewis Shapter
Henry Charrington Martin
Arthur James Macdonald Bentley

SESSION CXXXVI. 1872–73
James Crawford Renton
Henry Macdonald Church
John Edward Shaw
Alfred Charles Edward Harris

SESSION CXXXVII. 1873–74
George Thomas Beatson
Alexander James
James Stevenson Forrester
Charles Watson MacGillivray

SESSION CXXXVIII. 1874–75
Robert Saundby
William Garton
Magnus Retzius Simpson
Robert Alexander Gibbons

SESSION CXXXIX. 1875–76
Robert Adam Turnbull
Alexander Robert Coldstream
Thomas Rutherford Ronaldson
Thomas Duddingston Wilson

SESSION CXL. 1876–77
John James Graham Brown
Joshua John Cox
Robert Kirk
James Baker

SESSION CXLI. 1877–78
Robert Roxburgh
Johnson Symington
David Berry Hart
George Alexander Gibson

SESSION CXLII. 1878–79
Charles Walker Cathcart
Charles Begg
German Sims Woodhead
Albert Wilson

SESSION CXLIII. 1879–80
Edward Hyla Greves
Thomas Francis Spittal Caverhill
Alexander Bruce
Edward Fowler Scougal

SESSION CXLIV. 1880–81
William Henry Dobie
Robert Alexander Lundie
Alexander Hugh Freeland Barbour
Archibald Lyle Macleish

SESSION CXLV. 1881–82
Robert Mackenzie Johnstone
Patrick William Maxwell
John Lockhart Gibson
James Greig Soutar
Robert William Philip (vice J. G. Soutar, resigned)

SESSION CXLVI. 1882–83
James Greig Soutar
Thomas Peter Anderson Stuart
James Hewetson
Robert Sydney Marsden
John Lockhart Gibson (vice T. P. A. Stuart, resigned)

SESSION CXLVII. 1883–84
Arthur William Hare
William Hunter
George Mackay
Diarmid Noël Paton
Arthur Henry Weiss Clemow (vice D. N. Paton, resigned)

SESSION CXLVIII. 1884–85
Diarmid Noël Paton
James Haig Ferguson
George Armstrong Atkinson
John Frederick Sturrock

SESSION CXLIX. 1885–86
John Mackintosh Balfour
Henry Alexis Thomson
Robert Fraser Calder Leith

Charles James Lewis
George Brooke French (vice J. M. Balfour, resigned)

SESSION CL. 1886–87
James Taylor
Frederick Howorth Jeffcoat
George Lovell Gulland
James Auriol Armitage

SESSION CLI. 1887–88
William Aldren Turner
George Owen Carr Mackness
Herbert Furnivall Waterhouse
Edward Henry Ezard

SESSION CLII. 1888–89
Henry Harvey Littlejohn
Alexander Lockhart Gillespie
Robert Abernethy
Ernest Christison Carter

SESSION CLIII. 1889–90
William Gordon Woodrow Sanders
Arthur Logan Turner
James Ritchie
Robert Oswald Adamson

SESSION CLIV. 1890–91
Robert Dawson Rudolf
Patrick Balfour Haig
Robert Durward Clarkson
Alexander Miles

SESSION CLV. 1891–92
Alexander Miles
Richard James Arthur Berry
Gerald Fitzgerald
Edward Barnard Fuller

SESSION CLVI. 1892–93
Archibald Nathaniel Shirley Carmichael
John William Crerar
Harry Rainy
James Stewart Fowler

SESSION CLVII. 1893–94
Robert Hutchison
George Loraine Kerr Pringle
Dugald Charles Bremner
George Elder

SESSION CLVIII. 1894–95
John Orr
James Purves Stewart
Charles Cromhall Easterbrook
James Gibson Cattanach

SESSION CLIX. 1895–96
Joseph Edward Bowes
William Macrae Taylor
Kenneth MacLean
Henry John Forbes Simson

SESSION CLX. 1896–97
Edward Scott Carmichael
James Brunton Blaikie
Edwin Bramwell
Harry Fowler

SESSION CLXI. 1897–98
Thomas Arthur Ross
Harold Sherman Ballantyne
George Lyall Chiene
Ernest Edward Porritt

SESSION CLXII. 1898–99
Robert Frederick M'Nair Scott
Charles Minor Cooper
Percy Theodore Herring
George Freeland Barbour Simpson

SESSION CLXIII. 1899–1900
Alexander Dingwell Fordyce
William John Barclay
John Dixon Comrie
George Mackie

SESSION CLXIV. 1900–1901
William James Stuart
Robert Ainslie Ross
George Lyon
Lionel Charles Peel Ritchie

ANNUAL PRESIDENTS

SESSION CLXV. 1901–2
Arthur Murray Wood
William Elliot Carnegie Dickson
James Graham M'Bride
George Scott Carmichael

SESSION CLXVI. 1902–3
Andrew Beaconsfield Ross
Benjamin Philp Watson
William Hogg Prentice
Samuel Alexander Kinnier Wilson

SESSION CLXVII. 1903–4
Charles John Shaw
Duncan Campbell Lloyd Fitz-
williams
Thomas Bogie Hamilton
Hubert Dunbar Shepherd

SESSION CLXVIII. 1904–5
Hugh Nethersole Fletcher
Auckland Campbell Geddes
Henry John Dunbar
Robert William Johnstone

SESSION CLXIX. 1905–6
James Methuen Graham
Robert Alexander Chambers
Joseph Douglas Wells
Alexander William Neill

SESSION CLXX. 1906–7
Alexander Murray Drennan
Thomas Graham Brown
David Percival Dalbreck Wilkie
Norman Scott Carmichael

SESSION CLXXI. 1907–8
Alexander Church Brodie
McMurtrie
David Malcolmson Barcroft
George Herbert Rae Gibson
James Sutherland Edwards

SESSION CLXXII. 1908–9
William Kelman MacDonald
Mark Stewart Fraser

Andrew Fergus Hewat
John Gilmour

SESSION CLXXIII. 1909–10
Dermid Maxwell Ross
Richard Charles Alexander
Ronald Chesney MacQueen
Francis Esmond Reynolds

SESSION CLXXIV. 1910–11
Francis Richard Fraser
Edward Burton Gunson
Joseph le Fleming Coy Burrow
Eben Stuart Burt Hamilton

SESSION CLXXV. 1911–12
Ronald Gray Gordon
Thomas Clark Ritchie
Francis Richard Luke
John Tertius Morrison

SESSION CLXXVI. 1912–13
David Murray Lyon
Stanley James Linzell
Duncan Metcalfe Morison
William Charles Bernhard Meyer

SESSION CLXXVII. 1913–14
William Alister Alexander
John Fearby Campbell Haslam
Sydney Alfred Smith
John Hamilton Boag

SESSION CLXXVIII. 1914–15
Thomas Arthur Fuller
Peter MacCallum
Donald Watson
Charles George Lambie

SESSION CLXXIX. 1915–16
James Norman Jackson Hartley
Robert George Bannerman
John Mitchell Watt
Hedley Duncan Wright

SESSION CLXXX. 1916–17
Robert George Bannerman
Adam Prentice
James Tait Cowie McAuslin
James Godfrey Lyon Brown
George Louis Malcolm Smith (vice
  J. G. L. Brown, resigned)

SESSION CLXXXI. 1917–18
Robert George Bannerman
Adam Prentice
Frank Holmes
Thomas Burns Moyes

SESSION CLXXXII. 1918–19
Francis Evelyn Jardine
Robert George Bannerman
John Sinclair Westwater
James Duff Stewart

SESSION CLXXXIII. 1919–20
Alfred George Norton Weatherhead
Robert Lightbody Galloway
David Murray Lyon
William Ashley Lethem

SESSION CLXXXIV. 1920–21
James Davidson
John Lewis Owen
John Mitchell Watt
John Fearby Campbell Haslam

SESSION CLXXXV. 1921–22
William Alister Alexander
Norman Bruce Williamson
John William Alexander Hunter
David Cook Wilson
Edward Arnold Carmichael (vice
  W. A. Alexander, resigned)

SESSION CLXXXVI. 1922–23
Thomas McWalter Millar
Hope Pitcairn Anderson
George Dunlop Steven
Edward Robert Charles Walker

SESSION CLXXXVII. 1923–24
Alexander Boyd Williamson
Alexander Robert McClure
William McKie
Gavin Alexander Dunlop

SESSION CLXXXVIII. 1924–25
Thomas Drummond Shiels
John William Starkey
David Gibb Anderson
John Gibb McCrie

SESSION CLXXXIX. 1925–26
John Gibb McCrie
George Lionel Alexander
William Ritchie Russell
Robert Hall Sanderson
Lucien Benedict Wevill (vice G. L.
  Alexander, resigned)

SESSION CXC. 1926–27
William Ritchie Russell
Frank McLean Richardson
Derrick Melville Dunlop
James Ernest Monro

SESSION CXCI. 1927–28
William Mitchell-Innes
Lucien Benedict Wevill
John Alastair Bruce
Ian George Wilson Hill

SESSION CXCII. 1928–29
Ian George Wilson Hill
Thomas Arthur Howard Munro
Colin Panton Beattie
Arthur Spencer Paterson

SESSION CXCIII. 1929–30
Arthur George Graham Melville
Thomas Arthur Howard Munro
Alick Fleming Kerr Clarkson
William Davidson

SESSION CXCIV. 1930–31
William Ian Clinch Morris
Dyson Milroy Blair

ANNUAL PRESIDENTS

Hugh Adair Raeburn
Ian Charles Monro

SESSION CXCV. 1931–32
William Melville Arnott
Frank Leighton Ker
Ian Donald Cruickshank Veitch
Duncan Scott Napier

SESSION CXCVI. 1932–33
Ronald Leslie Cormie
James Gilbert Murdoch Hamilton
James Johnston Mason Brown
Robert Mitchell

SESSION CXCVII. 1933–34
James Gilbert Murdoch Hamilton
John Gordon Bate
James Johnston Mason Brown
Kenneth Cameron

SESSION CXCVIII. 1934–35
John Louis Henderson
Keith Maxwell Morris
Geoffrey Gilbert Sherriff
John Gordon Bate

SESSION CXCIX. 1935–36
Allan Menzies McFarlan
Robert Tait Campbell
Henry Matthew Adam
Arthur Fawcett Miller Barron

SESSION CC. 1936–37
Andrew Gilchrist Ross Lowdon
Ronald Fraser Dawson
James MacMaster Macfie
Ainslie Sanderson Crawford

SESSION CCI. 1937–38
Gavin John Cleland
Raleigh Barclay Lucas
Walter Gifford Kerr
Robert Diarmuid Hutchinson
  Baigrie

SESSION CCII. 1938–39
Robert Maxwell Johnstone
Douglas Arthur Clouston McRae
Robert Brockie Hunter
Peter Esmond Brown

SESSION CCIII. 1939–40
Robert Murray MacDonald
George William Baker
Charles William Alexander Falconer
James Alexander Lyon Naughton
John Cornelius Blair Serjeant (vice
  J. A. L. Naughton, resigned)

SESSION CCIV. 1940–41
William Bertrand Dawson
Thomas Gordon Band
Hamish Alexander Stewart
Kenneth Patrick Geddes Mears

SESSION CCV. 1941–42
Charles William Alexander Falconer
Alexander Alan Guild
John Ernest Tinne
Leo Wollman

SESSION CCVI. 1942–43
Charles Stewart Ross Lowdon
David Ross Wallace
John Norrie Swanson
Robert McKenzie Fulton
John Archibald Simpson
David Hazell Clark

SESSION CCVII. 1943–44
William Malcolm Murray Lyon
David Ian Hunter Smith
William Donald Munro
Thomas Ffrancon Elias-Jones
Donald Greenshields Mackay

SESSION CCVIII. 1944–45
Thomas Ffrancon Elias-Jones
Douglas Telfer Kay

Robert Tyrie Ritchie
Gordon Herbert Dargavel
  McNaught

SESSION CCIX. 1945–46
William John Stedman
Rae Llewelyn Lyon
Ian Scoon Ferguson
Boris Ruebner
David Francis Fisk Stephens (vice
  I. S. Ferguson, resigned)

SESSION CCX. 1946–47
Ian Ferguson Sommerville
Donald Stewart McLaren
Alexander Duff Robertson
Boris Ruebner

SESSION CCXI. 1947–48
Alastair Morrison Nelson
Johnston Douglas Haldane
Alexander Duff Robertson
Lindsay Alexander Gordon
  Davidson

SESSION CCXII. 1948–49
Malcolm David Webster Low
James Stanislaus Barrett
John Allan Dalrymple Anderson
James Henderson Brown

SESSION CCXIII. 1949–50
John Allan Dalrymple Anderson
David Spens Alexander
Iain MacDonald Clark
Ivan Ballantyne Tait

SESSION CCXIV. 1950–51
Ivan Ballantyne Tait
Kenneth MacDonald Wood
Charles William Mercer
James Jeffrey Maccabe

SESSION CCXV. 1951–52
James Barr McWhinnie
Arthur Rowland Isaac
John Alastair Duncan Gillies
William Daniel Roberts

INDEX

Abercrombie, John, 166, 176

Aberdeen, George Hamilton Gordon, 4th Earl of, 174

Abernethy, Robert, President (1888–89), 324

Academy of Physics. *See* Edinburgh

Accumulating Fund (1818), 143-146

Adair, Charles, 149

Adair, James M'Kittrick, member of committee to adjudge Prize Question (1793, 1795), 69 ; and Robert Burns, 250 ; President (1788–89), 317

Adam, Henry Matthew, President (1935–1936), 327

Adamson, Robert Oswald, President (1889–1890), 324

Addison, Thomas, 62, 115-116

Aitchison, James Edward Tierney, 220

Aitken, John, 53, 77 ; President (1774–1776), 315, 316

Aitken, Lachlan, 245

Akenside, Mark, 18, 27, 28-29, 37, 245

Albert, Prince Consort of Queen Victoria, Loyal Address presented to (1842), 174 ; his death (1861), 240

Alexander, David Spens, President (1949–1950), 328

Alexander, George Lionel, President (1925–26), 326

Alexander, Richard Charles, President (1909–10), 325

Alexander, William, President (1786–87), 316

Alexander, William Alister, President (1913–14, 1921–22), 325, 326

Alison, William Pulteney, appointed to Chair of Physiology at Edinburgh (1821), 131 ; attends Centenary dinner of the Society (1837), 166 ; elected Honorary Member (1841), 172 ; signs Sir James Y. Simpson's diploma of honorary membership (1850), 158 ; and new Hall in Melbourne Place (1851), 200, 202 ; reads paper to the Society (1858), 219-220 ; protagonist for blood-letting, 140,

178 ; and Kay-Shuttleworth, 136 ; and John Reid, 159

Allbutt, Sir Thomas Clifford, 33, 259

Allen, John, 84, 85-86, 89, 110 ; President (1790–91), 317

Allman, George James, Professor of Natural History, 219

Alston, Charles, Professor of Botany, 10, 26

Altham, James, 213

American College of Surgeons, 49

American Physical Society. *See* Edinburgh

Anaesthesia, 274-275. *See also* Chloroform

Anatomy : Society's efforts to improve facilities for obtaining subjects for dissection, 146-150

Anatomy Act (1832), 150

Ancrum, William Kerr, Lord. *See* Lothian

Anderson, Alexander Purcell, President (1790–91), 317

Anderson, David Gibb, President (1924–1925), 326

Anderson, Hope Pitcairn, President (1922–23), 326

Anderson, James Keith, President (1865–1866), 322

Anderson, John, President (1861–62), 322

Anderson, John Allan Dalrymple, President (1948–50), 328

Anderson, Thomas [Professor of Chemistry at Glasgow], elected first Hon. Secretary (1840), 168 ; signs Sir J. Y. Simpson's diploma of honorary membership (1850), 158 ; takes part in negotiations for a new Hall (1850–51), 189, 190, 196, 199, 200 ; subscribes to New Hall fund, 202 ; draws Lister's attention to work of Pasteur, 168-169 ; President (1840–1841), 168, 320

Annals of Medicine, 67

Annandale, Thomas [father of Professor Thomas Annandale, *q.v.*], joins Society (1824), 236; reads dissertation on puerperal fever (1825), 133

INDEX

INDEX

McNaught, Gordon Herbert Dargavel, President (1944–45), 328

Macpherson, Hugh, President (1792–93), 317

MacQueen, Ronald Chesney, President (1909–10), 325

McRae, Douglas Arthur Clouston, President (1938–39), 327

McWhinnie, James Barr, President (1951–52), 328

Madden, William Herries, President (1837–38), 320

Maddocks, James, President (1766–67), 315

Magendie, François, 111

Magrane, Patrick, President (1797–98), 317

Maitland, —, 54

Malpighi, Marcello, 33

Marat, Jean Paul, 72

Marcet, Alexander Jean Gaspard, 91–92, 93, 116

Marcet, William, President (1849–50), 321

Marsden, Robert Sydney, 137 ; President (1882–83), 323

Marshall, Henry, President (1854–56), 321

Martin, Charles James, 294

Martin, Henry Charrington, President (1871–72), 323

Martineau, Philip Meadows, 98

Martland, Robert Thomas, President (1844–45), 321

Martyn, John Richard, 57–58

Maw, George, President (1817–18), 318

Maxwell, Patrick William, President (1881–82), 323

Maycock, James Dottin, 70 ; President (1810–11), 318

Mayer, Robert, 243

Maynard, Alleyne, President (1842–43), 320

Mayow, John, 34

Mead, Richard, 1

Meakins, Jonathan Campbell, 309

Mears, Kenneth Patrick Geddes, President (1940–41), 327

Medical and Philosophical Commentaries (1773–95), 67

Medical Essays and Observations. See Edinburgh. Society for the Improvement of Medical Knowledge

Medical Observations and Inquiries. See London. Society of Physicians

Melliar, James, 55, 56 ; President (1776–1778), 316

Melville, Arthur George Graham, President (1929–30), 326

Melville, Henry Dundas, 1st Viscount, 53

Melville, Robert Saunders Dundas, 2nd Viscount, 150

Membership :
  Ordinary, petition for seat rejected by single negative, 31 ; alterations of laws relating to (1799–1806), 110 ; decline in, considered (1868), 75, 261, 262–263

  Corresponding, institution of order of (1784), 68

  Extraordinary, controversy over attempted disfranchisement of, in election of Presidents (1808), 104–108 ; law relating to, altered (1816), 109–110 ; that title should be changed to Fellows proposed (1859), 218 ; first official use of " Fellow " (1887), 218, 299

  Honorary, first non-member to be elected an Honorary Member (1762), 67 ; honorary membership by rotation abolished (1776), 27

Mercer, Charles William, President (1950–1951), 328

Meyer, William Charles Bernhard, President (1912–13), 325

Middleton, Peter, 40, 46

Miles, Alexander, 302, 312 ; President (1890–92), 324

Millar, Thomas McWalter, President (1922–23), 326

Miller, James [Professor of Surgery], 202, 226

Miller, John, Secretary (1782–83), 168

Mitchell, Robert, President (1932–33), 327

Mitchell-Innes, William, President (1927–1928), 326

Moir, John Wilson, President (1866–67), 322

Moncrieff, James Moncrieff, 1st Baron, 76

Moncrieff, John, 141

Moncrieff, William, 141

Monro, Alexander, *Primus*, and foundation of Edinburgh Medical School, 1, 2, 3, 7-8 ; and unsuccessful attempt to found Infirmary (1720), 13 ; Secretary of the Society for the Improvement of Medical Knowledge, 2, 67 ; grants students use of his anatomical theatre for private dissection (1734), 15, 16 ; and George Cleghorn, 18 ; Goldsmith on, 36 ; and John Rutty, 19 ; his fame attracts men to Edinburgh, 71

347

INDEX

Rutherford, Daniel, 69, 113
Rutherford, John, 8-9, 14, 28, 30
Rutherford, William, 240-244 ; member of committee appointed to prepare pamphlet on the Society (1864), 239 ; takes part in inauguration of Murchison Memorial Scholarship, 182 ; member of the finance committee, 231 ; mentioned as President, 238 ; Haldane on, 297 ; President (1863–64), 322
Rutty, John, 19, 270

St. Andrews University, 151, 152-153
St. Clair, Andrew, 8-9, 19
Salmond, Robert, Secretary, 167
Salt, John Butt, President (1792–93), 317
Sandberg, Peter, President (1812–13), 318
Sanders, George, 178 ; President (1810–1811), 318
Sanders, James, President (1805–6), 318
Sanders, William Gordon Woodrow, President (1889–90), 324
Sanders, William Rutherford, 178-179 ; signs Sir J. Y. Simpson's diploma of honorary membership (1850), 158 ; member of New Hall committee (1850), 189 ; takes part in inauguration of Murchison Memorial Scholarship, 182 ; mentioned, 176 ; President (1847–48), 321
Sanderson, John Scott Burdon. *See* Burdon-Sanderson, Sir J. S.
Sanderson, Robert Hall, President (1925–1926), 326
Saundby, Robert, 287 ; President (1874–1875), 323
Saunders, William [Member, 1762], 93, 116, 174
Saunders, William [Member, 1798], President (1801–2), 317
Saussure, Horace Bénédict de, 92
Scarlett, Robert, President (1794–95), 317
Schäfer, Edward Albert. *See* Sharpey-Schafer, Sir E. A.
Scholefield, Matthew, 123 ; President (1822–23), 319
Schultze, Alexander, President (1848–49), 321
Scot-Skirving, Archibald Adam, 249
Scot-Skirving, Robert, 294
Scott, James Robinson, President (1818–1819), 318
Scott, Robert Frederick M'Nair, President (1898–99), 324

Scott, Sir Walter, Bart. [author of the Waverley Novels], 14, 26, 39, 80, 84, 92, 97, 99, 111-112, 114-115, 136, 137
Scougal, Edward Fowler, 266 ; President (1879–80), 323
Secretaries. *See* Office-bearers
Serjeant, John Cornelius Blair, President (1939–40), 327
Sewell, Stephen Charles, President (1834–1835), 320
Shand, John, President (1844–45), 321
Shand, John Sanders, President (1809–10), 318
Shapter, Lewis, 271 ; President (1871–72), 323
Sharpey, William, 128-129 ; subscribes to fund for new Hall (1851), 202 ; introduces Lister to Syme (1853), 209 ; elected Honorary Member (1855), 210 ; mentioned, 124, 127, 165, 179
Sharpey-Schafer, Sir Edward Albert [formerly E. A. Schäfer], 129
Shaw, Charles John, President (1903–4), 325
Shaw, Doyle Money, 205 ; President (1852–53), 321
Shaw, John Edward, President (1872–73), 323
Sheil, John Barclay, 129 ; President (1819–20), 319
Shepherd, Hubert Dunbar, President (1903–4), 325
Sherriff, Geoffrey Gilbert, President (1934–1935), 327
Sherrington, Sir Charles Scott, 306
Shiels, Sir Thomas Drummond, President (1924–25), 326
Shippen, William, 47, 48
Shute, Hardwick, President (1807–8), 318
Sibbald, Sir John, 184-185 ; President (1855–56), 321
Sibbald, Sir Robert, 1, 6
Simmons, Samuel Foart, 40
Simpson, Sir Alexander Russell, chairman of Chloroform Committee (1856), 186 ; presentation of gift by the Society to J. R. Young made by (1896), 268 ; stands for Parliament (1910), 233 ; mentioned, 211, 239, 272, 277, 278 ; President (1855–56), 321
Simpson, David James [eldest son of Sir J. Y. Simpson], 238-240, 246 ; President (1863–64), 322

351

INDEX